ScottForesman

EXPLORING
MATHEMATICS

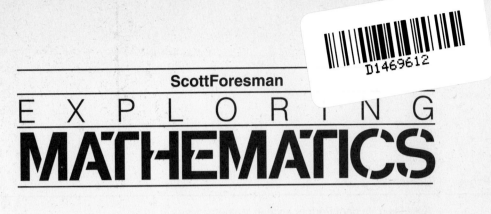

Assessment Handbook

- Performance and Alternative Assessments

- Free-Response and Multiple-Choice Tests

- Informal Assessment Forms

- Management Forms

- Answer Keys

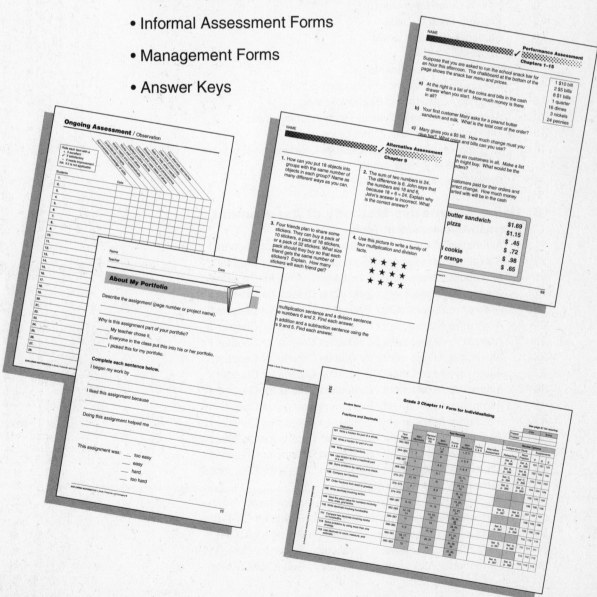

Contents

Assessing Student Performance in Mathematics

The Changing Face of Mathematics Instruction and Assessment

In the past decade, the National Council of Teachers of Mathematics and other mathematics education organizations and professionals have examined the methods teachers use to instruct students in mathematics and have recommended ways to improve this instruction. Their recommendations stress the importance of providing more diverse methods of instruction including activities, open-ended investigations, and long-term projects, many of which utilize cooperative learning. They challenge us to make the goal of mathematics the acquisition of the dynamic processes of critical thinking and problem solving, rather than merely the mastery of a static body of facts and procedures.

Instruction and its assessment are closely linked. As instructional methods change, the methods of evaluation need to change. New forms of assessment being proposed provide a more authentic way of evaluating the depth of our students' knowledge of mathematics rather than their ability to memorize facts and procedures. These alternative methods of assessment offer the opportunity for the students to display how they approach problem situations, collect and organize information, formulate and test conjectures, and communicate their mathematical insights.

An authentic assessment program contains tasks that are appropriate to the topics the students are learning and that provide outcomes that are valuable to the students. Such an assessment program allows for such highly individual factors as a school's curriculum objectives, a teacher's style of instruction, and a student's maturity level. Each individual teacher determines the assessment program best suited to the needs of his or her students.

In an instructional environment that demands a deeper understanding of mathematics, testing instruments that call for only identification of single correct responses no longer suffice. Instead, our instruments must reflect the scope and intent of our instructional program to have students solve problems, reason, and communicate.

NCTM Standards

To help teachers select the most appropriate evaluation tools for his or her classroom, this Assessment Handbook provides the following materials.

Informal Assessment Forms
- student-completed forms
- teacher-completed forms for individual, group, and class activities

Formal Assessment Instruments
- alternative chapter assessments comprised of several open-ended questions
- free-response chapter tests which parallel the Chapter Review/Test in the student text
- multiple-choice chapter, inventory, and cumulative tests
- task-oriented performance assessments for each quarter

Management Forms
- forms for individualizing
- class record forms

To assess development of a student's mathematical power, a teacher needs to use a mixture of means: essays, homework, projects, short answers, quizzes, blackboard work, journals, oral interviews, and group projects.

Everybody Counts:
A Report to the Nation on the Future of Mathematics Education

Guidelines for Developing an Authentic Assessment Program

Developing an authentic program of assessment is an ongoing process. Some assessment instruments will seem perfectly suited to the teacher and his or her students from the start. Others may be effective only after the teacher has had a chance to experiment with and refine them. Still others may be inappropriate for a given class or instructional situation. The following are some guidelines that may be helpful when choosing the types of assessment for a particular program.

Assessment serves many purposes.

- For the teacher, assessment yields feedback on the appropriateness of instructional methods and offers some clues as to how the content or pace of instruction could be modified.
- For the students, assessment should not only identify areas for improvement, but should also affirm their successes.
- Traditional forms of assessment yield a tangible score.

Make the assessment process a positive experience for students.

- Use a variety of assessment techniques.
- Provide opportunities for students to demonstrate their mathematical capabilities in an atmosphere that allows maximum performance.
- Emphasize what students *do* know and *can* do, not what they do not know and cannot do.
- Motivate students to achieve by using tasks that reflect the value of their efforts.

Authentic assessment focuses on higher-order thinking skills.

- Provides a picture of the student as a critical thinker and problem solver.
- Identifies *how* the student does mathmatics, not just what answer he or she gets.

Provide assessment activities that resemble day-to-day tasks.

- Use activities similar to instructional activities to assess.
- Use assessment activities to further instruction.
- Give students the immediate and detailed feedback they need to further the learning process.
- Encourage students to explore how the mathematics they are learning applies to everyday life.

Include each student as a partner in the assessment process.

- Encourage students to reflect on what they have done.
- Encourage students to share their goals.

Making and Using an Assessment Portfolio

A portfolio is a collection of a student's work — projects, reports, drawings, reflections, assessment instruments — that displays the student's mathematical accomplishments over an extended period. The following suggestions for use should be adapted to the needs and organizational style of the individual classroom teacher.

Getting Started

- Provide two file folders for each student.
- Label one *Work Portfolio* and the other *Assessment Portfolio*.

The Work Portfolio

- The *Work Portfolio* is for "work in progress" and recently completed materials. The student should have access to it on a day-to-day basis and should keep in it all class work, group work, homework, reports, and projects for the current period, including student assessment forms such as *My Math Log*.
- Every two to six weeks students review their *Work Portfolios* to determine the materials they would like to transfer to their *Assessment Portfolios*. (See below.)
- The teacher also selects student materials for the *Assessment Portfolio* and includes any appropriate formal assessment instruments.
- The student completes the *About My Portfolio* form and takes home all items remaining in the *Work Portfolio*.

The Assessment Portfolio

- The *Assessment Portfolio* is used as the basis for assessing a student's achievements. The focus of the *Assessment Portfolio* should be on:

    student thinking;

    growth in understanding over time;

    making mathematical connections;

    positive attitudes about mathematics;

    and the problem-solving process.

> *The opportunity to share mathematical ideas through portfolios can mark a real turning point in student attitudes.*
>
> **Mathematics Assessment (NCTM Publication)**

- *Assessment Portfolios* may include:

    student-selected items from the *Work Portfolio*

    a letter from the student about the work

    a math autobiography

    other work selected by the teacher including math surveys, formal assessments, and informal assessments such as interviews and observations.

Evaluating a Portfolio

- Keep in mind that portfolio evaluation is a matter of ongoing discussion.
- Set aside time to discuss the *Assessment Portfolio* with the student.
- Use the *Assessment Portfolio* when discussing the student's progress with his or her family.
- Use it as a basis for identifying strengths and weaknesses and for setting goals for the next period.
- Consider developing your own criteria for evaluating portfolios, for example, numeric scales.

Using Assessment Forms

Using Student-Completed Forms

To do meaningful work in our fast-paced and ever-changing technological world, students must learn to assess their own progress.

This handbook provides six forms that can be used to help students with self-assessment. Use one or more depending upon the needs of the students.

Form	Purpose	Suggested Uses
My Math Log	Student journal of experiences in mathematics	Model for keeping a daily journal in a notebook Lets student reflect on the work he or she has done
Student Survey	Checklist of student attitudes toward various math activities	Periodically monitor the change in student attitudes toward math
How We Worked in Our Group	Checklist of student interaction with the members of their groups	Completed at the conclusion of projects
Problem-Solving Guide	Tool for organizing problem-solving efforts Follows the steps found in the textbook	Aid in following the steps of the problem-solving process Monitor student progress in understanding the problem-solving process
Student Self-Assessment	Checklist of student awareness of how well he or she works independently	Monitor student progress in working independently
About My Portfolio	Form to describe the contents of student's portfolio	Completed when student transfers work from the *Work Portfolio* to the *Assessment Portfolio* Students can use one form for several work selections or for each selection.

Using Teacher-Completed Forms

This handbook provides seven assessment forms that are designed to help the teacher keep a record of authentic but informal assessments. Some forms are for use with individual students, while others are for use with groups of students. Determine which would be best suited for use in your classroom.

Form	Purpose	Suggested Uses
Assessing Performance in Problem Solving	Form to assess each student in a problem-solving situation	Describe level of student performance Modify the level to meet individual needs
Ongoing Assessment / Problem Solving	Checklist to assess groups of students in problem-solving situations	Assess the entire class Assess small groups over time
Assessment of an Individual Through Observation	Checklist to determine the student's thought processes, performance, and attitudes	Record observation of student in classroom
Ongoing Assessment / Observation	Checklist for observing several students at one time	Provide a mathematical profile of the entire class Identify common strengths and weaknesses Help in modifying pace or content Help in determining appropriate groupings
Ongoing Assessment / Cooperative Learning	Checklist to assess student abilities to work constructively in groups	Assess one or more cooperative groups
Overall Student Assessment	Summary of each student's overall performance	Evaluate student performance over an entire instructional period
Project / Presentation Checklist	Checklist for evaluating oral presentations or extended projects	Evaluate an individual or group presentation or project Prepare students for presentations or projects

My Math Log

It's fun to do math when...

I discovered that math is useful for...

I like math because...

I could do better in math if...

Use this sheet to help you write about math.

You may use the phrases above to help you get started.

You may use the space at the bottom for math drawings or sample problems.

_____

_____

_____

_____

_____

_____

_____

_____

_____

_____

_____

Student Survey

Make a check mark to tell how you feel.

	Most of the time	Some of the time	Hardly ever
I am good in math.			
I am getting better in math.			
I need help on most problems.			
I see how math is used in real life.			
I understand word problems.			
I can usually solve most problems.			
I like to try new strategies.			
I give up easily.			
I keep an organized notebook.			
I think math is fun.			

Name a project you would like the class to work on. _____

_____

What is your favorite kind of math? _____

Tell why. _____

_____

_____

List some activities where you have used math.

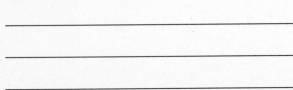

_____

_____

How We Worked in Our Group

Reader: _____   Writer: _____

Materials Handler: _____   Checker: _____

Other Group Members: _____

Materials Used: _____

Check the sentences that describe what happened.

_____ We had a new idea or made a suggestion.

_____ We asked for more information.

_____ We shared the information we found.

_____ We tried different ways to solve the problem.

_____ We helped someone explain his or her ideas better.

_____ We pulled our ideas together.

_____ We were reminded to work together.

_____ We encouraged those who did not understand.

Complete each sentence below.

We learned _____

_____

We found an answer by _____

_____

After we found an answer, we _____

_____

By working together, we _____

_____

Understand

QUESTION   What are you asked to find?

_____

_____

FACTS   What facts are given?

_____

_____

KEY IDEA   How are the facts and the

question related? _____

_____

_____

PROBLEM SOLVING GUIDE

Understand
QUESTION
FACTS
KEY IDEA

Plan and Solve
STRATEGY
ANSWER

Look Back
SENSIBLE ANSWER
ALTERNATE APPROACH

Plan and Solve

STRATEGY   What can you do to solve the problem? _____

_____

Solve the problem.

ANSWER   Give the answer in a sentence. _____

_____

Look Back

SENSIBLE ANSWER   Did you check your work?

ALTERNATE APPROACH   Is there another way to get the same

answer?

Student Self-Assessment

Write about what you did.

What were you trying to learn?_____

_____

_____

How did you start your work?_____

_____

_____

What materials did you need?_____

_____

_____

What did you learn?_____

_____

_____

Check the sentences that describe your work.

_____ I made a plan before I began my work.

_____ I was able to do the work.

_____ I did not understand the directions.

_____ I followed the directions but got the wrong answer.

_____ I found a different way to do this activity.

_____ I could explain how to do this to someone else.

_____ The work was easier than I thought it would be.

_____ The work was harder than I thought it would be.

About My Portfolio

Describe the assignment (page number or project name).

_____

_____

Why is this assignment part of your portfolio?

_____ My teacher chose it.

_____ Everyone in the class put this into his or her portfolio.

_____ I picked this for my portfolio.

Complete each sentence below.

I began my work by _____

_____

_____

I liked this assignment because _____

_____

_____

Doing this assignment helped me _____

_____

_____

This assignment was: ____ too easy

                       ____ easy

                       ____ hard

                       ____ too hard

Assessing Performance in Problem Solving

Check each statement below that accurately describes the student's work.

Understand

_____ Tells what facts are given

_____ Restates the problem in his or her own words

_____ Tells how the facts and the question are related

_____ Relates the problem to a similar problem

Plan and Solve

_____ Chooses an appropriate strategy for solving the problem

_____ Estimates what the answer should be

_____ Works systematically

_____ Shows work in an organized fashion

_____ Computes correctly

_____ States the answer in a complete sentence

Look Back

_____ Uses appropriate labels or units to state the answer

_____ Tries alternate approaches to solve the problem

_____ Checks to see that the answer is reasonable

Use the following criteria to assess the student's performance.

Level 5 (12–13 items checked)

The student demonstrates an in-depth understanding of the problem and communicates that understanding in a clear and concise manner. He or she is able to relate the problem to other work previously accomplished.

Level 4 (9–11 items checked)

The student understands the problem. A correct solution is clearly shown.

Level 3 (6–8 items checked)

The student displays an adequate understanding of major concepts. However, errors may occur in some of the specific components.

Level 2 (3–5 items checked)

The student partially understands the problem. He or she does not complete the necessary work, uses an inappropriate strategy, and/or gives an incorrect answer.

Level 1 (0–2 items checked)

The student has no apparent understanding. Either no answer, an inappropriate response, or an incorrect answer with no work is shown.

Ongoing Assessment / Problem Solving

Rate each item with a
+ if excellent
✓ if satisfactory
− if needs improvement
NA if it is not applicable

Tells what facts are given
Restates problem in own words
Tells how facts and questions are related
Chooses an appropriate strategy
Works systematically
Does computations correctly
States answer(s) in a complete sentence
Uses correct labels or units in answer
Gives an alternate approach
Checks the answer

Students	Date										
1.											
2.											
3.											
4.											
5.											
6.											
7.											
8.											
9.											
10.											
11.											
12.											
13.											
14.											
15.											
16.											
17.											
18.											
19.											
20.											
21.											
22.											
23.											
24.											
25.											
26.											
27.											
28.											

Assessment of an Individual Through Observation

	Frequently	Sometimes	Never
Understanding			
Demonstrates knowledge of skills	_____	_____	_____
Understands concepts	_____	_____	_____
Selects appropriate solution strategies	_____	_____	_____
Solves problems accurately	_____	_____	_____
Work Habits			
Works in an organized manner	_____	_____	_____
Works neatly	_____	_____	_____
Gets work in on time	_____	_____	_____
Works well with others	_____	_____	_____
Uses time productively	_____	_____	_____
Asks for help when needed	_____	_____	_____
Confidence			
Initiates questions	_____	_____	_____
Displays positive attitude	_____	_____	_____
Helps others	_____	_____	_____
Flexibility			
Tries alternative approaches	_____	_____	_____
Considers and uses ideas of others	_____	_____	_____
Likes to try alternative methods, such as mental math or calculators	_____	_____	_____
Perseverance			
Shows patience and perseverance	_____	_____	_____
Works systematically	_____	_____	_____
Is willing to try	_____	_____	_____
Checks work without being told	_____	_____	_____
Other			
_____	_____	_____	_____
_____	_____	_____	_____
_____	_____	_____	_____
_____	_____	_____	_____

Ongoing Assessment / Observation

Rate each item with a
+ if excellent
✓ if satisfactory
– if needs improvement
NA if it is not applicable

Students	Date	Demonstrates knowledge of skills	Understands concepts	Works neatly and systematically	Works well with others	Displays positive attitude	Considers and uses ideas of others	Shows patience and perseverance	Asks for help when needed	Uses time productively	Tries alternate approaches
1.											
2.											
3.											
4.											
5.											
6.											
7.											
8.											
9.											
10.											
11.											
12.											
13.											
14.											
15.											
16.											
17.											
18.											
19.											
20.											
21.											
22.											
23.											
24.											
25.											
26.											
27.											
28.											

EXPLORING MATHEMATICS © Scott, Foresman and Company/3

Rate each item with a
+ if excellent
✓ if satisfactory
− if needs improvement
NA if it is not applicable

Students	Date	Demonstrates problem-solving ability	Works systematically	Works with others in the group	Tutors and helps others	Considers and uses ideas of others	Speaks quietly	Initiates questions	Has positive attitude	Shows patience and perseverance	Disagrees without being disagreeable
1.											
2.											
3.											
4.											
5.											
6.											
7.											
8.											
9.											
10.											
11.											
12.											
13.											
14.											
15.											
16.											
17.											
18.											
19.											
20.											
21.											
22.											
23.											
24.											
25.											
26.											
27.											
28.											

Overall Student Assessment

Rate each item with a
+ if excellent
✓ if satisfactory
– if needs improvement
NA if it is not applicable

Problem Solving
Cooperative Learning
Test Scores
Class Work
Homework
Participation in Discussion

Students	Date										
1.											
2.											
3.											
4.											
5.											
6.											
7.											
8.											
9.											
10.											
11.											
12.											
13.											
14.											
15.											
16.											
17.											
18.											
19.											
20.											
21.											
22.											
23.											
24.											
25.											
26.											
27.											
28.											

Project/Presentation Checklist

This form can be used to evaluate an oral or written student project made by one student or a group of students. This checklist also can be used to discuss successful methods for making presentations, or given to students to help guide them in planning their projects such as: mathematical art, scientific experiments, data gathering for charts and graphs, computer demonstrations, skits, or oral and written research projects.

Student(s) .... Date ....

Project ....

....

The Project

____ Demonstrates a mathematical concept properly

____ Communicates its idea clearly

____ Shows a connection to another subject

____ Shows time spent in planning and preparation

____ Is original

____ Is creative

____ Is colorful and neat

____ Stimulates further investigation of the topic

____ Includes a short written report if it is a model or demonstration

____ Lists resources used

The Oral Presentation

____ Demonstrates a knowledge of the mathematical concept

____ Is organized (includes an introduction, main section, and conclusion)

____ Uses audio-visual props where appropriate

____ Speaks clearly and paces presentation at a proper speed

____ Answers questions and stimulates further interest in the topic

____ Demonstrates a positive problem-solving attitude

____ Lists resources used

Rate each item with a
+ if excellent
✓ if satisfactory
− if needs improvement
NA if it is not applicable

EXPLORING MATHEMATICS © Scott, Foresman and Company/3

Using Alternative Methods of Assessment

In order to provide more authentic forms of assessment, this handbook provides two forms that focus on students' ability to demonstrate their understanding of mathematical concepts. For each chapter there is an alternative assessment and for each quarter there is a performance assessment.

Alternative Assessments

The alternative assessment items in this handbook help the teacher to make a better judgment of the students' understanding of mathematical concepts and their ability to interpret information, make generalizations, and communicate their ideas. Each assessment contains three to six open-ended questions that are keyed to objectives.

Administering Alternative Assessments

The tests can be administered in a way that is best suited for the students.

- Use all the assessment items.
- Use only one or two along with a free-response or a multiple-choice test.
- Use the assessment items to interview each student.
- Have students give the explanations orally, then write the answers.
- Provide manipulatives, calculators, and extra paper as needed.

Evaluating Alternative Assessments

Each alternative assessment item is accompanied by a list of two or more evaluation criteria that can be used as a basis for judging student responses. To rate how well students meet each criterion, a simple scale such as this may be used.

| + excellent |
| ✓ satisfactory |
| − inadequate |

Comparison of Alternative Assessments and Free-Response Tests

	Alternative Assessments	Free-Response Tests
Number of items	3–6	5–35
Sample format	Draw 3 different rectangles that each have an area of 12 square centimeters.	Find the area of a rectangle that is 4 centimeters long and 3 centimeters wide.
Mode of administration	Interview Written response Combination of interview and written responses	Written response
Answers	May have more than one May require an explanation by student	Single, short
Scoring	2–4 evaluation criteria given Use of simple rating scale	One correct answer for each item
Benefits	More accurate determination of instructional needs and strengths of students	Easy to score

Performance Assessments

The four performance assessments in this handbook are cumulative in nature and designed for use at the end of each quarter. They are composed of mathematical tasks which allow students to demonstrate a broad spectrum of their abilities:

- how they reason through difficult problems,
- how they make and test conjectures,
- how their number sense helps them give reasonable answers, and
- how they utilize alternative strategies.

Performance tasks also give teachers a means of assessing qualities of imagination, creativity, and perseverance.

Administering Performance Assessments

Some Classroom Management Tips for Performance Assessments	
• Whenever possible, conduct performance assessments as cooperative group activities.	• Have calculators, rulers, and a wide variety of manipulatives readily available.
• Ask students questions that will give you information about their thought processes.	• Cut out pictures or cards for younger students ahead of time.
• Be sure all students understand the purpose of the task. Offer assistance as needed.	• Listen as students interact in their groups.

Each performance assessment is accompanied by a set of teacher notes that identifies the mathematical concepts and skills involved in the performance task and lists any materials that are needed. The notes also include specific suggestions for classroom management, questions to guide students as they seek solutions, and ideas for extending the activity.

Evaluating Performance Assessments

For each assessment, a set of task-specific performance standards provides a means for judging the quality of the students' work. These standards identify six levels of peformance related to the particular task. The specific standards were created using the following characteristics of student performance as general guidelines.

Level 6: Accomplishes and extends the task; displays in-depth understanding; communicates effectively and completely.

Level 5: Accomplishes the task competently; displays clear understanding of key concepts; communicates effectively.

Level 4: Substantially completes the task; displays minor flaws in understanding or technique; communicates successfully.

Level 3: Only partially completes the task; displays one or more major errors in understanding or technique; communicates unclear or incomplete information.

Level 2: Attempts the task, but fails to complete it in any substantive way; displays only fragmented understanding; attempts communication, but is not successful.

Level 1: Makes little if any attempt at the task; gives little evidence of understanding; communicates extraneous, even irrelevant, information.

Since performance tasks are open-ended, student responses are as varied and individual as the students themselves. For this reason, it may be helpful to use these general guidelines as well as the task-specific standards when determining the level of each student's performance.

1. Write a sentence that includes the number 6. Tell whether you used the number 6 to count, to label, to measure, or to order.

2. Ellie says that the number under the sticker is 11. Paulo says that the number is 5. Which answer is correct? Tell how you know.

$$3 + \blacksquare = 8$$

3. Which fact does not belong in this group? Tell how you know. Cross it out and replace it with the correct fact.

$$5 + 7 = 12$$
$$7 + 5 = 12$$
$$12 - 4 = 8$$
$$12 - 7 = 5$$

4. Write five different even numbers. Write five different odd numbers. Tell how you decided which numbers are even and which are odd.

5. Draw oranges in the empty bowl so there are two fewer oranges than apples.

✓

Evaluation of Performance
(See page 19 for scoring.)

Chapter 1

---

1. Write a sentence that includes the number 6. Tell whether you used the number 6 to count, to label, to measure, or to order.

[objective 1]

_____ Demonstrates an understanding of uses of numbers.

_____ Writes an appropriate sentence.

_____ Correctly identifies the use of the number 6.

2. Ellie says that the number under the sticker is 11. Paulo says that the number is 5. Which answer is correct? Tell how you know.

$$3 + \boxed{} = 8$$

[objectives 2, 3]

_____ Demonstrates an understanding of addition facts.

_____ Demonstrates an ability to find a missing number in an addition.

_____ Recognizes that Paulo's answer is correct.

---

3. Which fact does not belong in this group? Tell how you know. Cross it out and replace it with the correct fact.

$$5 + 7 = 12$$
$$7 + 5 = 12$$
$$12 - 4 = 8$$
$$12 - 7 = 5$$

[objectives 2, 5]

_____ Demonstrates an understanding of fact families.

_____ Recognizes that $12 - 4 = 8$ does not belong.

_____ Identifies $12 - 5 = 7$ as the correct fact.

4. Write five different even numbers. Write five different odd numbers. Tell how you decided which numbers are even and which are odd.

[objective 6]

_____ Demonstrates an understanding of even and odd numbers.

_____ Gives appropriate examples.

_____ Gives a logical explanation, such as: even numbers make even groups of two, odd numbers do not.

---

5. Draw oranges in the empty bowl so there are two fewer oranges than apples.

[objective 7]

_____ Demonstrates an ability to use data from a picture.

_____ Demonstrates an understanding of _fewer_ and _more_.

_____ Draws five oranges in the empty bowl.

1. Use place-value models to show why 30 tens and 3 hundreds are names for the same number.

2. Draw a number line to show why 237 rounds to 240 when you round it to the nearest ten.

3. Write two different numbers that fit this description.

   It is greater than 7,000.

   It is less than 8,000.

   It has 4 in the hundreds place.

   The sum of the digits in the tens place and the ones place is 9.

   Which of your two numbers is less?

4. Donna said that this number is equal to 2,635.

   20,000 + 600 + 30 + 5

   Explain why Donna's answer is incorrect. What is the correct answer?

5. Does picture A or picture B show the greater number? Tell how you know.

A

B

1. Use place-value models to show why 30 tens and 3 hundreds are names for the same number.

   [objective 10]

   _____ Demonstrates an understanding of place-value models.

   _____ Shows that there are 30 tens in 3 hundreds.

2. Draw a number line to show why 237 rounds to 240 when you round it to the nearest ten.

   [objective 15]

   _____ Demonstrates an understanding of rounding.

   _____ Draws an appropriate number line.

3. Write two different numbers that fit this description.

   It is greater than 7,000.

   It is less than 8,000.

   It has 4 in the hundreds place.

   The sum of the digits in the tens place and the ones place is 9.

   Which of your two numbers is less?

   [objectives 16, 17, 18]

   _____ Demonstrates an understanding of place value.

   _____ Demonstrates an ability to compare numbers.

   _____ Demonstrates an ability to solve a problem by using logical reasoning.

   _____ Writes two appropriate numbers

   _____ Correctly identifies the lesser number.

4. Donna said that this number is equal to 2,635.

   $$20,000 + 600 + 30 + 5$$

   Explain why Donna's answer is incorrect. What is the correct answer?

   [objective 19]

   _____ Demonstrates an understanding of expanded form.

   _____ Recognizes that the digit 2 must appear in the ten-thousands place.

   _____ Identifies 20,635 as the correct answer.

   _____ States that there are no thousands in the number.

5. Does picture A or picture B show the greater number? Tell how you know.

   [objectives 10, 11, 12]

   _____ Demonstrates an understanding of place-value models.

   _____ Demonstrates an ability to compare numbers.

   _____ Recognizes that picture A shows the greater number since there is one more ten stick than in picture B.

A

B

EXPLORING MATHEMATICS © Scott, Foresman and Company/3

1. What number does this picture show?

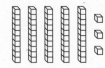

Draw a new picture that shows what happens when you trade 1 ten for 10 ones.

2. In which subtraction will you have to rename the first number?

$$\begin{array}{cccc} 81 & 62 & 96 & 57 \\ -50 & -35 & -32 & -14 \end{array}$$

Tell how you know. Then find the difference for that subtraction.

3. Write 3 two-digit numbers that are between 10 and 30. Find their sum.

4. Tell how to find the difference 79 − 23 using mental math.

5. Suppose that you have 80¢. Name two toys from the list at the right that you can buy. Tell how you know.

Can you buy three different toys from the list? Explain.

airplane	67¢
ball	26¢
balloon	59¢
doll	39¢
kite	48¢
truck	28¢
whistle	36¢

1. What number does this picture show?

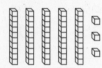

Draw a new picture that shows what happens when you trade 1 ten for 10 ones.

[objective 22]

_____ Recognizes that the number shown is 53.

_____ Demonstrates an ability to rename numbers.

_____ Draws an appropriate picture.

2. In which subtraction will you have to rename the first number?

$$\begin{array}{cccc} 81 & 62 & 96 & 57 \\ -50 & -35 & -32 & -14 \end{array}$$

Tell how you know. Then find the difference for that subtraction.

[objective 26]

_____ Recognizes that 62 − 35 requires renaming.

_____ Gives a logical explanation such as there are not enough ones in 62 to subtract 5 without trading.

_____ Identifies 27 as the difference.

3. Write 3 two-digit numbers that are between 10 and 30. Find their sum.

[objectives 23, 25]

_____ Demonstrates an understanding of the role of place value in addition.

_____ Demonstrates an ability to add two-digit numbers.

4. Tell how to find the difference 79 − 23 using mental math.

[objective 27]

_____ Demonstrates an understanding of mental math strategies for finding differences.

_____ Gives a logical explanation such as breaking 23 into 20 and 3 to subtract.

5. Suppose that you have 80¢. Name two toys from the list at the right that you can buy. Tell how you know.

Can you buy three different toys from the list? Explain.

airplane	67¢
ball	26¢
balloon	59¢
doll	39¢
kite	48¢
truck	28¢
whistle	36¢

[objectives 28, 29]

_____ Demonstrates an ability to estimate sums.

_____ Names two appropriate toys.

_____ Recognizes that 80¢ is not enough money to buy three toys.

1. Explain why picture A and picture B show the same amount of money.

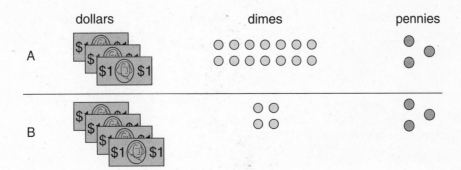

2. Fill in the boxes with the digits 4, 5, 6, 7, and 8. Use each digit only once. Find the sum.

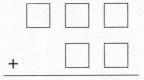

3. Write the digits 1, 4, and 6 to make a three-digit number you can subtract from 400. Explain how to find the difference. Find the difference.

4. Use the information in the map at the right. Write a problem about the distances between the cities. What is the solution to your problem?

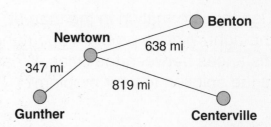

1. Explain why picture A and picture B show the same amount of money.

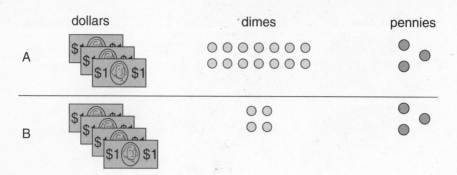

[objective 30]

_____ Demonstrates an ability to rename with dollars, dimes, and pennies.

_____ Gives a logical explanation such as ten dimes are same as one dollar.

2. Fill in the boxes with the digits 4, 5, 6, 7, and 8. Use each digit only once. Find the sum.

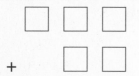

[objectives 32, 33]

_____ Demonstrates an ability to add two- and three-digit numbers.

_____ Writes an appropriate addition.

_____ Gives a correct sum for the chosen addition.

3. Write the digits 1, 4, and 6 to make a three-digit number you can subtract from 400. Explain how to find the difference. Find the difference.

[objectives 37, 38]

_____ Demonstrates an understanding of renaming.

_____ Demonstrates an ability to subtract three-digit numbers involving zeroes.

_____ Writes 146 or 164.

_____ Gives the difference as 254 or 236.

4. Use the information in the map at the right. Write a problem about the distances between the cities. What is the solution to your problem?

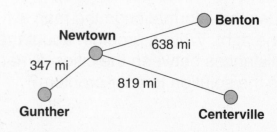

[objective 35]

_____ Demonstrates an ability to use data from a picture.

_____ Writes an appropriate problem.

_____ Gives a correct solution to the problem.

1. Suppose that June 15 is a Friday. What will the date be next Friday? Tell how you know.

2. The picture below shows one square centimeter. Draw two different figures that each have an area of 7 square centimeters.

3. Name something that you would measure in inches. Name something that you would measure in yards.

4. Explain why you would measure the line segment below in centimeters rather than meters or kilometers. About how many centimeters long do you think it is?

5. Fencing comes in 16-foot rolls and 24-foot rolls. How many rolls of each type should Dana buy to have enough fencing for the perimeter of this garden?

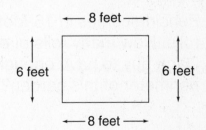

1. Suppose that June 15 is a Friday. What will the date be next Friday? Tell how you know.

[objective 42]

_____ Demonstrates an understanding of a calendar.

_____ Recognizes that June 22 is the date of the next Friday.

_____ Gives a logical explanation such as adding 7.

2. The picture below shows one square centimeter. Draw two different figures that each have an area of 7 square centimeters.

[objective 49]

_____ Demonstrates an understanding of area.

_____ Draws two appropriate figures.

3. Name something that you would measure in inches. Name something that you would measure in yards.

[objectives 43, 44]

_____ Demonstrates an understanding of customary units of length.

_____ Names an appropriate object to measure in inches.

_____ Names an appropriate object or distance to measure in yards.

4. Explain why you would measure the line segment below in centimeters rather than meters or kilometers. About how many centimeters long do you think it is?

[objectives 45, 46]

_____ Demonstrates an understanding of metric units of length.

_____ Gives a logical explanation such as km and m are used to measure longer lengths.

_____ Gives an appropriate estimate of the length of 5-7 cm.

5. Fencing comes in 16-foot rolls and 24-foot rolls. How many rolls of each type should Dana buy to have enough fencing for the perimeter of this garden?

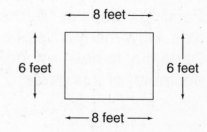

[objectives 48, 50]

_____ Demonstrates an understanding of perimeter.

_____ Recognizes that one roll of either size is not enough fencing.

_____ Suggest an appropriate purchase, such as two 16-foot rolls.

---

1. How are picture A and picture B alike? How are they different?

A 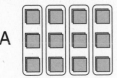 B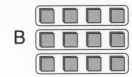

2. Write 5 numbers that are not doubles. Tell how you know.

---

3. Write a multiplication sentence for this addition.

$$17 + 17 + 17 + 17 + 17 = 85$$

4. Draw a picture to show this multiplication.

$$3 \times 9 = 27$$

---

5. Write a multiplication problem that you can solve using the data in the table at the right. Solve your problem. Then cross out the facts you did not use.

Yard Sale	
June 5	Rain or Shine!
books	$2.00 each
records	$4.00 each
dresses	$5.00 each
shirts	$3.00 each

1. How are picture A and picture B alike? How are they different?

[objectives 54, 58, 59]

_____ Demonstrates an understanding of an array as a means of showing a multiplication.

_____ Recognizes likeness such as:
Each picture shows 12 squares.
Each picture shows squares arranged in groups of equal size.

_____ Recognizes differences such as:
Picture A shows 4 groups of 3.
Picture B shows 3 groups of 4.

2. Write 5 numbers that are not doubles. Tell how you know.

[objective 56]

_____ Demonstrates an understanding of a double as a number that can be shown as 2 groups of equal size.

_____ Gives 5 odd numbers.

3. Write a multiplication sentence for this addition.

$$17 + 17 + 17 + 17 + 17 = 85$$

[objective 53]

_____ Demonstrates an understanding of multiplication as repeated addition.

_____ Identifies $5 \times 17 = 85$ as the related multiplication.

4. Draw a picture to show this multiplication.

$$3 \times 9 = 27$$

[objective 58]

_____ Demonstrates an understanding of the meaning of multiplication.

_____ Draws an appropriate picture.

5. Write a multiplication problem that you can solve using the data in the table at the right. Solve your problem. Then cross out the facts you did not use.

[objectives 55, 56, 58, 59, 60]

_____ Demonstrates an understanding of multiplication as a means of solving a problem.

_____ Writes an appropriate problem.

_____ Gives a correct solution of the problem.

_____ Correctly identifies the facts that were not used.

Yard Sale	
June 5	Rain or Shine!
books	$2.00 each
records	$4.00 each
dresses	$5.00 each
shirts	$3.00 each

1. What multiplication is shown on this number line?
Explain. What is the product?

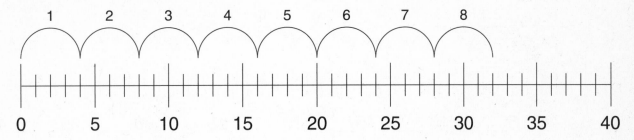

2. Tell how you can use the fact
$10 \times 6 = 60$ to find the product
9×6.

3. Draw a picture to show this
multiplication.

$$7 \times 8 = 56$$

4. Describe the pattern that you see
in these multiplications.

1	2	3	4	5
×6	×6	×6	×6	×6
6	12	18	24	30

Write the next three multiplications
in the pattern.

5. Explain how you could use either
addition or multiplication to solve
this problem. What is the solution?

Mike planted 4 rows of trees with
7 trees in each row. How many
trees did he plant in all?

Evaluation of Performance
(See page 19 for scoring.)

1. What multiplication is shown on this number line?
Explain. What is the product?

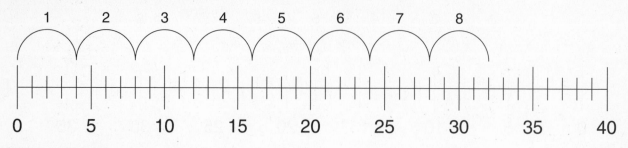

[objectives 62, 63]

_____ Demonstrates an understanding of a number line model for multiplication.

_____ Recognizes that the multiplication shown is $8 \times 4 = 32$.

_____ Gives a logical explanation.

2. Tell how you can use the fact
$10 \times 6 = 60$ to find the product
9×6.

[objective 66]

_____ Demonstrates an ability to use tens to multiply by 9.

_____ Recognizes that 9×6 is 6 less than 10×6.

_____ Identifies the product of 9 and 6 as 54.

3. Draw a picture to show this multiplication.

$7 \times 8 = 56$

[objective 67]

_____ Demonstrates an understanding of multiplication concepts.

_____ Draws an array, number line, or other appropriate picture.

4. Describe the pattern that you see in these multiplications.

1	**2**	**3**	**4**	**5**
×6	**×6**	**×6**	**×6**	**×6**
6	**12**	**18**	**24**	**30**

Write the next three multiplications in the pattern.

[objective 68]

_____ Demonstrates an understanding of multiplication patterns.

_____ Recognizes that the top factors increase by 1.

_____ Recognizes that the products increase by 6.

_____ Identifies the next three multiplications:
$6 \times 6 = 36$ $6 \times 7 = 42$ $6 \times 8 = 48$

5. Explain how you could use either addition or multiplication to solve this problem. What is the solution?

Mike planted 4 rows of trees with 7 trees in each row. How many trees did he plant in all?

[objective 64]

_____ Demonstrates an ability to choose an appropriate operation to solve a problem.

_____ Recognizes that the problem can be solved using the addition $7 + 7 + 7 + 7$.

_____ Recognizes that the problem can be solved using the multiplication 4×7.

_____ Gives a logical explanation.

_____ Identifies 28 trees as the solution.

1. Draw a figure with six sides. How many angles does your figure have? How many corners does it have? Draw a second figure that is congruent to it.

2. Complete the figure below so that the dashed line is a line of symmetry.

3. Name an object that you think weighs about 2 pounds. Explain how you decided on your answer.

4. Does shape A or shape B have the greater volume? Explain.

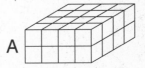 

A   B

5. Match the name with each shape. Then name an object with that shape.

**cylinder   sphere
rectangular prism   cube**

1. Draw a figure with six sides. How many angles does your figure have? How many corners does it have? Draw a second figure that is congruent to it.

[objectives 71, 72, 74]

_____ Demonstrates an understanding of geometric figures.

_____ Draws an appropriate figure.

_____ Recognizes that the figure has six angles and six corners.

_____ Demonstrates an understanding of congruent figures.

_____ Draws a congruent figure.

2. Complete the figure below so that the dashed line is a line of symmetry.

[objective 73]

_____ Demonstrates an understanding of line symmetry.

_____ Completes the shape correctly.

3. Name an object that you think weighs about 2 pounds. Explain how you decided on your answer.

[objectives 79, 82]

_____ Demonstrates an understanding of customary units of weight.

_____ Names an appropriate object.

_____ Gives a logical explanation.

4. Does shape A or shape B have the greater volume? Explain.

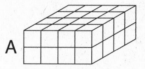 

A   B

[objective 76]

_____ Demonstrates an understanding of volume.

_____ Recognizes that shape B has the greater volume (36 cubic units).

_____ Gives a logical explanation.

5. Match the name with each shape. Then name an object with that shape.

cylinder   **sphere**
rectangular prism   **cube**

[objective 70]

_____ Recognizes the correct name for each shape.

_____ Names appropriate objects of each shape.

1. How can you put 18 objects into groups with the same number of objects in each group? Name as many different ways as you can.

2. The sum of two numbers is 24. The difference is 6. John says that the numbers are 18 and 6, because 18 + 6 = 24. Explain why John's answer is incorrect. What is the correct answer?

3. Four friends plan to share some stickers. They can buy a pack of 10 stickers, a pack of 18 stickers, or a pack of 32 stickers. What size pack should they buy so that each friend gets the same number of stickers? Explain. How many stickers will each friend get?

4. Use this picture to write a family of four multiplication and division facts.

5. Write a multiplication sentence and a division sentence using the numbers 6 and 2. Find each answer.

Write an addition and a subtraction sentence using the numbers 9 and 5. Find each answer.

Chapter 9

1. How can you put 18 objects into groups with the same number of objects in each group? Name as many different ways as you can.

[objective 84]

_____ Demonstrates an understanding of division as grouping.

_____ Identifies two or more groupings, such as:

    3 groups of 6   6 groups of 3

    2 groups of 9   9 groups of 2

2. The sum of two numbers is 24. The difference is 6. John says that the numbers are 18 and 6, because 18 + 6 = 24. Explain why John's answer is incorrect. What is the correct answer?

[objective 88]

_____ Recognizes that John's answer is incorrect because the difference of 18 and 6 is not 6.

_____ Uses an appropriate strategy to solve the problem, such as try and check.

_____ Identifies 15 and 9 as the numbers.

3. Four friends plan to share some stickers. They can buy a pack of 10 stickers, a pack of 18 stickers, or a pack of 32 stickers. What size pack should they buy so that each friend gets the same number of stickers? Explain. How many stickers will each friend get?

[objectives 83, 87]

_____ Demonstrates an understanding of division as sharing.

_____ Recognizes that the pack of 32 stickers can be shared equally.

_____ Gives a logical explanation.

_____ Recognizes that each will get 8 stickers.

4. Use this picture to write a family of four multiplication and division facts.

[objectives 85, 86, 87, 91]

_____ Demonstrates an understanding of multiplication and division fact families.

_____ Identifies the correct family of facts:

    $12 \div 4 = 3$ $12 \div 3 = 4$

    $4 \times 3 = 12$ $3 \times 4 = 12$

5. Write a multiplication sentence and a division sentence using the numbers 6 and 2. Find each answer.

Write an addition and a subtraction sentence using the numbers 9 and 5. Find each answer.

[objectives 85, 86]

_____ Demonstrates an understanding of multiplication/division families.of facts.

_____ Distinguishes between multiplication/division families and addition/subtraction families of facts.

_____ Writes appropriate number sentences, such as:

    $6 \times 2 = 12$, $12 \div 6 = 2$ or $6 \div 2 = 3$, $2 \times 3 = 6$;

    $9 + 5 = 14$, $14 - 9 = 5$ or $9 - 5 = 4$, $4 + 5 = 9$.

✓

---

1. Find each quotient. Describe the pattern that you see.

$6\overline{)36}$ $7\overline{)49}$ $8\overline{)64}$ $9\overline{)81}$

2. Write a family of multiplication and division facts using three of these numbers.

9   6   72

7   42   54   64

56

---

3. Give two examples of division whose quotient is 1. Give two examples of division facts whose quotient is 0.

4. Draw a picture to show this division.

$$14 \div 6$$

What is the remainder?

---

5. Write a word problem that involves the numbers 8 and 2. Tell whether you need to add, subtract, multiply, or divide to solve your problem. Then show how to solve the problem.

6. A class of 44 students is going on a field trip. One van can carry the driver and 6 students, so the teacher plans to have 8 vans. On the day of the field trip, two new students join the class. Is another van needed? Explain.

1. Find each quotient. Describe the pattern that you see.

$$6\overline{)36} \quad 7\overline{)49} \quad 8\overline{)64} \quad 9\overline{)81}$$

[objectives 92, 93, 94, 95]

_____ Demonstrates an ability to find quotients with divisors of 6, 7, 8, and 9.

_____ Recognizes one or more patterns, such as:
In each division, the quotient is equal to the divisor.
The divisors increase by 1.
The quotients increase by 1.

2. Write a family of multiplication and division facts using three of these numbers.

9   6   72

7   42   64

    56   54

[objective 96]

_____ Demonstrates an understanding of multiplication and division fact families.

_____ Chooses three appropriate numbers.

_____ Writes a correct family of facts for the chosen numbers.

3. Give two examples of division whose quotient is 1. Give two examples of division facts whose quotient is 0.

[objective 98]

_____ Demonstrates an understanding of division facts involving 1.

_____ Gives appropriate examples of 1 as a quotient.

_____ Demonstrates an understanding of division facts involving 0.

_____ Gives appropriate examples of 0 as a quotient.

4. Draw a picture to show this division.

$$14 \div 6$$

What is the remainder?

[objective 99]

_____ Demonstrates an understanding of remainders in division.

_____ Draws an appropriate picture.

_____ Correctly identifies 2 as the remainder.

5. Write a word problem that involves the numbers 8 and 2. Tell whether you need to add, subtract, multiply, or divide to solve your problem. Then show how to solve the problem.

[objective 97]

_____ Demonstrates an ability to choose the correct operation to solve a problem.

_____ Writes an appropriate problem.

_____ Gives a correct solution of the problem.

6. A class of 44 students is going on a field trip. One van can carry the driver and 6 students, so the teacher plans to have 8 vans. On the day of the field trip, two new students join the class. Is another van needed? Explain.

[objective 100]

_____ Demonstrates an ability to interpret a remainder in solving a problem involving division.

_____ Recognizes that another van is not needed.

_____ Gives a logical explanation.

1. Draw a picture to show why $\frac{2}{3}$ and $\frac{4}{6}$ are equal fractions.

2. Write two fractions that are less than $\frac{1}{2}$.

3. Group the hearts so there are the same number of hearts in each group. What fraction of all the hearts is in each group? Explain.

4. Give an example to show how decimals are used in measurement.

5. Color the first box to show a decimal greater than 0.5. Write the decimal. Color the second box to show a decimal less than 0.50. Write the decimal. Compare the two decimals. Which is less? Which is greater?

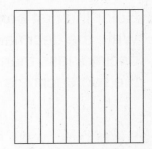

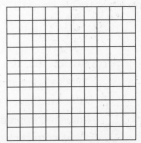

1. Draw a picture to show why $\frac{2}{3}$ and $\frac{4}{6}$ are equal fractions.

[objectives 101, 102, 103]

_____ Demonstrates an understanding of a fraction as part of a whole or as part of a set.

_____ Demonstrates an understanding of equivalent fractions.

_____ Draws an appropriate picture.

2. Write two fractions that are less than $\frac{1}{2}$.

[objective 106]

_____ Demonstrates an ability to compare fractions.

_____ Writes two appropriate fractions.

3. Group the hearts so there are the same number of hearts in each group. What fraction of all the hearts is in each group? Explain.

[objectives 102, 104]

_____ Demonstrates an understanding of fractional parts of a set.

_____ Makes an appropriate grouping.

_____ Correctly identifies the fraction for one group.

4. Give an example to show how decimals are used in measurement.

[objective 113]

_____ Demonstrates an understanding of uses of decimals.

_____ Gives an appropriate example.

5. Color the first box to show a decimal greater than 0.5. Write the decimal. Color the second box to show a decimal less than 0.50. Write the decimal. Compare the two decimals. Which is less? Which is greater?

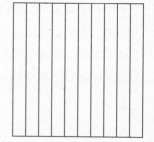

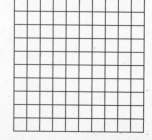

[objectives 107, 108, 109, 110, 111]

_____ Demonstrates an understanding of decimals as tenths and as hundredths.

_____ Demonstrates an ability to compare decimals.

_____ Writes two appropriate decimals.

_____ Draws correct models for the decimals.

1. What time does this clock show? Write the time as many different ways as you can.

2. At the grocery store, you buy items whose total cost is $3.59. Name a set of coins and bills that can be used to pay for the items exactly.

Suppose that you only have a $5.00 bill. How much change should the cashier give you?

3. How are these additions alike? How are they different?

```
  1,247        $12.47
+   253      +   2.53
```

4. The ride from your bus stop to school takes 15 minutes. Starting at 7:15, buses leave your stop every 10 minutes. If school starts at 8:05, what time do you think you should be at your stop? Explain.

5. Betty Ann has made the shopping list at the right. At the store, she discovers that she has only $8.00. Which items can she buy? Suppose she goes shopping tomorrow. How much money should she take with her to buy the rest of the items on her list?

notebook	*$3.98*
lined paper	*$2.19*
pencils	*$1.25*
calculator	*$5.39*
erasers	*$0.95*
ruler	*$1.09*

NAME

▓▓▓▓▓▓▓▓▓▓▓▓▓▓▓▓▓▓▓▓ ✓ ▓▓▓▓▓▓▓▓▓▓▓▓▓▓▓

Alternative Assessment

Evaluation of Performance
(See page 19 for scoring.)

Chapter 12

1. What time does this clock show? Write the time as many different ways as you can.

[objective 114]

_____ Demonstrates an ability to tell time to the nearest minute on a standard clock.

_____ Writes the time in two or more ways, such as *10:37, 37 minutes after 10,* and *23 minutes before 11.*

2. At the grocery store, you buy items whose total cost is $3.59. Name a set of coins and bills that can be used to pay for the items exactly.

Suppose that you only have a $5.00 bill. How much change should the cashier give you?

[objectives 117, 118, 119, 120]

_____ Demonstrates an understanding of the value of coins and bills through $5.00.

_____ Names an appropriate set of coins and bills.

_____ Demonstrates an ability to find an amount of change.

_____ Identifies $1.41 as the correct change.

3. How are these additions alike? How are they different?

1,247	$12.47
+ 253	+ 2.53

[objective 119]

_____ Demonstrates an ability to add amounts of money.

_____ Recognizes likenesses such as:
the digits involved
the alignment of the digits.

_____ Recognizes differences such as:
the place value of the digits involved
the need to include a dollar sign and decimal point in the sum involving money.

4. The ride from your bus stop to school takes 15 minutes. Starting at 7:15, buses leave your stop every 10 minutes. If school starts at 8:05, what time do you think you should be at your stop? Explain.

[objectives 116, 121]

_____ Demonstrates an ability to solve multiple-step problems involving time.

_____ Chooses a reasonable time, such as 7:35 or 7:45.

_____ Demonstrates an ability to determine elapsed time.

5. Betty Ann has made the shopping list at the right. At the store, she discovers that she has only $8.00. Which items can she buy? Suppose she goes shopping tomorrow. How much money should she take with her to buy the rest of the items on her list?

notebook	$3.98
lined paper	$2.19
pencils	$1.25
calculator	$5.39
erasers	$0.95
ruler	$1.09

[objective 122]

_____ Demonstrates an ability to estimate amounts of money.

_____ Chooses an appropriate set of items.

_____ Estimates a reasonable amount for the rest of the items.

1. Tell the number of tens in all.

   4 × **6 tens** = ____

   Then write the number sentence using the standard form of the numbers.

2. Choose a one-digit number and a two-digit number. Explain how to estimate the product of those numbers.

3. What multiplication does this picture show? Describe how to use the models in the picture to find the product.

4. Write a number with three different digits less than 5. Multiply it by 4. How could you find the answer without multiplying?

5. Use the facts in the chart to write a multiplication problem. Cross out any facts that are not needed to solve your problem. Then show how to solve it.

> Balloons come in packs of 18 each.
> Janelle bought 6 bags of marbles.
> Nadia bought 4 packs of balloons.
> Henry bought 3 packs of stickers.
> Marbles come in bags of 24 each.

1. Tell the number of tens in all.

$$4 \times 6 \text{ tens} = \underline{\quad}$$

Then write the number sentence using the standard form of the numbers.

[objectives 123, 124]

_____ Demonstrates an ability to multiply by tens.

_____ Writes the multiplication as $4 \times 60 = 240$.

2. Choose a one-digit number and a two-digit number. Explain how to estimate the product of those numbers.

[objective 125]

_____ Chooses appropriate numbers.

_____ Demonstrates an understanding of estimation in multiplication by rounding the two-digit numbers to the nearest ten and multiplying.

_____ Gives a correct estimate for the numbers used.

3. What multiplication does this picture show? Describe how to use the models in the picture to find the product.

[objective 126, 127, 129]

_____ Demonstrates an ability to multiply a two-digit number by a one-digit number.

_____ Identifies the multiplication as 4×26.

_____ Describes an appropriate method for finding the product.

_____ Identifies the product as 104.

4. Write a number with three different digits less than 5. Multiply it by 4. How could you find the answer without multiplying?

[objective 131]

_____ Writes an appropriate three-digit number.

_____ Multiplies correctly.

_____ Uses regrouping correctly when necessary.

_____ Recognizes that addition could be used to find the answer.

5. Use the facts in the chart to write a multiplication problem. Cross out any facts that are not needed to solve your problem. Then show how to solve it.

[objectives 128, 130]

_____ Demonstrates an ability to use multiplication to solve a problem.

_____ Demonstrates an ability to choose the correct operation for solving a problem.

_____ Writes an appropriate problem.

_____ Correctly identifies the facts that are not needed.

_____ Gives a correct solution to the problem.

Balloons come in packs of 18 each.

Janelle bought 6 bags of marbles.

Nadia bought 4 packs of balloons.

Henry bought 3 packs of stickers.

Marbles come in bags of 24 each.

1. The tally chart below shows some data that Yung-Mi collected from her classmates. What question or questions do you think she asked them? How many of her classmates answered?

school bus	⦀⦀ ⦀⦀ ⫼
car	⦀⦀ ⏐
walk	⦀⦀ ⫼⫼

2. Alan made this bar graph to show data he collected. However, he forgot to write the numbers along the bottom. What do you think the numbers should be? Use your numbers to tell how many students like each type of pizza topping.

Favorite Pizza Toppings

plain cheese

mushroom

pepperoni

Number of Students

3. Karen looked at the grid below and said that the number pair for the letter M is (4, 2). Explain why her answer is incorrect. What is the correct number pair?

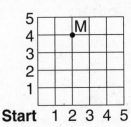

4. Draw and color a spinner with 4 parts so that each outcome is equally likely. Draw and color another spinner with 4 parts so that one outcome is more likely than any other.

✓

Evaluation of Performance
(See page 19 for scoring.)

1. The tally chart below shows some data that Yung-Mi collected from her classmates. What question or questions do you think she asked them? How many of her classmates answered?

school bus	卌 卌 ‖
car	卌 ‖
walk	卌 ‖‖

[objectives 132, 133]

_____ Demonstrates an understanding of data collected to solve a problem.

_____ Demonstrates an ability to interpret a tally chart.

_____ Writes an appropriate question, such as: *Did you come to school this morning by school bus, by car, or did you walk?*

_____ Recognizes that 26 students answered.

2. Alan made this bar graph to show data he collected. However, he forgot to write the numbers along the bottom. What do you think the numbers should be? Use your numbers to tell how many students like each type of pizza topping.

Favorite Pizza Toppings

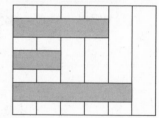

plain cheese

mushroom

pepperoni

Number of Students

[objectives 135, 136]

_____ Demonstrates an ability to read and interpret a bar graph.

_____ Gives an appropriate set of numbers.

_____ Gives a correct number of students for each type of pizza topping.

3. Karen looked at the grid below and said that the number pair for the letter M is (4, 2). Explain why her answer is incorrect. What is the correct number pair?

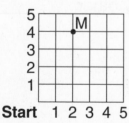

Start 1 2 3 4 5

[objective 137]

_____ Demonstrates an ability to locate points on a grid.

_____ Gives a logical explanation.

_____ Identifies (2, 4) as the correct number pair.

4. Draw and color a spinner with 4 parts so that each outcome is equally likely. Draw and color another spinner with 4 parts so that one outcome is more likely than any other.

[objectives 138, 139]

_____ Demonstrates an understanding of basic probability concepts.

_____ Demonstrates an ability to identify outcomes.

_____ Recognizes the meaning of *equally likely*.

_____ Recognizes the meaning of *more likely*.

_____ Colors the spinner appropriately.

1. Show a way to divide the money below into equal groups with none left over. How many groups did you make? How much money is in each group?

| $10 | $10 | $10 | $10 | $10 | $10 | $10 |

| $1 | $1 | $1 | $1 | $1 | $1 | $1 | $1 |

2. Explain how you can use multiplication to check the quotient in this division.

$$266 \div 7 = 38$$

3. Draw a picture to show this division.

$$44 \div 3$$

What is the remainder?

4. Write a problem that you can solve using this division.

$$73 \div 5 = 14, \text{ remainder } 3$$

Show how to solve your problem. What is the answer? Why?

✓

Evaluation of Performance
(See page 19 for scoring.)

1. Show a way to divide the money below into equal groups with none left over. How many groups did you make? How much money is in each group?

$10	$10	$10	$10	$10	$10	$10

$1	$1	$1	$1	$1	$1	$1	$1

[objective 141]

_____ Demonstrates an understanding of division as sharing.

_____ Shows an appropriate grouping.

_____ Correctly identifies the number of groups, such as: 2, 3, 6, 13, 26, or 39.

_____ Correctly identifies the amount in each group, such as: 39, 26, 13, 6, 3, or 2.

2. Explain how you can use multiplication to check the quotient in this division.

$$266 \div 7 = 38$$

[objective 142]

_____ Recognizes the relationship between division and multiplication.

_____ Identifies $7 \times 38 = 266$ as the related multiplication.

3. Draw a picture to show this division.

$$44 \div 3$$

What is the remainder?

[objective 143]

_____ Demonstrates an ability to divide a two-digit number by a one-digit number.

_____ Draws an appropriate picture.

_____ Identifies 2 as the remainder.

4. Write a problem that you can solve using this division.

$$73 \div 5 = 14, \text{ remainder } 3$$

Show how to solve your problem. What is the answer? Why?

[objective 144]

_____ Demonstrates an ability to interpret a remainder in a problem involving division.

_____ Writes an appropriate problem.

_____ Gives the correct answer for the problem.

Performance Assessment

Chapters 1–3

Materials: crayons or markers, poster board (optional)

Concepts and Skills This activity requires children to:
- add and subtract one- and two-digit numbers
- collect and organize data
- solve multiple-step problem
- summarize results

Management Suggestions
- Encourage students to make a rough sketch of their posters before attempting to calculate amounts and costs of materials.
- Be sure students understand that one package of letter/number sets contains the entire set of 26 letters and 10 digits, in the amounts given.
- Students could work in groups and thus cut costs by sharing supplies.

Helpful Questions
 What do you need to decide before you can determine how many letter/number sets to buy?
- Will you need more than one package of paint brushes? Why or why not?
- What will you need to know before you can find the cost of your poster?

Extend the Problem
- You may wish to have students plan and make posters for a real upcoming event in your school's schedule. Use available materials and display the posters in the school.
- Students could be asked to work within a certain budget. For example, a maximum amount per poster could be set.

Chapters 1–7

Materials: rulers, grid paper, calendars

Concepts and Skills This activity requires children to:
- use data from a table
- create arrays for given products
- use multiplication facts
- find perimeter
- interpret a calendar
- solve a problem by drawing a plan

Management Suggestion
- In planning their gardens, be sure students understand that they are to consider each type of vegetable individually.
- Note that there is no requirement that the garden be rectangular. Encourage students to be creative.

Helpful Questions
- Is there more than one way that you can arrange the green pepper plants?
- How many different ways can you arrange the lettuce plants?
- How can you decide which way to arrange the three types of plants?
- How will you find the perimeter of your garden?
- How will you figure out or determine when the lettuce will be ready?

Extend the Problem
- Have students plan a flower garden for an area in the school yard. Suggest that they research annual and perennial plants, their growing seasons, and their ability to survive the area's climate.

Performance Assessment

Chapters 1–11

Materials: crayons or markers, poster board (optional)

Concepts and Skills This activity requires children to:

- use data from a table
- make and extend number patterns
- use multiplication and division facts
- use fraction concepts
- make a pictograph

Management Suggestions

- To help students review pictographs, you may wish to begin the activity by having a volunteer explain the meaning of the term.
- Encourage students to try and check different values before making a final decision about the amount each symbol should represent.

Helpful Questions

- How large will you make your graph?
- How large should you make each symbol?
- How will you arrange your graph?
- Will all of the students in the school (including the first graders) be able to read and understand your graph?
- What will half of a shirt symbol represent on your graph?

Extend the Problem

- Tell students that the data in the table represents the first two weeks of the T-shirt sale. Have students use their graphs to predict the number of T-shirts that each grade will sell in the next week.

Chapters 1–15

Materials: coins and bills, calculators, restaurant order slips (optional)

Concepts and Skills This activity requires children to:

- read data from a table
- find the value of a collection of coins and bills
- add and subtract with amounts of money
- make change
- make an organized list

Management Suggestions

- Encourage students having difficulty to use coins and bills to act out the situation.
- Some students may feel overwhelmed when finding the total cost of six orders. Encourage these students to add just two costs at a time, but caution them to keep a careful record of these partial sums.

Helpful Questions

- How can you find the total amount of money in the cash drawer?
- How can you decide on the amount of change Mary should get from the $5 bill?
- How can you find the total cost of all the orders? How could you find the total using a different way?
- How will you figure out how much money is in the drawer at the end of the hour?

Extend the Problem

- Have students add some of their favorite foods to the menu and determine prices for them. They could then take "food orders" from each other, determine the total bill, and give change to customers.

Your teacher wants you to design a poster for a food drive to be held at your school two weeks from today. Make a list of what you will need and tell how much the supplies will cost. Choose supplies from the list at the right.

a. Write down the information you need to put on your poster. Think about the time, the place, and what you want people to bring.

b. You will use packages of letter/number sets to make all the words and numbers. How would you decide how many sets you need to make the poster?

c. Rewrite the information for your poster using fewer letters than you did the first time. Will the second poster be cheaper? Which copy do you want to use? Why?

d. How many jars of paint will you need for the art on your poster? Tell each color needed.

e. How much will it cost to make your poster?

Poster Board

white $1

red, green, yellow, blue, $2

orange, black, brown,

purple

Jars of paint

(all colors) each $1

Paint brushes

pack of 3 $2

Letter/Number Sets

One package has
3 each of:
A, E, I, O, U, Y, R, S, T, L, N

2 each of:
W, D, B, P, C, F, G, H, K, M,
0, 1, 2, 3, 4, 5, 6, 7, 8, 9 and

1 each of:
Q, X, Z, V, J

NAME

Performance Assessment

Evaluation of Performance
(For further explanation of scoring, see page 20.)

Chapters 1–3

Level   *Standard to be achieved for performance at specified level*

6   The student answers all questions completely and accurately. Responses indicate a considerable amount of reflection. The planned poster clearly displays all relevant information, and the proposed design is creative and imaginative. The list of supplies is thorough, accurate, and easy to read.

5   The student answers all questions completely and accurately, demonstrating a thorough understanding of the mathematics involved. The planned poster clearly displays all relevant information. The list of supplies is thorough, accurate, and easy to read.

4   The student answers all questions completely but makes some minor errors in calculation. The planned poster clearly displays all relevant information. The list of supplies is complete, but the amounts identified may reflect minor errors in computation.

3   The student attempts to answer all questions, but responses may be incomplete and may reflect one or more major errors in calculation. The student may experience considerable difficulty rewriting the information. The planned poster is essentially complete. There is an attempt to list the needed supplies in an organized manner, but the list may be inaccurate or incomplete.

2   The student attempts to answer all questions, but responses reflect a fundamental difficulty with the mathematics involved. There is an attempt to calculate a total cost for the poster, but the student omits one or more major steps of the process. The student makes a plan for the poster, but the information displayed may be mixed up and difficult to interpret. The list of supplies is disorganized and incomplete.

1   Responses are incomplete and reflect little, if any, understanding of the problem to be solved and the mathematics involved. The student either chooses no supplies from the list or chooses unnecessary ones. The plan for the poster is jumbled, and it may contain items that are irrelevant.

People who plant a garden usually like to arrange all the plants of one kind in rows. They try to put the same number of plants in each row.

Your parents want to plant a vegetable garden. They ask you to help them arrange the plants in rows in their 6 × 12 foot garden. The table at the right shows the number of each kind of plant your parents have.

Kind of Plant	Number of Plants
tomato	24
green pepper	18
lettuce	30
green bean	16

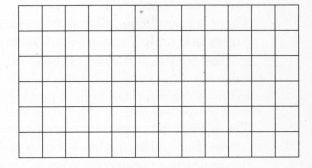

a. Show one way of arranging the green pepper plants on the grid by placing a symbol for each plant in the center of each square.

b. Can you arrange all the lettuce plants in 4 rows with the same number of plants in each row? Tell why or why not.

c. Draw a plan for the garden. Be sure that each kind of plant is labeled clearly in your drawing.

d. In a gardening book, you read that there should be one foot of space between each plant. Find the perimeter of your garden.

e. The gardening book states that lettuce takes 6 weeks to grow. If you plant lettuce on May 10, when should it be ready?

NAME

Performance Assessment

✓

Evaluation of Performance
(For further explanation of scoring, see page 20.)

Chapters 1–7

Level   *Standard to be achieved for performance at specified level*

6   The student demonstrates an in-depth understanding of the mathematical concepts involved. The student's plan for the garden is thorough and neat, and it may be rendered imaginatively. One or more alternative plans may be suggested. The student's perimeter and calendar calculations are accurate and complete. The student may ask good questions or offer additional insights.

5   The student demonstrates a clear understanding of the relationship between arrays and multiplication. The student creates an effective garden plan, and the drawing is thorough, accurate, and easy to read. All perimeter and calendar calculations are correct and complete.

4   There is a fundamental understanding of the relationship between arrays and multiplication, but the student may make minor errors in calculating the perimeter of the garden or in working with the calendar. The student creates an effective plan for the garden and makes a drawing that is neat and organized.

3   The student has a basic understanding of the relationship between arrays and multiplication but may make one or more errors in determining an appropriate array for a given number. The plan for the garden is essentially complete, but it reflects errors in multiplication. The student understands appropriate procedures for calculating perimeter and finding dates on a calendar but makes one or more major errors or omissions.

2   The student displays only minimal understanding of the relationship between arrays and multiplication and has a great deal of difficulty in drawing an appropriate array for a given number. There is an attempt to create a plan for the garden, but the result is disorganized and incomplete. The student is unable to determine the correct perimeter or find appropriate dates on a calendar.

1   There is little or no evidence that the student understands the relationship between arrays and multiplication, and there is no attempt to calculate the required perimeter or to find dates on a calendar. The student produces a drawing that is jumbled or irrelevant.

The students at Jefferson Elementary School are selling T-shirts. The table at the right shows the number of sales so far.

The students decided to make a pictograph to show the number of T-shirts sold. They want to use this symbol on the graph.

Jefferson Elementary School	
Grade	Number of T-Shirts Sold
1	32
2	48
3	72
4	52
5	66

a. Some students think it is not a good idea to use one symbol to stand for just one T-shirt. Do you agree? Explain your answer.

b. Suppose that one symbol stands for 2 T-shirts. How many symbols would stand for the number of T-shirts sold by the third-graders?

c. Suppose that one symbol stands for 4 T-shirts. How could you use the symbol to show just 2 T-shirts?

d. What other number could you let the symbol stand for?

e. Look at all the data. Decide how many T-shirts you think each symbol should stand for. Then make a pictograph to show the T-shirt sales.

NAME

Performance Assessment

Evaluation of Performance
(For further explanation of scoring, see page 20.)

Chapters 1–11

Level   Standard to be achieved for performance at specified level

6   The student demonstrates an in-depth understanding of the situation and of the mathematics involved. All questions are answered completely and correctly. The graph is accurate and easy to interpret, and it may be rendered imaginatively. The student may ask good questions or offer additional insights.

5   The student demonstrates a clear understanding of multiplication and division concepts and is able to utilize them effectively in the given situation. All questions are answered completely and accurately. The graph is neat, thorough, and easy to read.

4   The student demonstrates a fundamental understanding of multiplication and division concepts and is able to apply them to the given situation. All questions are answered completely, but the student may make some minor errors. The graph is well-organized and clearly labeled, but it may reflect errors in multiplication or division.

3   The student has a basic understanding of multiplication and division concepts and understands how to apply them to the given situation but may make one or more major errors. The student attempts to answer all questions, but responses may be incomplete. The student produces a graph as directed, but there may be errors or omissions. (For example, the student may omit the key that indicates what each symbol stands for.)

2   The student attempts to answer all questions, but responses reflect a fundamental difficulty with multiplication and division concepts, and the student is unsure how to apply them to the given situation. The student produces a graph, but it is disorganized and incomplete.

1   Responses are incomplete and reflect little, if any, understanding of the situation and of the mathematics involved. The student produces a drawing that is disorganized. Any attempts at communication are fragmented or jumbled.

Suppose that you are asked to run the school snack bar for an hour this afternoon. The chalkboard at the bottom of the page shows the snack bar menu and prices.

1 $10 bill
2 $5 bills
8 $1 bills
1 quarter
16 dimes
3 nickels
24 pennies

a. At the right is a list of the coins and bills in the cash drawer when you start. How much money is there in all?

b. Your first customer, Mary, asks for a peanut butter sandwich and milk. What is the total cost of the order?

c. Mary gives you a $5 bill. How much change must you give her? What coins and bills can you use?

d. Suppose that you have six customers in all. Make a list of what you think each might buy. What would be the total cost of all their orders?

e. Suppose that all six customers paid for their orders and you gave them the correct change. How much money including what you started with will be in the cash drawer?

peanut butter sandwich	**$1.69**
slice of pizza	**$1.15**
milk	**$ .45**
juice	**$ .72**
oatmeal cookie	**$ .98**
apple or orange	**$ .65**

NAME

Performance Assessment

✓

Evaluation of Performance
(For further explanation of scoring, see page 20.)

Chapters 1–15

Level   Standard to be achieved for performance at specified level

6   The student manipulates coins and bills and adds and subtracts amounts of money with ease. All questions are answered completely and correctly, and the student creates reasonable orders for the six customers. The student may ask good questions or offer additional insights. (For example, the student may attempt to determine the greatest amount that the six customers might reasonably spend.)

5   The student has a clear understanding of the value of coins and bills and adds and subtracts amounts of money with no difficulty. All questions are answered completely and accurately, and the student creates a reasonable order for the six customers.

4   The student has a fundamental understanding of the value of coins and bills but may make minor errors in computing totals or in determining an amount of change. The student answers all questions completely, but the responses reflect minor errors in computation. The student creates reasonable orders for the six customers.

3   The student has a basic understanding of the value of coins and bills but makes one or more major errors in computing totals or in determining an amount of change. The student attempts to answer all the questions, but responses may be incomplete and may reflect computational errors. The student may need some assistance in creating reasonable orders for the six customers.

2   The student attempts to answer all the questions, but responses indicate only a minimal understanding of the value of coins and bills. The student is unable to compute totals or determine an amount of change without assistance. The student is only able to create reasonable orders for the six customers with a considerable amount of assistance.

1   The student makes little, if any, attempt to answer the questions. Responses give no evidence that the student understands the value of coins and bills, and there is no attempt to find totals or to determine an amount of change. The student either does not create orders for the six customers or simply copies items from the menu at random.

Using Free-Response and Multiple-Choice Tests

Teachers use written tests for many purposes. Particularly when it is objective-referenced, a test can be a relatively quick and efficient method of diagnosing the scope of a student's mathematical knowledge. Tests can also provide valuable instructional feedback. And, of course, grades are a traditional instrument for reporting student achievement to parents, administrators, and the community. This handbook provides two forms of written tests that are commonly used, the free-response test and the multiple-choice test.

Free-Response Tests

A free-response test, sometimes called a completion test, is a collection of items for which a student must supply requested information.

This handbook contains free-response tests for each chapter which:

- come in two forms: Form A and Form B

- parallel the Chapter Review/Tests in the Pupil Edition

- are made up of items that are keyed to objectives (at least one for each objective in the chapter)

- can be used as a diagnostic tool for gaining insight into students' understanding of specific mathematical concepts and/or skills

- can be used as chapter pretests and posttests
  to help plan individualized instruction
  to help determine what type of reteaching, if any, needs to take place. (See the Forms for Individualizing on pages 312–334.)

Administering Free-Response Tests

Because Forms A and B parallel the Chapter Review/Test in the student text, the student text form can be used as a practice test helping students feel more at ease when taking the actual test. It also may be helpful to suggest that students show the work they do on a separate sheet of paper and turn it in with the test.

While free-response tests are generally designed for written responses, they may also be used orally with individual students, especially those with limited English proficiency.

Evaluating Free-Response Tests

Answer keys for the free-response tests are found following the tests. While most numerical answers are straightforward, it is important to keep in mind that a student may not use the exact wording given for problems requiring written explanation. Also, it is a good idea to refer to students' work and grant partial credit if the work is correct, but the answer is not. A Percent Table for Scoring is found on the inside back cover of this book.

When administering the free-response or multiple-choice tests, this scale can be used to determine satisfactory performance for each objective tested.

Items per objective	Number correct
1–2	1
3	2
4	3
5	4
6–7	5

Multiple-Choice Tests

A multiple-choice test consists of many well-defined problems or questions. The student is given a set of four or five possible answers for each item and is asked to select the correct or best answer. The other answers, often called distractors, usually reflect common misconceptions or errors.

This handbook provides a comprehensive set of multiple-choice tests. All test items are objective-referenced.

- A four-page inventory test helps assess students' skill levels at the beginning of the school year.

- Multiple-choice chapter tests are provided in two forms, Form C and Form D, with three items for each objective. Like the free-response chapter tests, these can be used as chapter pre- and posttests.

- Four cumulative tests, one for each quarter, help maintain ongoing assessment of students' mastery of the course objectives.

Administering Multiple-Choice Tests

If students have never taken a multiple-choice test before, it might be helpful to give them several multiple-choice items with which to practice. A Test Answer Form for recording answer choices is found on page 305. Further suggestions for administering multiple-choice tests are provided on pages 139–140.

Evaluating Multiple-Choice Tests

The answer key for the multiple-choice tests is located on pages 306–310. There is also a Computer Management System offered with *Exploring Mathematics* that can be used to score the tests and to print out various reports based on the scores.

Advantages of using multiple-choice tests	Disadvantages to using multiple-choice tests
Possible to test many objectives with a single test	Difficult to assess a student's critical-thinking skills
Easy to understand	Does not assess students' ability to communicate mathematics
Easy to determine student errors	Students may guess
Easy to score and interpret	Major conceptual errors and minor computational errors not differentiated in scoring

EXPLORING MATHEMATICS © Scott, Foresman and Company/3

1. Tell if the number in the picture is used to count, to label, to measure, or to tell order.

1. _____

2. Use the rule − 5.
Find the missing number.

− 5	
7	2
11	■
14	9

2. _____

Add or subtract.

3. 7
   +9

4. 1 3
   − 5

5. 6
   +5

3. _____

4. _____

5. _____

Tell what sign belongs in each box.

6. 6 ■ 9 = 15

7. 2 1 ■ 9 + 12

6. _____

7. _____

8. Which fact does not belong to the family?

   1 2 − 7 = 5
   7 + 5 = 1 2
   1 2 − 5 = 7
   7 − 5 = 2
   5 + 7 = 1 2

8. _____

Tell if each number is odd or even.

9. 116

10. 65

11. 321

9. _____

10. _____

11. _____

12. How many more apples are there than bananas?

12. _____

13. Put in order, starting with the season it is now.

summer, winter, fall, spring

13. _____

14. Look at the numbers in the top row. Tell what pattern was used to get the numbers in the bottom row.

14. _____

12	6	10	4	13
9	3	7	1	10

Read this problem and use it for Exercises 15 and 16.

Anya's pencil box holds 10 pencils, 5 erasers, and 1 ruler. If Anya has 6 pencils, how many does she need to buy to fill up her box?

15. What facts are given about the pencils?

15. _____

16. The answer to the problem above is 4. Write the answer in a sentence.

16. _____

17. Write About Math Explain how a family of facts can be useful.

_____

_____

EXPLORING MATHEMATICS © Scott, Foresman and Company/3

1. Tell if the numbers in the picture are used to count, to label, to measure, or to tell order.

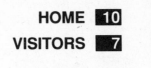

| HOME | 10 |
| VISITORS | 7 |

1. _____

2. Use the rule + 3.
   Find the missing number.

	+ 3
3	6
8	■
5	8

2. _____

Add or subtract.

3. 4
   +8

4. 1 5
   − 9

5. 1 2
   − 7

3. _____

4. _____

5. _____

Tell what sign belongs in each box.

6. 1 8 ■ 7 + 1 1   7. 9 ■ 5 = 4

6. _____

7. _____

8. Which fact does not belong to the family?

   17 − 9 = 8
    8 + 9 = 17
    9 + 9 = 18
   17 − 8 = 9
    9 + 8 = 17

8. _____

Tell if each number is odd or even.

9. 95   10. 72   11. 538

9. _____

10. _____

11. _____

12. How many more eggs are there than birds?

12. _____

13. Put in alphabetical order: horse, elephant, zebra, monkey, bear.

13. _____

14. Look at the numbers in the top row. Tell what pattern was used to get the numbers in the bottom row.

14. _____

4	6	10	3	1
11	13	17	10	8

Read this problem and use it for Items 15 and 16.

Sam planted 4 bean seeds, 8 lettuce seeds, and 6 pumpkin seeds. If 4 bean plants, 5 lettuce plants, and 6 pumpkin plants have started growing, how many lettuce seeds have not started to grow?

15. What facts are given about the lettuce?

15. _____

16. The answer to the problem above is 3. Write the answer in a sentence.

17. **Write About Math** Explain why the fact you wrote for Item 8 does not belong to the family of facts.

16. _____

_____

_____

_____

_____

Use ☐, ■, and • to show how many hundreds, tens, and ones are in

1. 43 ones.   **2.** 29 ones.

3. 14 tens.   **4.** 56 tens.

Write the standard form of each.

5. eight hundred thirty-five

6. six thousand, four hundred ninety-two

In 591,746, which digit is in

7. the hundred-thousands place?

8. the hundreds place?

9. the thousands place?

10. the ten-thousands place?

Decide whether < or > belongs in the ●.

11. 4 5 ● 3 9

12. 5 1 6 ● 6 1 2

13. 7,5 9 8 ● 6,0 3 4

14. Write the numbers in order from least to greatest.

     372   465   391

Write the numbers as you

15. count by twos from 44 to 52.

16. count by fives from 290 to 310.

1. _____

2. _____

3. _____

4. _____

5. _____

6. _____

7. _____

8. _____

9. _____

10. _____

11. _____

12. _____

13. _____

14. _____

15. _____

16. _____

17. Round 34 to the nearest ten.

17. _____

18. Round 762 to the nearest hundred.

18. _____

19. In a three-digit number, if you subtract the ones digit from the tens digit, the answer is the hundreds digit. The hundreds digit is less than the ones digit. Use the numbers below to write this special three-digit number.

19. _____

4   5   9

20. Carlo sold 65 tickets. Only his friend Matt sold more tickets. Choose the most sensible answer for the number of tickets sold by Matt.

20. _____

52 tickets   65 tickets   83 tickets

21. Read this problem. Then answer the question below.

Erin collected 547 plastic bottles on trash cleanup day. Rico collected 822 plastic bottles. How many bottles did the two of them collect?

Choose the question that has the same meaning as the question in the problem.

21. _____

a. How many bottles did Erin and Rico collect altogether?

b. Who collected more bottles, Erin or Rico?

c. How many more bottles did Rico collect than Erin collected?

22. Write About Math Explain which number is the larger one and how you know the answer.

429,581   629,581

_____

_____

_____

Use □, ■, and • to show how many hundreds, tens, and ones are in

1. 36 ones.   2. 75 ones.

3. 21 tens.   4. 48 tens.

Write the standard form of each.

5. seven hundred sixty-eight

6. two thousand, nine hundred fifty-three

In 863,574, which digit is in the

7. hundred-thousands place?

8. hundreds place?

9. thousands place?

10. ten-thousands place?

Decide whether < or > belongs in the ●.

11. 6 8 ● 9 7

12. 7 8 3 ● 9 3 2

13. 3,4 9 1 ● 2,9 5 8

14. Write the numbers in order from least to greatest.

467   371   488

Write the numbers as you

15. count by twos from 62 to 72.

16. count by fives from 385 to 410.

1. _____

2. _____

3. _____

4. _____

5. _____

6. _____

7. _____

8. _____

9. _____

10. _____

11. _____

12. _____

13. _____

14. _____

15. _____

16. _____

17. Round 57 to the nearest ten.

17. _____

18. Round 428 to the nearest hundred.

18. _____

19. In a three-digit number, if you add the ones digit and the tens digit, the answer is the hundreds digit. The ones digit is greater than the tens digit. Use only the following digits to write this special three-digit number.

   2   4   6

19. _____

20. Ellen collected 83 shells. Her friend Cindy did not collect as many. Choose the most sensible answer for the number of shells collected by Cindy.

72 shells   95 shells   83 shells

20. _____

21. Read this problem. Then answer the question below.

Tony counted 89 birds while on the class nature walk. Cara counted 67 birds.
How many did the two of them count?

Choose the question that has the same meaning as the question in the problem.

21. _____

  a. Who counted more birds, Tony or Cara?

  b. How many more birds did Tony count than Cara counted?

  c. How many birds did Tony and Cara count altogether?

22. Write About Math In which number below does the 8 mean a larger amount? Explain.

836,715   683,715

_____

_____

_____

EXPLORING MATHEMATICS © Scott, Foresman and Company/3

Rename. Make all the new tens you can.

1.

Tens	Ones
4	16

2.

Tens	Ones
8	11

Rename. Trade 1 ten for 10 ones.

3.

Tens	Ones
6	4

4.

Tens	Ones
1	9

Add.

5.
$$\begin{array}{r} 67 \\ +25 \\ \hline \end{array}$$

6.
$$\begin{array}{r} 22 \\ +38 \\ \hline \end{array}$$

7.
$$\begin{array}{r} 54 \\ +17 \\ \hline \end{array}$$

8. Add $48 + 25$ mentally. Write which method you used.

Add.

9. $36 + 27 + 12$

10. $41 + 33 + 16 + 8$

Subtract.

11.
$$\begin{array}{r} 72 \\ -46 \\ \hline \end{array}$$

12.
$$\begin{array}{r} 34 \\ -8 \\ \hline \end{array}$$

13.
$$\begin{array}{r} 52 \\ -39 \\ \hline \end{array}$$

	Tens	Ones
1.		

	Tens	Ones
2.		

	Tens	Ones
3.		

	Tens	Ones
4.		

5. _____

6. _____

7. _____

8. _____

9. _____

10. _____

11. _____

12. _____

13. _____

Find each difference mentally. Write which method
you used.

14. 86 − 53   15. 72 − 29

14. _____

15. _____

Estimate each sum or difference.

16. 23 + 61   17. 68 − 19

16. _____

17. _____

18. Gina's club planted 32 maple trees. They
planted 15 more oak trees than maples. How
many oaks did the club plant?

18. _____

19. With $1.00, can Henry buy a 69¢ toy truck and
a 29¢ ball?

19. _____

20. Ramon bought a bag of apples. He gave
10 apples to Luisa and 5 apples to Bob.
Ramon still had 18 apples. Which sentence
below tells how many apples were in the bag
when Ramon bought it?

20. _____

a. Ramon bought a bag with 33 apples in it.

b. Ramon gave 15 apples away altogether.

c. Ramon has 18 apples more than Luisa and
Bob.

21. **Write About Math** Explain the method you
used to answer Item 19.

_____

_____

_____

EXPLORING MATHEMATICS © Scott, Foresman and Company/3

Rename. Make all the new tens you can.

1.
Tens	Ones
6	18

2.
Tens	Ones
3	12

Rename. Trade 1 ten for 10 ones.

3.
Tens	Ones
1	7

4.
Tens	Ones
9	5

Add.

5.
```
  3 4
+ 1 8
```

6.
```
  1 7
+ 4 9
```

7.
```
  6 3
+ 2 8
```

8. Add 46 + 32 mentally. Write which method you used.

Add.

9. 3 1 + 2 5 + 1 7

10. 3 9 + 2 5 + 1 7 + 8

Subtract.

11.
```
  5 2
- 3 5
```

12.
```
  4 3
- 1 9
```

13.
```
  6 7
- 2 8
```

Tens	Ones

1. _____

Tens	Ones

2. _____

Tens	Ones

3. _____

Tens	Ones

4. _____

5. _____

6. _____

7. _____

8. _____

9. _____

10. _____

11. _____

12. _____

13. _____

Find each difference mentally. Write which method you used.

14. 9 5 − 4 2   **15.** 8 1 − 3 7

14. _____

15. _____

Estimate each sum or difference.

16. 4 3 + 5 1   **17.** 7 7 − 3 9

16. _____

17. _____

18. Taro folded 29 paper birds. Ramon folded 13 more paper birds than Taro did. How many paper birds did Ramon fold?

18. _____

19. With 80¢, can Judy buy a 47¢ box of chalk and a 39¢ chalk eraser?

19. _____

20. Eddie ordered a box of pencils. He sold 25 pencils to Marisa and 20 pencils to Fred. He still had 55 pencils left to sell. Which sentence below tells how many pencils were in the box he ordered?

20. _____

a. Eddie sold 45 pencils to Marisa and Fred.

b. Eddie ordered a box of 100 pencils.

c. Marisa has 5 more pencils than Fred has.

21. Write About Math Explain the method you used to answer Item 16.

_____

_____

_____

EXPLORING MATHEMATICS © Scott, Foresman and Company/3

1. Rename 10 pennies as 1 dime. Then write the new amount.

   4 dollars, 6 dimes, 13 pennies.

   1. _____

2. Rename 1 dollar as 10 dimes. Then write the new amount.

   5 dollars, 8 dimes, 9 pennies

   2. _____

Tell how many dollars, dimes, and pennies

3. there are in all.   4. are left.

   3. _____

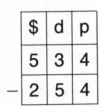

$	d	p
6	2	7
+ 2	7	5

$	d	p
5	3	4
− 2	5	4

   4. _____

Add.

5.   552
  +144

6.   427
  +391

   5. _____
   6. _____

7. 7,338
 + 271

8. 4,587
 + 227

   7. _____
   8. _____

Subtract.

9.   663
 −257

10.   306
 −195

   9. _____
   10. _____

11.   570
 −378

12.   428
 −378

   11. _____
   12. _____

13. 3,194
 −1,415

14. 6,006
 − 592

   13. _____
   14. _____

Use paper and pencil, mental math, or a calculator
to find each answer. Tell which method you used.

15. _____

16. _____

17. _____

15.	2	16.	568	17.	15
	+6		+392		+30

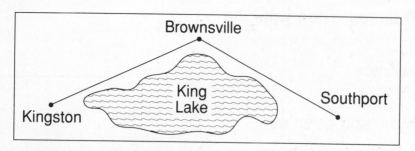

Town	Population
Brownsville	1,971 people
Kingston	3,576 people
Southport	5,324 people

18. Using the map, name the city you would go
through on your way from Kingston to
Southport.

18. _____

19. What facts from the table would you use to
compare the populations of Brownsville and
Southport?

19. _____

20. How many more people live in Southport than
in Brownsville?

20. _____

21. **Write About Math**   What numbers
would you have to rename in   5,903
5,903 to do this problem?   −3,758
Tell how you would rename them.

_____

_____

1. Rename 10 pennies as 1 dime.
   Then write the new amount.

   6 dollars, 4 dimes, 18 pennies

   1. _____

2. Rename 1 dollar as 10 dimes.
   Then write the new amount.

   8 dollars, 3 dimes, 6 pennies

   2. _____

Tell how many dollars, dimes, and pennies

3. there are in all.   4. are left.

   3. _____

$	d	p
5	3	6
+ 4	2	8

$	d	p
8	5	7
− 4	6	3

   4. _____

Add.

5.　 368
   +237

6.　 582
   +259

   5. _____
   6. _____

7.　5,407
   + 368

8.　2,936
   + 517

   7. _____
   8. _____

Subtract.

9.　 528
   −277

10.　 407
    −216

   9. _____
   10. _____

11.　 630
    −239

12.　 826
    −256

   11. _____
   12. _____

13.　4,258
    −2,371

14.　3,009
    − 726

   13. _____
   14. _____

Use paper and pencil, mental math, or a calculator
to find each answer. Tell which method you used.

15.   8
  +5

16.   4 5 7
  +2 3 3

17.   2 5
  +1 5

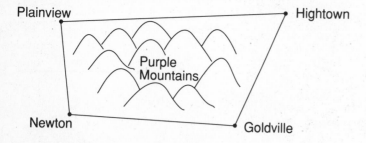

City	Year Settled
Goldville	1880
Hightown	1907
Newton	1892
Plainview	1913

18. Using the map, name the city that is closest
to Plainview.

18. _____

19. What facts from the table would you use to
compare the years when Goldville and
Plainview were settled?

19. _____

20. How many years after Goldville was settled
was Plainview settled?

20. _____

21. **Write About Math**   What numbers
would you have to rename to do this
problem? Tell how you would rename them.

  8,6 2 1
  −5,3 4 7

_____

_____

What time is shown on each clock?

1.

2.

_____ minutes after _____

1. _____

2. _____

JANUARY						
S	M	T	W	T	F	S
	1	2	3	4	5	6
7	8	9	10	11	12	13
14	15	16	17	18	19	20
21	22	23	24	25	26	27
28	29	30	31			

3. Which day of the week is January 19?

3. _____

4. What is the date of the fifth Monday in January?

4. _____

Choose the best estimate for the length of each segment.

5. _____

1 in.   2 in.   3 in.

5. _____

6. _____

1 in.   1½ in.   2 in.

6. _____

Choose the more sensible unit of measure.

7. Width of a chair seat

inch   foot

7. _____

8. Height of a building

mile   foot

8. _____

9. Length of a piece of chalk

centimeter   meter

9. _____

10. Distance across the playground

kilometer   meter

10. _____

11. Find the perimeter.

11. _____

12. Find the area of
the figure in
square centimeters.

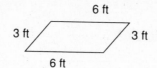

12. _____

13. Choose the most sensible temperature for
swimming lessons.

25°F   50°F   85°F

13. _____

14. Lisa is making prize ribbons for awards. Each
ribbon is 6 inches long. She needs to make 30
ribbons. Should she buy three or four 50-inch
rolls of ribbon?

14. _____

Read this problem. Then make a table to answer
the questions below.

Al, Tina, and Pete are hungry after school. They
find an apple, a peach, and a banana. Al doesn't
like peaches. Pete would like a banana. Who gets
each piece of fruit so everyone is happy?

15. What fruit does Al get?

15. _____

16. What fruit does Tina get?

16. _____

17. What fruit does Pete get?

17. _____

18. Write About Math   Would you use the same
unit of measure for both the height of a tree and
the distance around it? Explain your answer.

_____

_____

_____

_____

What time is shown on each clock?

1.

2.

_____ minutes after _____

1. _____

2. _____

MARCH						
S	M	T	W	T	F	S
				1	2	3
4	5	6	7	8	9	10
11	12	13	14	15	16	17
18	19	20	21	22	23	24
25	26	27	28	29	30	31

3. Which day of the week is March 13?

4. What is the date of the fourth Friday in March?

3. _____

4. _____

Choose the best estimate for the length of each segment.

5. _____

1 in.   2 in.   3 in.

6. _____

$\frac{1}{2}$ in.   1 in. $1\frac{1}{2}$ in.

5. _____

6. _____

Choose the more sensible unit of measure.

7. Width of a skateboard

inch   foot

8. Length of a swimming pool

yard   mile

9. Height of the playground slide

centimeter   meter

10. Distance from Florida to California

meter   kilometer

7. _____

8. _____

9. _____

10. _____

11. Find the perimeter.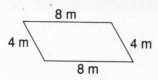

11. _____

12. Find the area of the figure in square inches.

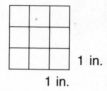

12. _____

13. Choose the most sensible temperature at which to bake cookies.

50°F   100°F   300°F

13. _____

14. Ted is making bookmarks to sell at the craft fair. Each bookmark is 5 inches long. He wants to make 50 bookmarks. Should Ted buy two or three 100-inch rolls of ribbon?

14. _____

Read this problem. Then make a table to answer the questions below.

Su, Lynn, and Raul are buying pets. The pet store has a kitten, a puppy, and a rabbit. Kittens make Su sneeze. Lynn wants a rabbit. Which animal should each person buy so everyone is happy?

15. What animal does Su buy?

15. _____

16. What animal does Lynn buy?

16. _____

17. What animal does Raul buy?

17. _____

18. **Write About Math**   Why did you choose the answer you chose for Item 10?

_____

_____

_____

1. Write an addition sentence for this picture.

○ ○ ○ ○
○ ○ ○ ○
○ ○ ○ ○

1. _____

Write an addition and a multiplication sentence for each picture.

2. 🔔 🔔 🔔
   🔔 🔔 🔔
   🔔 🔔 🔔

2. _____

3. ☆ ☆ ☆ ☆ ☆
   ☆ ☆ ☆ ☆ ☆
   ☆ ☆ ☆ ☆ ☆
   ☆ ☆ ☆ ☆ ☆

3. _____

Write each product.

4. $\begin{array}{r} 5 \\ \times 6 \\ \hline \end{array}$

5. $\begin{array}{r} 4 \\ \times 2 \\ \hline \end{array}$

4. _____

5. _____

6. $\begin{array}{r} 2 \\ \times 8 \\ \hline \end{array}$

7. $\begin{array}{r} 2 \\ \times 9 \\ \hline \end{array}$

6. _____

7. _____

8. $\begin{array}{r} 3 \\ \times 3 \\ \hline \end{array}$

9. $\begin{array}{r} 3 \\ \times 8 \\ \hline \end{array}$

8. _____

9. _____

10. $\begin{array}{r} 5 \\ \times 5 \\ \hline \end{array}$

11. $\begin{array}{r} 4 \\ \times 6 \\ \hline \end{array}$

10. _____

11. _____

12. $\begin{array}{r} 0 \\ \times 6 \\ \hline \end{array}$

13. $\begin{array}{r} 7 \\ \times 1 \\ \hline \end{array}$

12. _____

13. _____

14. $\begin{array}{r} 3 \\ \times 0 \\ \hline \end{array}$

15. $\begin{array}{r} 1 \\ \times 8 \\ \hline \end{array}$

14. _____

15. _____

16. Which picture can help you find the product for 4 times 6?

16. _____

a. ☆ ☆ ☆ ☆ ☆
   ☆ ☆ ☆ ☆ ☆
   ☆ ☆ ☆ ☆ ☆
   ☆ ☆ ☆ ☆ ☆

b. ☆ ☆ ☆ ☆
   ☆ ☆ ☆ ☆
   ☆ ☆ ☆ ☆
   ☆ ☆ ☆ ☆
   ☆ ☆ ☆ ☆

c. ☆ ☆ ☆ ☆
   ☆ ☆ ☆ ☆
   ☆ ☆ ☆ ☆
   ☆ ☆ ☆ ☆
   ☆ ☆ ☆ ☆
   ☆ ☆ ☆ ☆

d. ☆ ☆
   ☆ ☆
   ☆ ☆
   ☆ ☆
   ☆ ☆

17. Arlene's garden has 6 daisies and 8 sunflowers. Each daisy has 4 blossoms. How many daisy blossoms are there in all?

17. _____

18. There are 8 children and 2 teachers in the room. Each child has 4 pencils. Which information is *not* needed to find how many pencils the children have?

18. _____

a. 8 children   b. 2 teachers   c. 4 pencils

19. **Write About Math** Look at the choices for Item 16. Explain the difference between answer **a** and answer **b**.

_____

_____

_____

1. Write an addition sentence for this picture.

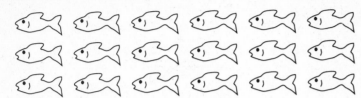

1. _____

Write an addition and a multiplication sentence for each picture.

2.

2. _____

3.

3. _____

Write each product.

4. 5
  ×4

5. 7
  ×2

4. _____

5. _____

6. 2
  ×6

7. 2
  ×8

6. _____

7. _____

8. 5
  ×3

9. 9
  ×3

8. _____

9. _____

10. 8
  ×5

11. 4
  ×7

10. _____

11. _____

12. 0
  ×9

13. 4
  ×1

12. _____

13. _____

14. 6
  ×0

15. 1
  ×5

14. _____

15. _____

16. Which picture can help you find the product for
    3 times 5?

16. _____

a.
◇ ◇ ◇
◇ ◇ ◇
◇ ◇ ◇
◇ ◇ ◇
◇ ◇ ◇

b.
◇ ◇ ◇ ◇
◇ ◇ ◇ ◇
◇ ◇ ◇ ◇
◇ ◇ ◇ ◇

c.
◇ ◇ ◇ ◇
◇ ◇ ◇ ◇
◇ ◇ ◇ ◇
◇ ◇ ◇ ◇
◇ ◇ ◇ ◇

d.
◇ ◇
◇ ◇
◇ ◇
◇ ◇
◇ ◇

17. At the park, there are 8 playground sets.
    Each set has 1 slide and 4 swings. How many
    swings are there in all?

17. _____

18. On Saturday, 6 children went to the fair
    together. Each child bought 1 stuffed animal
    and 3 books of tickets. Which information is not
    needed to find how many books of tickets the
    children bought in all?

18. _____

    a. 6 children
    b. 1 stuffed animal
    c. 3 books of tickets

19. **Write About Math**   In Item 18, how could
    you use drawing a picture to solve the
    problem?

    _____

    _____

    _____

1. A section of fence has 8 boards in it.

1. _____

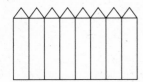

Which product shows the number of boards in 5 sections of the fence?

a. 5×8 **b.** 8×8 **c.** 5×5

Find each product.

2. $\begin{array}{r} 5 \\ \times 6 \\ \hline \end{array}$	3. $\begin{array}{r} 7 \\ \times 7 \\ \hline \end{array}$

2. _____

3. _____

4. $\begin{array}{r} 7 \\ \times 6 \\ \hline \end{array}$	5. $\begin{array}{r} 8 \\ \times 5 \\ \hline \end{array}$

4. _____

5. _____

6. $\begin{array}{r} 9 \\ \times 6 \\ \hline \end{array}$	7. $\begin{array}{r} 5 \\ \times 5 \\ \hline \end{array}$

6. _____

7. _____

8. $\begin{array}{r} 8 \\ \times 7 \\ \hline \end{array}$	9. $\begin{array}{r} 7 \\ \times 9 \\ \hline \end{array}$

8. _____

9. _____

10. $\begin{array}{r} 8 \\ \times 8 \\ \hline \end{array}$	11. $\begin{array}{r} 9 \\ \times 8 \\ \hline \end{array}$

10. _____

11. _____

12. $\begin{array}{r} 9 \\ \times 5 \\ \hline \end{array}$	13. $\begin{array}{r} 9 \\ \times 3 \\ \hline \end{array}$

12. _____

13. _____

14. Think of the multiplication facts for 6 in order, starting with 0×6. What pattern is made by the ones digits?

14. _____

15. How many layers?
How many rows?
How many in each
row?

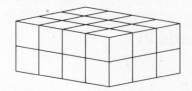

Fill in the missing numbers to find how many in
all.

15. _____

Tell whether you would add, subtract, or multiply to
solve each problem.

16. Gary makes stuffed animals. He made 2 bears,
3 penguins, 4 seals, and 2 fish to sell at the
craft fair. How many stuffed animals did Gary
make in all?

16. _____

17. Nina paints small wooden boats. At the craft
fair, Nina had 5 rows with 6 boats in each row.
How many boats did Nina have in all?

17. _____

18. Tony and Miyo helped set up the craft fair.
They set up 4 rows of booths. Each row had
9 booths in it. How many booths were there in
all?

18. _____

19. Solve Problem 18.

19. _____

20. **Write About Math** Janice has 3 shelves
with 6 books on each shelf. Ralph has
6 shelves with 3 books on each shelf. Do
Janice and Ralph have the same number of
books? Explain your answer.

_____

_____

1. A section of fence has 7 boards in it.

1. _____

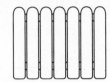

Which product shows the number of boards in 6 sections of the fence?

a. 6 × 6   b. 6 × 7   c. 7 × 8

Find each product.

2.   5
   ×7

3.   9
   ×9

2. _____

3. _____

4.   8
   ×6

5.   9
   ×5

4. _____

5. _____

6.   9
   ×8

7.   8
   ×8

6. _____

7. _____

8.   7
   ×9

9.   7
   ×6

8. _____

9. _____

10.   7
   ×7

11.   6
   ×9

10. _____

11. _____

12.   4
   ×9

13.   5
   ×8

12. _____

13. _____

14. Think of the multiplication facts for 4 in order, starting with 0 × 4. What pattern is made by the ones digits?

14. _____

Continued

15. How many layers?
How many rows?
How many in each row?
How many in all?

■ × ■ × ■ = ■

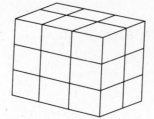

15. _____

Tell whether you would add, subtract, or multiply to solve each problem.

16. Jeff bought hot dogs for the class picnic. He needed 9 hot dogs for each table. There would be 7 tables at the picnic. How many hot dogs did Jeff need to buy?

16. _____

17. Tara and Liz served juice at the picnic. They had 100 cups when they started. At the end of the picnic, they had 65 cups left. How many cups of juice did they serve?

17. _____

18. Allan made fruit salad for the class picnic. He used 4 apples, 5 pears, 2 bananas, and 6 oranges. How many pieces of fruit did Allan use in all?

18. _____

19. Solve the problem in Item 16.

19. _____

20. Write About Math Harry lives in a building with 4 floors. Each floor has 7 apartments. Anne lives in a 7-story building. Each floor has 4 apartments. How are the number of apartments in Harry's building related to the number in Anne's building? Why?

_____

_____

1. Give the name for this shape. Use *sphere*, *cylinder*, or *cube*.

1. _____

2. Give the name for this shape. Use *square*, *pentagon*, or *hexagon*.

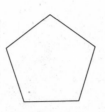

2. _____

3. Is this angle a right angle?

3. _____

4. Is the broken line a line of symmetry?

4. _____

5. Which two figures are congruent?

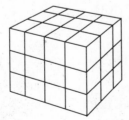

A   B   C

5. _____

6. Find the volume in cubic units.

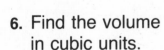

6. _____

Choose the more sensible measure for each.

7. plastic wading pool
   (quart   gallon)

8. Large cooking pot
   (milliliter   liter)

9. Bottle of nail polish
   (milliliter   liter)

10. Mass of a couch
    (gram   kilogram)

11. Weight of 10 peanuts
    (ounce   pound)

12. Mass of a light bulb
    (gram   kilogram)

Write how many of each object would make about 1 pound.

13. 3-ounce apples

14. 8-ounce books

7. _____

8. _____

9. _____

10. _____

11. _____

12. _____

13. _____

14. _____

Mystery Books Read This Year	
Roger	x x x x
Gail	x x x x x
Marco	x x x x x x
Sandra	x x

x = 1 mystery book read

15. Which problem can be solved with data from the graph?

   a. How many more mystery books did Gail read than Sandra?

   b. How many books of all kinds did Roger read?

   c. How many children like to read science books?

16. Solve the problem you chose in Item 15.

15. _____

16. _____

17. **Write About Math**   Explain why the two figures you chose in Item 5 are congruent.

_____

_____

1. Give the name for this shape.
   Use *sphere*, *cylinder*, or *cube*.

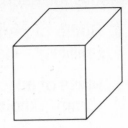

1. _____

2. Give the name for this shape.
   Use *square*, *pentagon*,
   or *hexagon*.

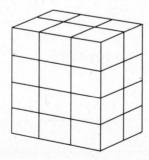

2. _____

3. Is this angle a right angle?

3. _____

4. Is the broken line a line
   of symmetry?

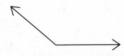

4. _____

5. Which two figures are congruent?

A   B   C

5. _____

6. Find the volume
   in cubic units.

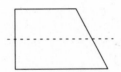

6. _____

Choose the more sensible measure for each.

7. Pot of water
   (cup   quart)

8. Bottle of perfume
   (milliliter   liter)

9. Aquarium for goldfish
   (milliliter   liter)

10. Mass of an ice cube
    (gram   kilogram)

11. Weight of 4 watermelons
    (ounce   pound)

12. Mass of a horse
    (gram   kilogram)

7. _____

8. _____

9. _____

10. _____

11. _____

12. _____

Write how many of each object would make about
1 pound.

13. 6-ounce boxes of cereal

14. 4-ounce pads of paper

13. _____

14. _____

Boxes of Pencils Sold to Raise Money for Charity

Erin	x x x x x x
Kate	x x x x x x x x x x x x x
Raul	x x x x x x x x x
Yuri	x x x

x = 1 box of pencils sold

15. Which problem can be solved with data from
    the graph?

    a. How much money did the children raise
       altogether?

    b. How many pencils did Erin sell?

    c. How many boxes of pencils did the children
       sell altogether?

15. _____

16. Solve the problem you chose in Item 15.

16. _____

17. **Write About Math** Explain how you arrived
    at your answer to Item 5.

_____

_____

_____

_____

The garden club has 6 buckets for members to use.

1. If the club has 18 small shovels, how many shovels go in each bucket?

1. _____

2. If the club has 30 sticks to hold plants up, how many sticks go in each bucket?

2. _____

There are 40 members of the garden club.

3. If the members work together in 5 groups, how many members will be in each group?

3. _____

4. If the members work in 10 groups, how many members will be in each group?

4. _____

5. Write the missing numbers.

5. _____

   ■ tools in all 5 buckets

   ■ ÷ 5 = ■

Write each quotient.

6. 16 ÷ 2   7. 12 ÷ 3

6. _____

7. _____

8. 28 ÷ 4   9. 30 ÷ 5

8. _____

9. _____

10. 2)‾18   11. 3)‾24

10. _____

11. _____

12. 4)‾20   13. 5)‾35

12. _____

13. _____

Write the missing number. Then write three more
sentences to make a family of facts.

14. $3 \times 9 = $ ■   **15.** $5 \times 8 = $ ■

14. _____

15. _____

16. $4 \times 6 = $ ■   **17.** $2 \times 7 = $ ■

16. _____

18. Paula and Jody like to play a computer game.
As of this week, their combined scores are 900.
Paula's score is 40 points higher than Jody's
score. What is each of their scores?

17. _____

18. _____

19. Read this problem. Then answer the questions
below.

Susi works in a pet store taking care of the
mice. Today she is ordering new cages. <u>There
are 36 mice, and there should be no more than
4 mice in each cage.</u>

What does the underlined statement tell you?

19. _____

a. Susi must get rid of some mice.
b. Susi must find a much bigger cage.
c. Susi must buy more than one cage.

20. In Item 19, how many cages should Susi
order?

20. _____

21. Write About Math   When will a family of
facts have only 1 multiplication sentence and
1 division sentence?

_____

_____

_____

            EXPLORING MATHEMATICS © Scott, Foresman and Company/3

The First-Aid Club has 8 kits for members to use.

1. If the club has 40 rolls of tape, how many rolls can go in each kit?

1. _____

2. If the club has 32 special bandages, how many of them should be put in each kit?

2. _____

There are 24 members of the First-Aid Club.

3. If the members work together in 8 groups, how many members will be in each group?

3. _____

4. If the members work in 6 groups, how many members will be in each group?

4. _____

5. Write the missing numbers.

■ rolls in all 6 kits

■ ÷ 6 = ■

5. _____

Write each quotient.

6. $21 \div 3$

7. $10 \div 2$

8. $24 \div 4$

9. $45 \div 5$

10. $2\overline{)16}$

11. $3\overline{)27}$

12. $4\overline{)24}$

13. $5\overline{)25}$

6. _____

7. _____

8. _____

9. _____

10. _____

11. _____

12. _____

13. _____

Write the missing number. Then write three more sentences to make a family of facts.

14. $2 \times 9 = \blacksquare$ **15.** $4 \times 8 = \blacksquare$

16. $5 \times 6 = \blacksquare$ **17.** $3 \times 5 = \blacksquare$

14. _____

15. _____

16. _____

18. City workers counted a total of 850 cars and trucks using the First Street Bridge on Friday. They counted 50 more cars and trucks in the afternoon than they counted in the morning. How many did they count in the morning and how many in the afternoon?

17. _____

18. _____

19. Read this problem.

Pete's teacher asked him to get a new supply of pencils for the class. There are 32 students in the class and each box contains 8 pencils.

What does the underlined statement tell you?

a. Pete can't get a pencil for everyone.
b. Pete must get more than one box of pencils.
c. Pete must find boxes with more pencils.

19. _____

20. In Item 19, how many boxes should Pete get?

20. _____

21. **Write About Math**   How could a family of facts help you solve Item 19? Write the family of facts that goes with the problem.

_____

_____

_____

_____

EXPLORING MATHEMATICS © Scott, Foresman and Company/3

✓

Write each quotient.

1. $42 \div 6$ **2.** $6 \div 1$

3. $45 \div 9$ **4.** $64 \div 8$

5. $0 \div 9$ **6.** $56 \div 7$

7. $6\overline{)54}$ **8.** $7\overline{)35}$

9. $8\overline{)48}$ **10.** $9\overline{)81}$

1. _____
2. _____
3. _____
4. _____
5. _____
6. _____
7. _____
8. _____
9. _____
10. _____

Write the letter of the fact that does *not* belong to the family of facts.

11. a. 7×7 **12. a.** $40 \div 5$
   b. $49 \div 7$ **b.** 5×8
   c. $42 \div 7$ **c.** 8×5
                  d. $40 \div 4$
                  e. $40 \div 8$

11. _____
12. _____

Divide. Write each quotient and remainder.

13. $23 \div 9$ **14.** $70 \div 8$

15. $61 \div 7$ **16.** $58 \div 6$

13. _____
14. _____
15. _____
16. _____

Tell whether you would add, subtract, multiply, or divide to solve each problem.

17. Harold bought a box of 24 pencils. He gave an equal number of pencils to each of 6 friends. How many pencils did each friend get?

17. _____

18. Josie sold 18 packs of seeds. Kelly sold 7 more packs than Josie. How many packs of seeds did Kelly sell?

18. _____

19. There were 65 boxes of baseball cards on the shelf. How many boxes were left after Wally bought 9 boxes?

19. _____

20. Solve Item 17.

20. _____

21. Sara collected 14 pine cones to use in making bird feeders. Each feeder uses 3 pine cones. Choose the most sensible answer for the number of bird feeders Sara can make.

    a. 17 feeders   b. 4 feeders
    c. 5 feeders   d. 11 feeders

21. _____

22. In Item 21, if Sara makes all the bird feeders she can, how many pine cones will be left over?

22. _____

23. **Write About Math**   If you divide objects into groups of 6, the greatest number of objects that can be left over is 5. Explain why.

_____

_____

_____

EXPLORING MATHEMATICS © Scott, Foresman and Company/3

Write each quotient.

1. $54 \div 6$ **2.** $8 \div 1$

1. _____

2. _____

3. $54 \div 9$ **4.** $56 \div 8$

3. _____

4. _____

5. $0 \div 7$ **6.** $63 \div 7$

5. _____

6. _____

7. $6\overline{)30}$ **8.** $7\overline{)28}$

7. _____

8. _____

9. $8\overline{)64}$ **10.** $9\overline{)72}$

9. _____

10. _____

Write the letter of the fact that does not belong to the family of facts.

11. a. 7×9 **12. a.** $81 \div 9$

   b. $42 \div 7$ **b.** 9×9

   c. $63 \div 9$ **c.** $72 \div 9$

   d. 9×7

   e. $63 \div 7$

11. _____

12. _____

Divide. Write each quotient and remainder.

13. $21 \div 4$ **14.** $36 \div 8$

13. _____

14. _____

15. $45 \div 7$ **16.** $60 \div 9$

15. _____

16. _____

Tell whether you would add, subtract, multiply,
or divide to solve each problem.

17. Karla collected 24 shells. Tomas collected 11
    more than Karla did. How many shells did Karla
    and Tomas collect altogether?

17. _____

18. There were 90 packs of stickers on the shelf.
    After Jo-Ann bought stickers, there were 78
    packs left. How many packs of stickers did
    Jo-Ann buy?

18. _____

19. A shipment of 48 goldfish arrived. If Terry put
    6 fish in each tank, how many tanks are there?

19. _____

20. Solve Item 19.

20. _____

21. The computer lab has 6 computers. All
    28 students in Ms. Brown's class go to the lab
    in groups so that each student can use a
    computer alone. Choose the most sensible
    answer for the number of groups of students
    that will go to the computer lab.

21. _____

    a. 4 groups   **b.** 5 groups

    c. 3 groups   **d.** 10 groups

22. In Item 21, one group will have fewer students
    than the other groups. How many students will
    be in the smallest group?

22. _____ _____

23. **Write About Math**   If you separate objects
    into groups of 5, what is the greatest number
    that can be left over? Why?

_____

_____

_____

_____

What fraction names the shaded part?

1.   **2.**

3. What fraction of the glasses are full?

3. _____

Complete each number sentence to show
equal fractions.

4.   **5.**

4. _____

5. _____

$$\frac{2}{3} = \blacksquare$$ $$\frac{5}{8} = \blacksquare$$

Find each answer.

6. $\frac{1}{4}$ of 12   **7.** $\frac{1}{5}$ of 30

6. _____

7. _____

Write $<$ or $>$ to compare the fractions.

8.   **9.**

8. _____

9. _____

$$\frac{7}{8} \bullet \frac{5}{8}$$ $$\frac{1}{5} \bullet \frac{2}{5}$$

Write the fractions in order from least to greatest.

10. $\frac{5}{8}, \frac{2}{8}, \frac{1}{2}$

10. _____

Write each decimal.

11. 2 tenths   **12.** 7 tenths

13. fifty-three hundredths

For each decimal, tell what place the 4 is in.

14. 29.4   **15.** 45.3   **16.** 84.6

Write < or > to compare the decimals.

17. 0.5 ● 0.7

18. 0.4 ● 0.36

19. What decimal part of a dollar is one half-dollar?

20. There are four stores in the mall. A record store is at the far left. A bookstore is between the shoe store and the record store. The toy store is at the far right. What does the underlined statement mean?

    a. The store on the right end sells toys.
    b. The toy store has a bookstore on its right.
    c. The toy store is the best store of the five.

21. Write the letter that shows the order of the stores in Item 20, from left to right.

    a. Record store, shoe store, bookstore, toy store
    b. Toy store, shoe store, bookstore, record store
    c. Record store, bookstore, shoe store, toy store

22. **Write About Math**   Explain the meaning of each part of the fraction you wrote in Item 1.

_____

_____

_____

_____

11. _____

12. _____

13. _____

14. _____

15. _____

16. _____

17. _____

18. _____

19. _____

20. _____

21. _____

EXPLORING MATHEMATICS © Scott, Foresman and Company/3

What fraction names the shaded part?

1.

2.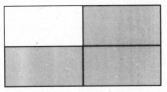

1. _____

2. _____

3. What fraction of the arrows point up?

3. _____

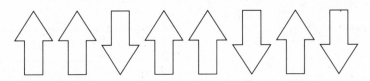

Complete each number sentence to show equal fractions.

4.

4. _____

5.

5. _____

 $\frac{1}{2} = \frac{\blacksquare}{\blacksquare}$

 $\frac{2}{5} = \frac{\blacksquare}{\blacksquare}$

Find each answer.

6. $\frac{1}{6}$ of 18

7. $\frac{1}{4}$ of 28

6. _____

7. _____

Write < or > to compare the fractions.

8.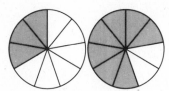

9.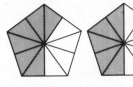

8. _____

9. _____

$\frac{3}{9}$ ● $\frac{7}{9}$

 $\frac{6}{10}$ ● $\frac{5}{10}$

Write the fractions in order from least to greatest.

10. $\frac{5}{6}, \frac{11}{12}, \frac{7}{12}$

10. _____

Write each decimal.

11. 4 tenths   **12.** 9 tenths

13. seventy-one hundredths

For each decimal, tell what place the 7 is in.

14. 47.3   **15.** 75.6   **16.** 35.7

Write < or > to compare the decimals.

17. 0.8 ● 0.3   **18.** 0.51 ● 0.6

19. What decimal part of a dollar is one quarter?

20. There are five cars in the lot. The red car is in the center. The blue car is between the red car and the yellow car. The green car is on the right side of the red car. The gray car is on the right side of the green car. Which statement has the same meaning as the underlined statement?

    a. The green car is the newest car.

    b. The red car is on the left side of the green car.

    c. The green car is in the wrong place.

21. Write the letter that shows the order of the cars in Item 20, from left to right.

    a. Yellow car, blue car, red car, green car, gray car

    b. Red car, blue car, yellow car, green car, gray car

    c. Gray car, green car, red car, blue car, yellow car

22. Write About Math Explain the meaning of each part of the fraction you wrote in Item 2.

_____

_____

_____

11. _____

12. _____

13. _____

14. _____

15. _____

16. _____

17. _____

18. _____

19. _____

20. _____

21. _____

Write each time as minutes before the hour.

1.

2.

1. _____

2. _____

		JULY				
S	M	T	W	T	F	S
1	2	3	4	5	6	7
8	9	10	11	12	13	14
15	16	17	18	19	20	21
22	23	24	25	26	27	28
29	30	31				

		AUGUST				
S	M	T	W	T	F	S
			1	2	3	4
5	6	7	8	9	10	11
12	13	14	15	16	17	18
19	20	21	22	23	24	25
26	27	28	29	30	31	

3. Which day of the week is July 17?

4. What is the date of the third Monday in August?

3. _____

4. _____

Write the name of the coin or bill for each amount.

5. 50 pennies

6. 500 cents

5. _____

6. _____

Write the amount of money. Use a $ and . in your answers.

7. 1 quarter, 4 pennies

8. 2 dimes, 3 nickels, 2 pennies

7. _____

8. _____

Add or subtract.

9. $\begin{array}{r} \$5\,4.2\,7 \\ +6.4\,8 \\ \hline \end{array}$

10. $\begin{array}{r} \$9.2\,4 \\ -0.6\,8 \\ \hline \end{array}$

9. _____

10. _____

Write the change from $3.00 for a

11. $1.40 box of paints.

11. _____

12. $0.98 coloring book.

12. _____

13. Which is the better estimate for $3.69 + $0.89?

13. _____

    a. $4.00   **b.** $4.50

14. Work backward to complete the solution of this problem. Complete the number sentences.

14. _____

Elton's lunch costs $3 more than Gino's lunch. Gino's lunch costs $2 more than Terri's. If Elton's lunch costs $8, how much did Terri's lunch cost?

$8 − $■ = $■ $■ − $■ = $■

15. Maggie sold 4 bunches of flowers to Robyn. Later, she sold 3 bunches to Kirk. Altogether, Maggie sold 5 more bunches than she sold to Robyn and Kirk. Which would be the <u>first step</u> in finding how many bunches Maggie sold in all?

15. _____

    a. 4 + 3 = 7
    b. 4 + 3 − 5 = 2
    c. 4 × 3 = 20

16. In the problem in Item 15, how many bunches of flowers did Maggie sell in all?

16. _____

17. **Write About Math** Cara has 6 coins that are together worth $1.00. What coins might she have?

_____

_____

_____

Write each time as minutes before the hour.

1.

2.

1. _____

2. _____

	OCTOBER					
S	M	T	W	T	F	S
		1	2	3	4	5	6
7	8	9	10	11	12	13
14	15	16	17	18	19	20
21	22	23	24	25	26	27
28	29	30	31			

	NOVEMBER					
S	M	T	W	T	F	S
				1	2	3
4	5	6	7	8	9	10
11	12	13	14	15	16	17
18	19	20	21	22	23	24
25	26	27	28	29	30	

3. Which day of the week is November 15?

4. What is the date of the fourth Wednesday in October?

3. _____

4. _____

Write the name of the coin or bill for each amount.

5. 25 pennies

6. 1,000 cents

5. _____

6. _____

Write the amount of money. Use a $ and . in your answers.

7. 4 dimes, 2 pennies

8. 2 quarters, 1 nickel, 4 pennies

7. _____

8. _____

Add or subtract.

9. $37.14
  +   3.96

10. $8.35
  − 0.77

9. _____

10. _____

Write the change from $4.00 for a

11. $2.70 model car.

11. _____

12. $0.59 battery.

12. _____

13. Which is the better estimate for $4.79 + $0.59?

    a. $5.50   **b.** $6.00

13. _____

14. Complete the number sentences by working backward to find the solution.

A box with 300 crayons, a pad of tracing paper, and 500 sheets of drawing paper cost $7. The crayon box costs $2. The pad of tracing paper costs $3. How much does just the drawing paper cost?

$7 − $■ = $■ $■ − $■ = $■

14. _____

15. On Monday morning, Tony counted 3 birds at his bird feeder. On Tuesday morning, he counted 7 birds. In the week, Tony counted 6 more birds than he counted Monday and Tuesday mornings. Which would be the *first step* in finding out how many birds Tony counted in all?

    a. 7 − 3 = 4
    b. 7 + 3 = 10
    c. 7 − 3 + 6 = 4

15. _____

16. In the problem in Item 15, how many birds did Tony count in the week?

16. _____

17. Write About Math Adam has $2.00 in coins. He has 3 different kinds of coins. What coins might Adam have?

_____

_____

_____

1. Give the standard form for 4 groups of 5 hundreds.

1. _____

Find each product mentally.

2. 80×5

2. _____

3. 40×7

3. _____

Estimate each product.

4. 32×7

4. _____

5. 6×581

5. _____

6. Find how many are in 5 groups of 37.

6. _____

Use Exercises A and B to answer Items 7–12. Draw pictures to help you.

A. 33
   $\times 3$

B. 28
   $\times 5$

In Exercise A,

7. how many ones will there be?

7. _____

8. do you need to rename any ones as tens?

8. _____

9. how many tens will there be?

9. _____

In Exercise B,

10. how many ones will there be?

10. _____

11. do you need to rename any ones as tens?

11. _____

12. how many tens will there be in all?

12. _____

Find each product. Draw pictures to help.

13. 7 × 3 5

13. _____

14. 4 × 2 3

14. _____

15. 5 × 9 8

15. _____

16. 6 × 4 0 6

16. _____

17. Elaine planted 15 flower boxes for her building. Each flower box has 2 rows of flowers with 6 flowers in each row. How many flowers did she plant in each box?

17. _____

18. Fifteen students each drew the same number of pictures for the school fair. Each student drew 3 pictures. Would you add, subtract, multiply, or divide to find how many pictures the students drew?

18. _____

19. Simon worked the problem in Item 18 and got an answer of 12. Does his answer make sense? Why or why not?

19. _____

20. Solve the problem in Item 18.

20. _____

21. Write About Math Does Item 17 have too much information? If your answer is yes, tell what information was not needed and why it was not needed.

_____

_____

_____

EXPLORING MATHEMATICS © Scott, Foresman and Company/3

1. Give the standard form for 8 groups of 2 hundreds.

1. _____

Find each product mentally.

2. _____

2. 7 0 × 6   3. 3 0 × 7

3. _____

Estimate each product.

4. 4 3 × 5

4. _____

5. 4 × 7 9 3

5. _____

6. Find how many are in 6 groups of 28.

6. _____

Use Exercises A and B to answer Items 7–12.
Draw pictures to help you.

A.   1 2   B.   2 3
     × 4   × 5

In Exercise A,

7. how many ones will there be?

7. _____

8. do you need to rename any ones as tens?

8. _____

9. how many tens will there be?

9. _____

In Exercise B,

10. how many ones will there be?

10. _____

11. do you need to rename any ones as tens?

11. _____

12. how many tens will there be in all?

12. _____

Find each product. Draw pictures to help.

13. 6×18

13. _____

14. 3×76

14. _____

15. 4×86

15. _____

16. 5×398

16. _____

17. Jorge made 16 packages of thank-you notes to sell at the school fair. He will sell each package for $0.75. He put 8 note cards in each package. How many note cards did he use?

17. _____

18. At the class picnic, 7 students have the job of clearing tables. Each student will clear the same number of tables. There are 35 tables. Would you add, subtract, multiply, or divide to find how many tables each one will clear?

18. _____

19. Laurie worked the problem in Item 18 and got an answer of 42. Does her answer make sense? Why or why not?

19. _____

20. Solve the problem in Item 18.

20. _____

21. **Write About Math** In Item 17, is there too much information? If your answer is yes, tell what information was not needed and why it was not needed.

_____

_____

_____

1. Write two questions to help you gather the necessary data for this problem.

   Mrs. Jackson has some quarters to give to her children. Each child will get the same number of quarters. How many quarters will each child get?

   1. _____

Toys at School Fair

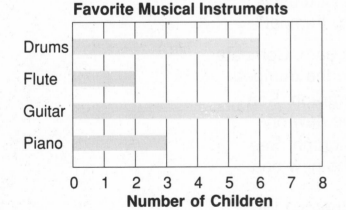

Bears	🐻 🐻 🐻 🐻 🐻
Cars	🚗 🚗
Ponies	🐴 🐴 🐴
Robots	🤖 🤖 🤖 🤖 🤖 🤖 🤖

Each picture means 2 toys.

2. How many more robots than bears were there?

   2. _____

Favorite Musical Instruments

```
Drums |████████████████
Flute |█████
Guitar|████████████████████
Piano |█████████
      0  1  2  3  4  5  6  7  8
        Number of Children
```

3. How many more children chose the guitar than the flute?

   3. _____

Use the grid at the right for Items 4 and 5.

```
4
3      C
2    B
1        A
Start 1 2 3 4
```

4. What letter is at (3, 1)?

   4. _____

5. What is the number pair for the letter C?

   5. _____

6. Tell whether it is certain, possible, or impossible for you to be 25 years old next year.

6. _____

7. A bowl is filled with black, white, and pink pebbles. There are more pink pebbles than either black or white ones. Which outcome is most likely?

   a. To pick a black pebble
   b. To pick a white pebble
   c. To pick a pink pebble

7. _____

8. You have a bowl of buttons. There are 10 gray buttons, 5 green ones, and 3 yellow ones. If you take one button without looking, what are you most likely to get?

8. _____

9. Make a tally chart for the information in Item 8.

9. _____

10. Look at the graph for Item 3. There were 4 other children who chose the trumpet. How could you show which musical instruments were chosen more often than the trumpet?

    a. Add the total numbers for the bars. Compare that to the number who chose the trumpet.
    b. Add a bar for trumpets to the graph. See which bars are longer than the new one.
    c. Add a bar for trumpets to the graph. See which bars are shorter than the new one.

10. _____

11. **Write About Math** Look at the grid for Items 4 and 5. Is the number pair (2, 1) correct for point *B*? Explain why or why not.

_____

_____

EXPLORING MATHEMATICS © Scott, Foresman and Company/3

1. Write two questions to help you gather the necessary data for this problem.

Each person in your club needs 2 new pencils. When you buy the pencils, how much money will you need?

1. _____

Animals in Our Pet Project

Cats	🐱 🐱 🐱 🐱
Dogs	🐕 🐕 🐕 🐕 🐕 🐕 🐕 🐕
Fish	🐟 🐟 🐟 🐟 🐟 🐟
Mice	🐭 🐭 🐭

Each picture means 2 pets.

2. How many more dogs than mice were part of the pet project?

2. _____

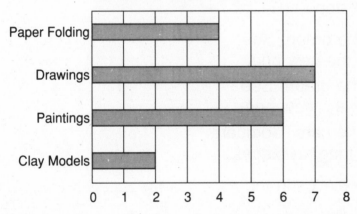

Artwork in Class Show

3. How many more paintings than clay models were in the class show?

3. _____

Use the grid at the right for Items 4 and 5.

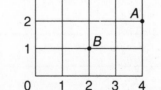

4. What letter is at (1, 3)?

4. _____

5. What is the number pair for the letter A?

5. _____

In Items 6 and 7, tell whether each is certain, possible, or impossible.

6. You will visit the moon and walk on its surface.

6. _____

7. You will live underwater without needing help to breath.

7. _____

8. Most of the leaves on a tree are yellow, but some are brown and some are red. Which outcome is most likely?

8. _____

   a. A brown leaf will fall.

   b. A yellow leaf will fall.

   c. A red leaf will fall.

9. In a bag, there are 15 green plastic clips, 10 orange clips, 5 blue ones, and 5 red ones. If you take one clip without looking, what are you most likely to get?

9. _____

10. Look at the graph for Item 3. There were 5 pieces of string art in the show, too. How would you show which kind(s) of art had more pieces in the class show than string art?

10. _____

   a. Add a bar for string art to the graph. See which bars are longer than the new one.

   b. Add a bar for string art to the graph. See which bars are shorter than the new one.

   c. Add the total numbers for the bars. Compare the sum to the number of string art pieces.

11. Which kind(s) of art had more pieces in the class show than string art?

11. _____

12. **Write About Math** Look at the grid for Items 4 and 5. If you put point D at (3, 2), would it be next to point A or directly above point B? Explain why.

_____

_____

_____

_____

Draw a picture to show how to divide

1. $40 into 4 equal groups.

2. $39 into 3 equal groups.

1. _____

Choose the division sentence for each
multiplication sentence. Then give the missing
factor.

2. _____

3. ■ × 13 = 52

    a. 52 ÷ 13 = 4   b. 52 ÷ 2 = 26

3. _____

4. 6 × ■ = 102

    a. 102 ÷ 6 = 17   b. 102 ÷ 3 = 34

4. _____

5. 3 × ■ = 156

    a. 156 ÷ 4 = 39   b. 156 ÷ 3 = 52

5. _____

Tell how many are in each group and how many
are left over. Draw pictures to help you.

6. $45 into 6 equal groups

6. _____

7. $62 into 5 equal groups

7. _____

8. $83 into 7 equal groups

8. _____

9. Bobbie is making toy carts. He needs 6 wheels
   for each cart. He has 75 wheels. How many
   carts can he make?

9. _____

Use the exercise below to answer Items 10–13.
Draw pictures to help you.

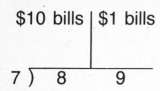

$10 bills | $1 bills

7) 8   9

When $89 is divided into 7 equal groups,

10. how many $10 bills will there in be in each group?

10. _____

11. do you need to trade any $10 bills for $1 bills?

11. _____

12. how many $1 bills will there be in each group?

12. _____

13. how many $1 bills will be left over?

13. _____

14. Draw pictures to divide $56 into 4 equal groups.

14. _____

15. Glory made 35 small jars of applesauce. She wants to give 3 jars to each friend. Would you multiply or divide to find how many friends Glory can give applesauce to?

15. _____

16. Solve the problem in Item 15.

16. _____

17. **Write About Math** How can drawing a picture help you when you divide?

_____

_____

EXPLORING MATHEMATICS © Scott, Foresman and Company/3

Draw a picture to show how to divide

1. $30 into 6 equal groups.

1. _____

2. $60 into 5 equal groups.

Choose the division sentence for each multiplication sentence. Then give the missing factor.

2. _____

3. _____

3. ■ × 17 = 68

   a. 68 ÷ 17 = 4   **b.** 68 ÷ 2 = 34

4. 7 × ■ = 105

4. _____

   a. 105 ÷ 5 = 21   **b.** 105 ÷ 7 = 15

5. 6 × ■ = 144

5. _____

   a. 144 ÷ 6 = 24   **b.** 144 ÷ 12 = 12

Tell how many are in each group and how many are left over. Draw pictures to help you.

6. $70 into 9 equal groups

6. _____

7. $46 into 7 equal groups

7. _____

8. $92 into 8 equal groups

8. _____

9. Jonah has 76 stickers. He wants to give an equal number to each of 7 friends. How many stickers will each friend get?

9. _____

Use the exercise below to answer Items 10–13.
Draw pictures to help you.

$10 bills | $1 bills

4) 9   7

When $97 is divided into 4 equal groups,

10. how many $10 bills will there be?

11. do you need to trade any $10 bills for $1 bills?

12. how many $1 bills will there be in each group?

13. how many $1 bills will be left over?

14. Draw pictures to divide $80
    into 5 equal groups.

10. _____

11. _____

12. _____

13. _____

14. _____

15. Louise made bracelets for her friends. She
    used 9 beads for each bracelet. She had
    115 beads. Would you multiply or divide to find
    out how many bracelets Louise could make?

16. Solve the problem in Item 15.

15. _____

16. _____

17. **Write About Math**   Explain what a
    remainder is when you draw a picture to help
    you divide.

_____

_____

_____

1. Tell if the number in the picture is used to count, to label, to measure, or to tell order.

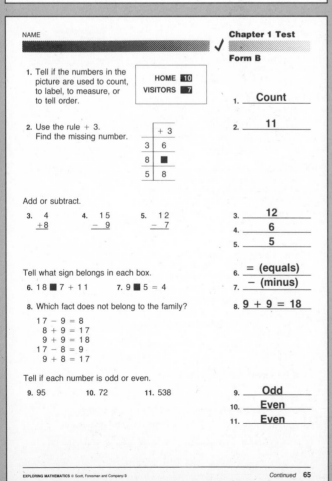

63

1. Label, tell order

2. Use the rule − 5. Find the missing number.

	− 5
7	2
11	■
14	9

2. ____ 6

Add or subtract.

3. 7   4. 13   5. 6
  +9   − 5   +5

3. ____ 16
4. ____ 8
5. ____ 11

Tell what sign belongs in each box.

6. 6 ■ 9 = 15   7. 21 ■ 9 + 12

6. ____ + (plus)
7. ____ = (equals)

8. Which fact does not belong to the family?

12 − 7 = 5
7 + 5 = 12
12 − 5 = 7
7 − 5 = 2
5 + 7 = 12

8. ____ 7 − 5 = 2

Tell if each number is odd or even.

9. 116   10. 65   11. 321

9. ____ Even
10. ____ Odd
11. ____ Odd

---

12. How many more apples are there than bananas?

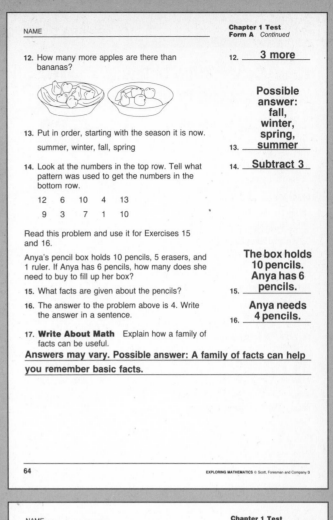

12. ____ 3 more

13. Put in order, starting with the season it is now.

summer, winter, fall, spring

13. ____ Possible answer: fall, winter, spring, summer

14. Look at the numbers in the top row. Tell what pattern was used to get the numbers in the bottom row.

12   6   10   4   13
9   3   7   1   10

14. ____ Subtract 3

Read this problem and use it for Exercises 15 and 16.

Anya's pencil box holds 10 pencils, 5 erasers, and 1 ruler. If Anya has 6 pencils, how many does she need to buy to fill up her box?

15. What facts are given about the pencils?

15. ____ The box holds 10 pencils. Anya has 6 pencils.

16. The answer to the problem above is 4. Write the answer in a sentence.

16. ____ Anya needs 4 pencils.

17. **Write About Math** Explain how a family of facts can be useful.

Answers may vary. Possible answer: A family of facts can help you remember basic facts.

---

1. Tell if the numbers in the picture are used to count, to label, to measure, or to tell order.

HOME ■ 10
VISITORS ■ 7

1. ____ Count

2. Use the rule + 3. Find the missing number.

	+ 3
3	6
8	■
5	8

2. ____ 11

Add or subtract.

3. 4   4. 15   5. 12
  +8   − 9   − 7

3. ____ 12
4. ____ 6
5. ____ 5

Tell what sign belongs in each box.

6. 18 ■ 7 + 11   7. 9 ■ 5 = 4

6. ____ = (equals)
7. ____ − (minus)

8. Which fact does not belong to the family?

17 − 9 = 8
8 + 9 = 17
9 + 9 = 18
17 − 8 = 9
9 + 8 = 17

8. ____ 9 + 9 = 18

Tell if each number is odd or even.

9. 95   10. 72   11. 538

9. ____ Odd
10. ____ Even
11. ____ Even

---

12. How many more eggs are there than birds?

12. ____ 4 more

13. Put in alphabetical order: horse, elephant, zebra, monkey, bear.

13. ____ Bear, elephant, horse, monkey, zebra

14. Look at the numbers in the top row. Tell what pattern was used to get the numbers in the bottom row.

4   6   10   3   1
11   13   17   10   8

14. ____ Add 7

Read this problem and use it for Items 15 and 16.

Sam planted 4 bean seeds, 8 lettuce seeds, and 6 pumpkin seeds. If 4 bean plants, 5 lettuce plants, and 6 pumpkin plants have started growing, how many lettuce seeds have not started to grow?

15. What facts are given about the lettuce?

15. ____ Sam planted 8 lettuce seeds. 5 are growing.

16. The answer to the problem above is 3. Write the answer in a sentence.

17. **Write About Math** Explain why the fact you wrote for Item 8 does not belong to the family of facts.

16. ____ 3 lettuce seeds have not started to grow.

Answers may vary. Possible answer: 9 + 9 = 18 does not belong because the family of facts is for 8, 9, and 17.

Use ☐, ▪, and • to show how many hundreds, tens, and ones are in

1. 43 ones.   2. 29 ones.

3. 14 tens.   4. 56 tens.

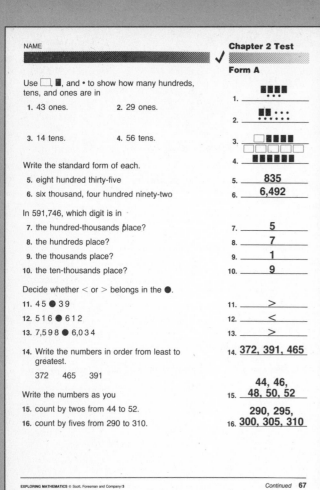

1. ▪▪▪▪ •••

2. ▪▪ •••••

3. ☐▪▪▪▪ / ☐☐☐☐☐

4. ▪▪▪▪▪▪

Write the standard form of each.

5. eight hundred thirty-five   5. **835**

6. six thousand, four hundred ninety-two   6. **6,492**

In 591,746, which digit is in

7. the hundred-thousands place?   7. **5**

8. the hundreds place?   8. **7**

9. the thousands place?   9. **1**

10. the ten-thousands place?   10. **9**

Decide whether < or > belongs in the ●.

11. 45 ● 39   11. **>**

12. 516 ● 612   12. **<**

13. 7,598 ● 6,034   13. **>**

14. Write the numbers in order from least to greatest.
372   465   391   14. **372, 391, 465**

Write the numbers as you

15. count by twos from 44 to 52.   15. **44, 46, 48, 50, 52**

16. count by fives from 290 to 310.   16. **290, 295, 300, 305, 310**

---

17. Round 34 to the nearest ten.   17. **30**

18. Round 762 to the nearest hundred.   18. **800**

19. In a three-digit number, if you subtract the ones digit from the tens digit, the answer is the hundreds digit. The hundreds digit is less than the ones digit. Use the numbers below to write this special three-digit number.
4   5   9   19. **495**

20. Carlo sold 65 tickets. Only his friend Matt sold more tickets. Choose the most sensible answer for the number of tickets sold by Matt.
52 tickets   65 tickets   83 tickets   20. **83 tickets**

21. Read this problem. Then answer the question below.

Erin collected 547 plastic bottles on trash cleanup day. Rico collected 822 plastic bottles. How many bottles did the two of them collect?

Choose the question that has the same meaning as the question in the problem.   21. **a**

a. How many bottles did Erin and Rico collect altogether?

b. Who collected more bottles, Erin or Rico?

c. How many more bottles did Rico collect than Erin collected?

22. **Write About Math** Explain which number is the larger one and how you know the answer.
429,581   629,581

629,581 is larger; Possible explanation: The number in the hundred-thousands place is larger.

Use ☐, ▪, and • to show how many hundreds, tens, and ones are in

1. 36 ones.   2. 75 ones.

3. 21 tens.   4. 48 tens.

1. ▪▪▪ ••••••

2. ▪▪▪▪▪▪▪ •••••

3. ☐☐▪

4. ▪▪▪▪▪▪▪▪

Write the standard form of each.

5. seven hundred sixty-eight   5. **768**

6. two thousand, nine hundred fifty-three   6. **2,953**

In 863,574, which digit is in the

7. hundred-thousands place?   7. **8**

8. hundreds place?   8. **5**

9. thousands place?   9. **3**

10. ten-thousands place?   10. **6**

Decide whether < or > belongs in the ●.

11. 68 ● 97   11. **<**

12. 783 ● 932   12. **<**

13. 3,491 ● 2,958   13. **>**

14. Write the numbers in order from least to greatest.
467   371   488   14. **371, 467, 488**

Write the numbers as you

15. count by twos from 62 to 72.   15. **62, 64, 66, 68, 70, 72**

16. count by fives from 385 to 410.   16. **385, 390, 395, 400, 405, 410**

---

17. Round 57 to the nearest ten.   17. **60**

18. Round 428 to the nearest hundred.   18. **400**

19. In a three-digit number, if you add the ones digit and the tens digit, the answer is the hundreds digit. The ones digit is greater than the tens digit. Use only the following digits to write this special three-digit number.
2   4   6   19. **624**

20. Ellen collected 83 shells. Her friend Cindy did not collect as many. Choose the most sensible answer for the number of shells collected by Cindy.
72 shells   95 shells   83 shells   20. **72 shells**

21. Read this problem. Then answer the question below.

Tony counted 89 birds while on the class nature walk. Cara counted 67 birds. How many did the two of them count?

Choose the question that has the same meaning as the question in the problem.   21. **c**

a. Who counted more birds, Tony or Cara?

b. How many more birds did Tony count than Cara counted?

c. How many birds did Tony and Cara count altogether?

22. **Write About Math** In which number below does the 8 mean a larger amount? Explain.
836,715   683,715

836,715; Possible explanation: In 836,715, the 8 means 8 hundred-thousand. In 683,715 it means 8 ten-thousand.

Rename. Make all the new tens you can.

1.	Tens	Ones
	4	16

2.	Tens	Ones
	8	11

Rename. Trade 1 ten for 10 ones.

3.	Tens	Ones
	6	4

4.	Tens	Ones
	1	9

Add.

5. 67
   +25

6. 22
   +38

7. 54
   +17

8. Add 48 + 25 mentally. Write which method you used.

Add.

9. 36 + 27 + 12

10. 41 + 33 + 16 + 8

Subtract.

11. 72
    −46

12. 34
    − 8

13. 52
    −39

1.	Tens	Ones
	5	6

2.	Tens	Ones
	9	1

3.	Tens	Ones
	5	14

4.	Tens	Ones
	0	19

5. ____92____

6. ____60____

7. ____71____

8. **73; Sample method:** $50 + 25 = 75$, $75 − 2 = 73$

9. ____75____

10. ____98____

11. ____26____

12. ____26____

13. ____13____

Find each difference mentally. Write which method you used. **Sample methods given**

14. 8 6 − 5 3   15. 7 2 − 2 9

Estimate each sum or difference.

16. 2 3 + 6 1   17. 6 8 − 1 9

18. Gina's club planted 32 maple trees. They planted 15 more oak trees than maples. How many oaks did the club plant?

19. With $1.00, can Henry buy a 69¢ toy truck and a 29¢ ball?

20. Ramon bought a bag of apples. He gave 10 apples to Luisa and 5 apples to Bob. Ramon still had 18 apples. Which sentence below tells how many apples were in the bag when Ramon bought it?

   a. Ramon bought a bag with 33 apples in it.

   b. Ramon gave 15 apples away altogether.

   c. Ramon has 18 apples more than Luisa and Bob.

21. **Write About Math** Explain the method you used to answer Item 19.

Answers may vary. Possible explanation: 69¢ rounds up to 70¢ and 29¢ rounds up to 30¢. 70¢ + 30¢ = $1.00.

14. **33;** $86 − 50 = 36$, ____$36 − 3 = 33$____

15. **43;** $72 − 30 = 42$, ____$42 + 1 = 43$____

Sample estimates given

16. ____80____

17. ____50____

18. ____47 oaks____

19. ____Yes____

20. ____a____

Rename. Make all the new tens you can.

1.	Tens	Ones
	6	18

2.	Tens	Ones
	3	12

Rename. Trade 1 ten for 10 ones.

3.	Tens	Ones
	1	7

4.	Tens	Ones
	9	5

Add.

5. 34
   +18

6. 17
   +49

7. 63
   +28

8. Add 46 + 32 mentally. Write which method you used.

Add.

9. 31 + 25 + 17

10. 39 + 25 + 17 + 8

Subtract.

11. 52
    −35

12. 43
    −19

13. 67
    −28

1.	Tens	Ones
	7	8

2.	Tens	Ones
	4	2

3.	Tens	Ones
	0	17

4.	Tens	Ones
	8	15

5. ____52____

6. ____66____

7. ____91____

8. **78; Sample method:** $46 + 30 = 76$, $76 + 2 = 78$

9. ____73____

10. ____89____

11. ____17____

12. ____24____

13. ____39____

Find each difference mentally. Write which method you used. **Sample methods given**

14. 9 5 − 4 2   15. 8 1 − 3 7

Estimate each sum or difference.

16. 4 3 + 5 1   17. 7 7 − 3 9

18. Taro folded 29 paper birds. Ramon folded 13 more paper birds than Taro did. How many paper birds did Ramon fold?

19. With 80¢, can Judy buy a 47¢ box of chalk and a 39¢ chalk eraser?

20. Eddie ordered a box of pencils. He sold 25 pencils to Marisa and 20 pencils to Fred. He still had 55 pencils left to sell. Which sentence below tells how many pencils were in the box he ordered?

   a. Eddie sold 45 pencils to Marisa and Fred.

   b. Eddie ordered a box of 100 pencils.

   c. Marisa has 5 more pencils than Fred has.

21. **Write About Math** Explain the method you used to answer Item 16.

Answers may vary. Possible answer: I rounded 43 to 40 and 51 to 50. 40 + 50 = 90.

14. **53;** $95 − 40 = 55$, ____$55 − 2 = 53$____

15. **44;** $81 − 40 = 41$, ____$41 + 3 = 44$____

Sample estimates given

16. ____90____

17. ____40____

18. ____42 birds____

19. ____No____

20. ____b____

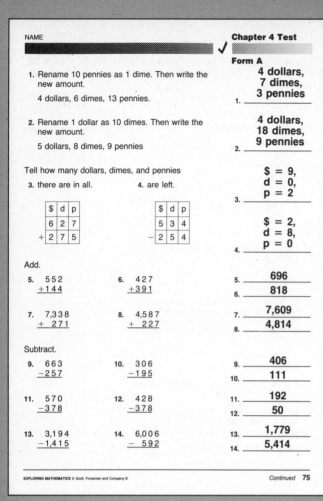

1. Rename 10 pennies as 1 dime. Then write the new amount.

   4 dollars, 6 dimes, 13 pennies.

1. ____ 4 dollars, 7 dimes, 3 pennies

2. Rename 1 dollar as 10 dimes. Then write the new amount.

   5 dollars, 8 dimes, 9 pennies

2. ____ 4 dollars, 18 dimes, 9 pennies

Tell how many dollars, dimes, and pennies

3. there are in all.

$	d	p
6	2	7
+2	7	5

3. ____ $ = 9, d = 0, p = 2

4. are left.

$	d	p
5	3	4
−2	5	4

4. ____ $ = 2, d = 8, p = 0

Add.

5. 552 +144   6. 427 +391

5. ____ 696
6. ____ 818

7. 7,338 + 271   8. 4,587 + 227

7. ____ 7,609
8. ____ 4,814

Subtract.

9. 663 −257   10. 306 −195

9. ____ 406
10. ____ 111

11. 570 −378   12. 428 −378

11. ____ 192
12. ____ 50

13. 3,194 −1,415   14. 6,006 − 592

13. ____ 1,779
14. ____ 5,414

Use paper and pencil, mental math, or a calculator to find each answer. Tell which method you used.

Method choices may vary.

15. 2 +6   16. 568 +392   17. 15 +30

15. ____ 8; M
16. ____ 960; P or C
17. ____ 45; M or P

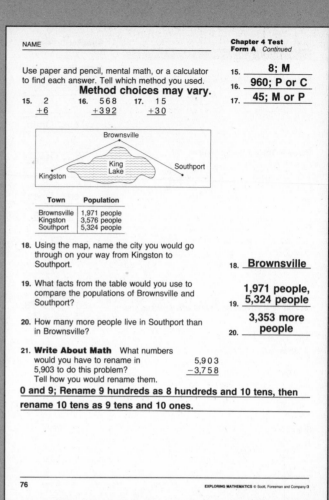

Town	Population
Brownsville	1,971 people
Kingston	3,576 people
Southport	5,324 people

18. Using the map, name the city you would go through on your way from Kingston to Southport.

18. ____ **Brownsville**

19. What facts from the table would you use to compare the populations of Brownsville and Southport?

19. ____ **1,971 people, 5,324 people**

20. How many more people live in Southport than in Brownsville?

20. ____ **3,353 more people**

21. **Write About Math** What numbers would you have to rename in 5,903 to do this problem? Tell how you would rename them.

   5,903 −3,758

0 and 9; Rename 9 hundreds as 8 hundreds and 10 tens, then rename 10 tens as 9 tens and 10 ones.

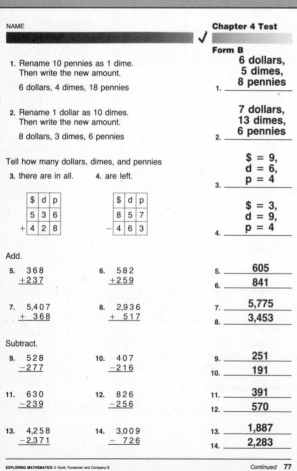

1. Rename 10 pennies as 1 dime. Then write the new amount.

   6 dollars, 4 dimes, 18 pennies

1. ____ 6 dollars, 5 dimes, 8 pennies

2. Rename 1 dollar as 10 dimes. Then write the new amount.

   8 dollars, 3 dimes, 6 pennies

2. ____ 7 dollars, 13 dimes, 6 pennies

Tell how many dollars, dimes, and pennies

3. there are in all.

$	d	p
5	3	6
+4	2	8

3. ____ $ = 9, d = 6, p = 4

4. are left.

$	d	p
8	5	7
−4	6	3

4. ____ $ = 3, d = 9, p = 4

Add.

5. 368 +237   6. 582 +259

5. ____ 605
6. ____ 841

7. 5,407 + 368   8. 2,936 + 517

7. ____ 5,775
8. ____ 3,453

Subtract.

9. 528 −277   10. 407 −216

9. ____ 251
10. ____ 191

11. 630 −239   12. 826 −256

11. ____ 391
12. ____ 570

13. 4,258 −2,371   14. 3,009 − 726

13. ____ 1,887
14. ____ 2,283

Use paper and pencil, mental math, or a calculator to find each answer. Tell which method you used.

Sample method choices given

15. 8 +5   16. 457 +233   17. 25 +15

15. ____ 13; M
16. ____ 690; P or C
17. ____ 40; M or P

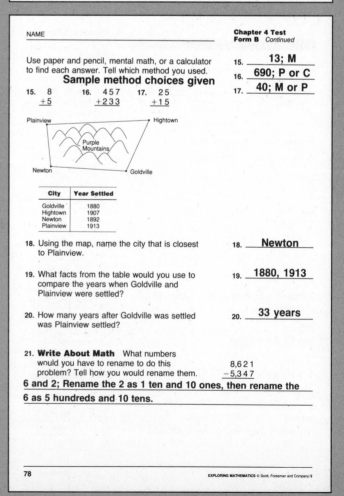

City	Year Settled
Goldville	1880
Hightown	1907
Newton	1892
Plainview	1913

18. Using the map, name the city that is closest to Plainview.

18. ____ **Newton**

19. What facts from the table would you use to compare the years when Goldville and Plainview were settled?

19. ____ **1880, 1913**

20. How many years after Goldville was settled was Plainview settled?

20. ____ **33 years**

21. **Write About Math** What numbers would you have to rename to do this problem? Tell how you would rename them.

   8,621 −5,347

6 and 2; Rename the 2 as 1 ten and 10 ones, then rename the 6 as 5 hundreds and 10 tens.

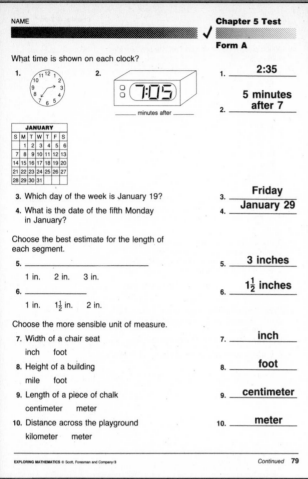

What time is shown on each clock?

1.
2.

1. _____ **2:35**
2. _____ **5 minutes after 7**

minutes after

JANUARY

S	M	T	W	T	F	S
		1	2	3	4	5	6
7	8	9	10	11	12	13
14	15	16	17	18	19	20
21	22	23	24	25	26	27
28	29	30	31			

3. Which day of the week is January 19?
4. What is the date of the fifth Monday in January?

3. _____ **Friday**
4. _____ **January 29**

Choose the best estimate for the length of each segment.

5. _____

   1 in.   2 in.   3 in.

6. _____

   1 in. $1\frac{1}{2}$ in.   2 in.

5. _____ **3 inches**
6. _____ **$1\frac{1}{2}$ inches**

Choose the more sensible unit of measure.

7. Width of a chair seat

   inch   foot

8. Height of a building

   mile   foot

9. Length of a piece of chalk

   centimeter   meter

10. Distance across the playground

   kilometer   meter

7. _____ **inch**
8. _____ **foot**
9. _____ **centimeter**
10. _____ **meter**

---

11. Find the perimeter.

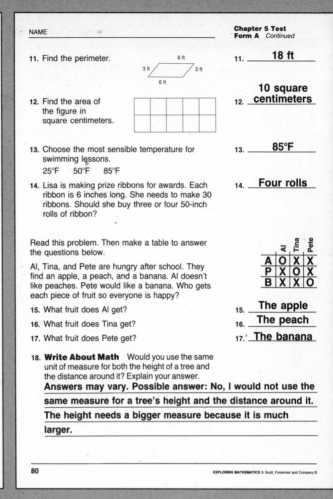

11. _____ **18 ft**

12. Find the area of the figure in square centimeters.

12. _____ **10 square centimeters**

13. Choose the most sensible temperature for swimming lessons.

   25°F   50°F   85°F

13. _____ **85°F**

14. Lisa is making prize ribbons for awards. Each ribbon is 6 inches long. She needs to make 30 ribbons. Should she buy three or four 50-inch rolls of ribbon?

14. _____ **Four rolls**

Read this problem. Then make a table to answer the questions below.

Al, Tina, and Pete are hungry after school. They find an apple, a peach, and a banana. Al doesn't like peaches. Pete would like a banana. Who gets each piece of fruit so everyone is happy?

	Al	Tina	Pete
A	O	X	X
P	X	O	X
B	X	X	O

15. What fruit does Al get?
16. What fruit does Tina get?
17. What fruit does Pete get?

15. _____ **The apple**
16. _____ **The peach**
17. _____ **The banana**

18. **Write About Math** Would you use the same unit of measure for both the height of a tree and the distance around it? Explain your answer.

Answers may vary. Possible answer: No, I would not use the same measure for a tree's height and the distance around it. The height needs a bigger measure because it is much larger.

What time is shown on each clock?

1.
2.

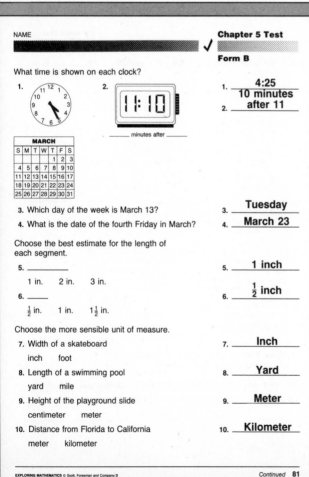

1. _____ **4:25**
2. _____ **10 minutes after 11**

minutes after

MARCH

S	M	T	W	T	F	S
					1	2	3
4	5	6	7	8	9	10
11	12	13	14	15	16	17
18	19	20	21	22	23	24
25	26	27	28	29	30	31

3. Which day of the week is March 13?
4. What is the date of the fourth Friday in March?

3. _____ **Tuesday**
4. _____ **March 23**

Choose the best estimate for the length of each segment.

5. ____

   1 in.   2 in.   3 in.

6. ____

   $\frac{1}{2}$ in.   1 in. $1\frac{1}{2}$ in.

5. _____ **1 inch**
6. _____ **$\frac{1}{2}$ inch**

Choose the more sensible unit of measure.

7. Width of a skateboard

   inch   foot

8. Length of a swimming pool

   yard   mile

9. Height of the playground slide

   centimeter   meter

10. Distance from Florida to California

   meter   kilometer

7. _____ **Inch**
8. _____ **Yard**
9. _____ **Meter**
10. _____ **Kilometer**

---

11. Find the perimeter.

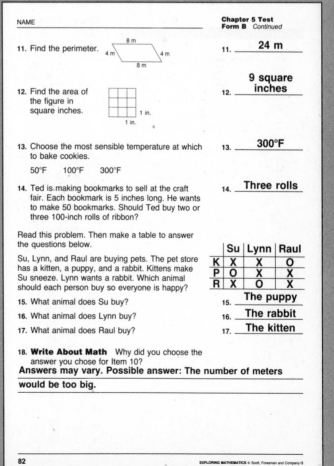

11. _____ **24 m**

12. Find the area of the figure in square inches.

12. _____ **9 square inches**

13. Choose the most sensible temperature at which to bake cookies.

   50°F   100°F   300°F

13. _____ **300°F**

14. Ted is making bookmarks to sell at the craft fair. Each bookmark is 5 inches long. He wants to make 50 bookmarks. Should Ted buy two or three 100-inch rolls of ribbon?

14. _____ **Three rolls**

Read this problem. Then make a table to answer the questions below.

Su, Lynn, and Raul are buying pets. The pet store has a kitten, a puppy, and a rabbit. Kittens make Su sneeze. Lynn wants a rabbit. Which animal should each person buy so everyone is happy?

	Su	Lynn	Raul
K	X	X	O
P	O	X	X
R	X	O	X

15. What animal does Su buy?
16. What animal does Lynn buy?
17. What animal does Raul buy?

15. _____ **The puppy**
16. _____ **The rabbit**
17. _____ **The kitten**

18. **Write About Math** Why did you choose the answer you chose for Item 10?

Answers may vary. Possible answer: The number of meters would be too big.

Chapter 6 Test

Form A

1. Write an addition sentence for this picture.

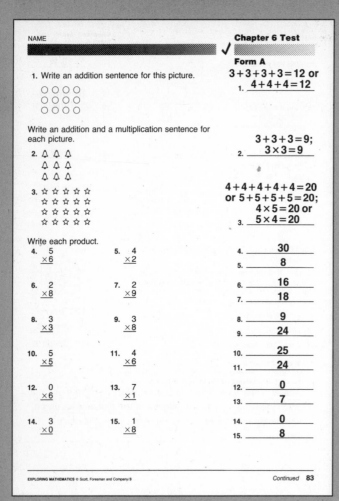

1. $3+3+3+3=12$ or $4+4+4=12$

Write an addition and a multiplication sentence for each picture.

2. 2. $3+3+3=9;$ $3\times3=9$

3. 3. $4+4+4+4+4=20$ or $5+5+5+5=20;$ $4\times5=20$ or $5\times4=20$

Write each product.

4. 5
×6

5. 4
×2

6. 2
×8

7. 2
×9

8. 3
×3

9. 3
×8

10. 5
×5

11. 4
×6

12. 0
×6

13. 7
×1

14. 3
×0

15. 1
×8

4. 30
5. 8
6. 16
7. 18
8. 9
9. 24
10. 25
11. 24
12. 0
13. 7
14. 0
15. 8

Chapter 6 Test
Form A *Continued*

16. Which picture can help you find the product for 4 times 6?

a. ☆ ☆ ☆ ☆
☆ ☆ ☆ ☆
☆ ☆ ☆ ☆
☆ ☆ ☆ ☆
☆ ☆ ☆ ☆

b. ☆ ☆ ☆ ☆
☆ ☆ ☆ ☆
☆ ☆ ☆ ☆
☆ ☆ ☆ ☆

c. ☆ ☆ ☆ ☆
☆ ☆ ☆ ☆
☆ ☆ ☆ ☆
☆ ☆ ☆ ☆
☆ ☆ ☆ ☆
☆ ☆ ☆ ☆

d. ☆ ☆
☆ ☆
☆ ☆
☆ ☆
☆ ☆
☆ ☆

16. **c**

17. Arlene's garden has 6 daisies and 8 sunflowers. Each daisy has 4 blossoms. How many daisy blossoms are there in all?

17. **24 blossoms**

18. There are 8 children and 2 teachers in the room. Each child has 4 pencils. Which information is *not* needed to find how many pencils the children have?

a. 8 children   b. 2 teachers   c. 4 pencils

18. **b**

19. **Write About Math**   Look at the choices for Item 16. Explain the difference between answer **a** and answer **b**.

Answers may vary. Possible answer: Answer a shows 4 rows of 5 stars and b shows 5 rows of 4 stars.

Chapter 6 Test

Form B

1. Write an addition sentence for this picture.

1. $3+3+3+3+3+3=18$ or $6+6+6=18$

Write an addition and a multiplication sentence for each picture.

2. 2. $3+3+3+3=12$ or $4+4+4=12;$ $3\times4=12$ or $4\times3=12$

3. 3. $4+4+4+4+4+4=24$ or $6+6+6+6=24;$ $4\times6=24$ or $6\times4=24$

Write each product.

4. 5
×4

5. 7
×2

6. 2
×6

7. 2
×8

8. 5
×3

9. 9
×3

10. 8
×5

11. 4
×7

12. 0
×9

13. 4
×1

14. 6
×0

15. 1
×5

4. 20
5. 14
6. 12
7. 16
8. 15
9. 27
10. 40
11. 28
12. 0
13. 4
14. 0
15. 5

Chapter 6 Test
Form B *Continued*

16. Which picture can help you find the product for 3 times 5?

a. ◇ ◇ ◇
◇ ◇ ◇
◇ ◇ ◇
◇ ◇ ◇
◇ ◇ ◇

b. ◇ ◇ ◇ ◇ ◇
◇ ◇ ◇ ◇ ◇
◇ ◇ ◇ ◇ ◇

c. ◇ ◇ ◇ ◇
◇ ◇ ◇ ◇
◇ ◇ ◇ ◇
◇ ◇ ◇ ◇
◇ ◇ ◇ ◇

d. ◇ ◇
◇ ◇
◇ ◇
◇ ◇
◇ ◇

16. **a**

17. At the park, there are 8 playground sets. Each set has 1 slide and 4 swings. How many swings are there in all?

17. **32 swings**

18. On Saturday, 6 children went to the fair together. Each child bought 1 stuffed animal and 3 books of tickets. Which information is not needed to find how many books of tickets the children bought in all?

a. 6 children
b. 1 stuffed animal
c. 3 books of tickets

18. **b**

19. **Write About Math**   In Item 18, how could you use drawing a picture to solve the problem?

Answers may vary. Possible answer: I could draw 6 children each holding three books of tickets and then count the books.

Chapter 7 Test

Form A

1. A section of fence has 8 boards in it.

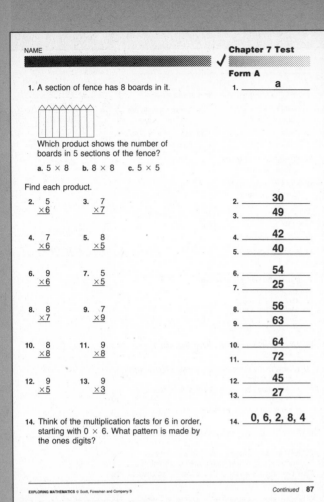

Which product shows the number of boards in 5 sections of the fence?

a. 5 × 8   **b.** 8 × 8   **c.** 5 × 5

Find each product.

2. $\begin{array}{r} 5 \\ \times 6 \end{array}$ 3. $\begin{array}{r} 7 \\ \times 7 \end{array}$

4. $\begin{array}{r} 7 \\ \times 6 \end{array}$ 5. $\begin{array}{r} 8 \\ \times 5 \end{array}$

6. $\begin{array}{r} 9 \\ \times 6 \end{array}$ 7. $\begin{array}{r} 5 \\ \times 5 \end{array}$

8. $\begin{array}{r} 8 \\ \times 7 \end{array}$ 9. $\begin{array}{r} 7 \\ \times 9 \end{array}$

10. $\begin{array}{r} 8 \\ \times 8 \end{array}$ 11. $\begin{array}{r} 9 \\ \times 8 \end{array}$

12. $\begin{array}{r} 9 \\ \times 5 \end{array}$ 13. $\begin{array}{r} 9 \\ \times 3 \end{array}$

14. Think of the multiplication facts for 6 in order, starting with 0 × 6. What pattern is made by the ones digits?

1. _____ **a** _____

2. _____ **30** _____
3. _____ **49** _____
4. _____ **42** _____
5. _____ **40** _____
6. _____ **54** _____
7. _____ **25** _____
8. _____ **56** _____
9. _____ **63** _____
10. _____ **64** _____
11. _____ **72** _____
12. _____ **45** _____
13. _____ **27** _____
14. _____ **0, 6, 2, 8, 4** _____

---

15. How many layers? How many rows? How many in each row?

Fill in the missing numbers to find how many in all.

■ × ■ × ■ = ■

Tell whether you would add, subtract, or multiply to solve each problem.

16. Gary makes stuffed animals. He made 2 bears, 3 penguins, 4 seals, and 2 fish to sell at the craft fair. How many stuffed animals did Gary make in all?

17. Nina paints small wooden boats. At the craft fair, Nina had 5 rows with 6 boats in each row. How many boats did Nina have in all?

18. Tony and Miyo helped set up the craft fair. They set up 4 rows of booths. Each row had 9 booths in it. How many booths were there in all?

19. Solve Problem 18.

20. **Write About Math** Janice has 3 shelves with 6 books on each shelf. Ralph has 6 shelves with 3 books on each shelf. Do Janice and Ralph have the same number of books? Explain your answer.

Yes. Possible explanation: Janice has 3 × 6 books. Ralph has 6 × 3 books. 3 × 6 = 6 × 3.

Order of numbers may vary.

15. _____ **2 × 4 × 3 = 24** _____

16. _____ **Add** _____

17. _____ **Multiply** _____

18. _____ **Multiply** _____

19. _____ **36 booths** _____

Chapter 7 Test

Form B

1. A section of fence has 7 boards in it.

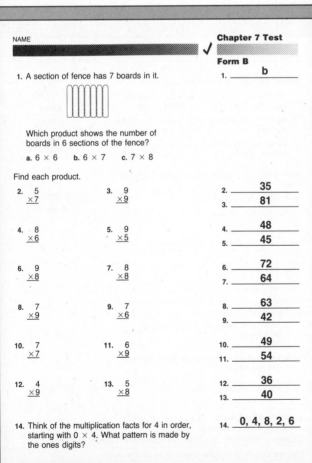

Which product shows the number of boards in 6 sections of the fence?

a. 6 × 6   **b.** 6 × 7   **c.** 7 × 8

Find each product.

2. $\begin{array}{r} 5 \\ \times 7 \end{array}$ 3. $\begin{array}{r} 9 \\ \times 9 \end{array}$

4. $\begin{array}{r} 8 \\ \times 6 \end{array}$ 5. $\begin{array}{r} 9 \\ \times 5 \end{array}$

6. $\begin{array}{r} 9 \\ \times 8 \end{array}$ 7. $\begin{array}{r} 8 \\ \times 8 \end{array}$

8. $\begin{array}{r} 7 \\ \times 9 \end{array}$ 9. $\begin{array}{r} 7 \\ \times 6 \end{array}$

10. $\begin{array}{r} 7 \\ \times 7 \end{array}$ 11. $\begin{array}{r} 6 \\ \times 9 \end{array}$

12. $\begin{array}{r} 4 \\ \times 9 \end{array}$ 13. $\begin{array}{r} 5 \\ \times 8 \end{array}$

14. Think of the multiplication facts for 4 in order, starting with 0 × 4. What pattern is made by the ones digits?

1. _____ **b** _____

2. _____ **35** _____
3. _____ **81** _____
4. _____ **48** _____
5. _____ **45** _____
6. _____ **72** _____
7. _____ **64** _____
8. _____ **63** _____
9. _____ **42** _____
10. _____ **49** _____
11. _____ **54** _____
12. _____ **36** _____
13. _____ **40** _____
14. _____ **0, 4, 8, 2, 6** _____

---

15. How many layers? How many rows? How many in each row? How many in all?

■ × ■ × ■ = ■

Tell whether you would add, subtract, or multiply to solve each problem.

16. Jeff bought hot dogs for the class picnic. He needed 9 hot dogs for each table. There would be 7 tables at the picnic. How many hot dogs did Jeff need to buy?

17. Tara and Liz served juice at the picnic. They had 100 cups when they started. At the end of the picnic, they had 65 cups left. How many cups of juice did they serve?

18. Allan made fruit salad for the class picnic. He used 4 apples, 5 pears, 2 bananas, and 6 oranges. How many pieces of fruit did Allan use in all?

19. Solve the problem in Item 16.

20. **Write About Math** Harry lives in a building with 4 floors. Each floor has 7 apartments. Anne lives in a 7-story building. Each floor has 4 apartments. How are the number of apartments in Harry's building related to the number in Anne's building? Why?

The buildings have the same number of apartments because 4 × 7 = 7 × 4.

Order of numbers may vary.

15. _____ **3 × 3 × 2 = 18** _____

16. _____ **Multiply** _____

17. _____ **Subtract** _____

18. _____ **Add** _____

19. _____ **63 hot dogs** _____

Chapter 8 Test

Form A

1. Give the name for this shape.
   Use *sphere*, *cylinder*, or *cube*.

   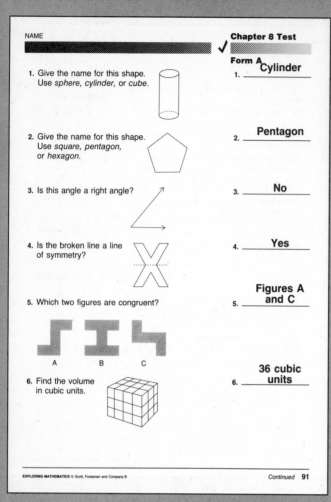

   1. __Cylinder__

2. Give the name for this shape.
   Use *square*, *pentagon*,
   or *hexagon*.

   2. __Pentagon__

3. Is this angle a right angle?

   3. __No__

4. Is the broken line a line
   of symmetry?

   4. __Yes__

5. Which two figures are congruent?

   5. __Figures A and C__

   A   B   C

6. Find the volume
   in cubic units.

   6. __36 cubic units__

Chapter 8 Test
Form A *Continued*

Choose the more sensible measure for each.

7. plastic wading pool
   (quart   gallon)

8. Large cooking pot
   (milliliter   liter)

9. Bottle of nail polish
   (milliliter   liter)

10. Mass of a couch
    (gram   kilogram)

11. Weight of 10 peanuts
    (ounce   pound)

12. Mass of a light bulb
    (gram   kilogram)

7. __Gallon__
8. __Liter__
9. __Milliliter__
10. __Kilogram__
11. __Ounce__
12. __Gram__

Write how many of each object would make about
1 pound.

13. 3-ounce apples

14. 8-ounce books

13. __5 apples__
14. __2 books__

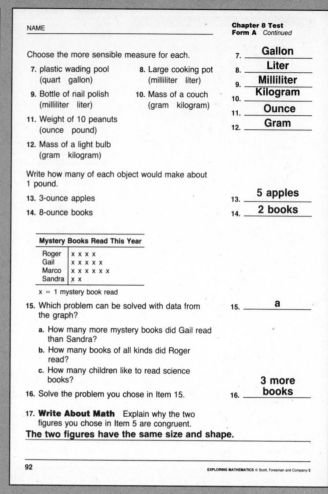

Mystery Books Read This Year	
Roger	x x x x
Gail	x x x x x
Marco	x x x x x x
Sandra	x x

x = 1 mystery book read

15. Which problem can be solved with data from
    the graph?

    a. How many more mystery books did Gail read
       than Sandra?
    b. How many books of all kinds did Roger
       read?
    c. How many children like to read science
       books?

    15. __a__

16. Solve the problem you chose in Item 15.

    16. __3 more books__

17. **Write About Math**   Explain why the two
    figures you chose in Item 5 are congruent.
    The two figures have the same size and shape.

Chapter 8 Test

Form B

1. Give the name for this shape.
   Use *sphere*, *cylinder*, or *cube*.

   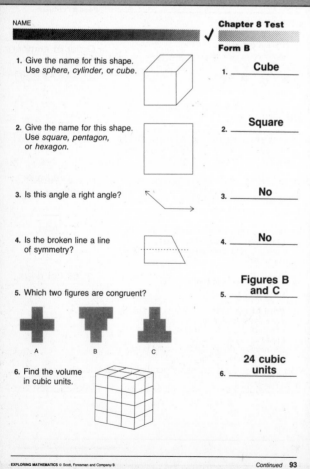

   1. __Cube__

2. Give the name for this shape.
   Use *square*, *pentagon*,
   or *hexagon*.

   2. __Square__

3. Is this angle a right angle?

   3. __No__

4. Is the broken line a line
   of symmetry?

   4. __No__

5. Which two figures are congruent?

   5. __Figures B and C__

   A   B   C

6. Find the volume
   in cubic units.

   6. __24 cubic units__

Chapter 8 Test
Form B *Continued*

Choose the more sensible measure for each.

7. Pot of water
   (cup   quart)

8. Bottle of perfume
   (milliliter   liter)

9. Aquarium for goldfish
   (milliliter   liter)

10. Mass of an ice cube
    (gram   kilogram)

11. Weight of 4 watermelons
    (ounce   pound)

12. Mass of a horse
    (gram   kilogram)

7. __Quart__
8. __Milliliter__
9. __Liter__
10. __Gram__
11. __Pound__
12. __Kilogram__

Write how many of each object would make about
1 pound.

13. 6-ounce boxes of cereal

14. 4-ounce pads of paper

13. __3 boxes__
14. __4 pads__

Boxes of Pencils Sold to Raise Money for Charity	
Erin	x x x x x x
Kate	x x x x x x x x x x x x x
Raul	x x x x x x x x
Yuri	x x x

x = 1 box of pencils sold

15. Which problem can be solved with data from
    the graph?

    a. How much money did the children raise
       altogether?
    b. How many pencils did Erin sell?
    c. How many boxes of pencils did the children
       sell altogether?

    15. __c__

16. Solve the problem you chose in Item 15.

    16. __29 boxes__

17. **Write About Math**   Explain how you arrived
    at your answer to Item 5.

    Answers may vary. Possible explanation: I could see that

    figures B and C are the same size and shape.

The garden club has 6 buckets for members to use.

1. If the club has 18 small shovels, how many shovels go in each bucket?

1. ___3 shovels___

2. If the club has 30 sticks to hold plants up, how many sticks go in each bucket?

2. ___5 sticks___

There are 40 members of the garden club.

3. If the members work together in 5 groups, how many members will be in each group?

3. ___8 members___

4. If the members work in 10 groups, how many members will be in each group?

4. ___4 members___

5. Write the missing numbers.

■ tools in all 5 buckets

■ ÷ 5 = ■

5. ___15; 15; 3___

Write each quotient.

6. $16 ÷ 2$ 7. $12 ÷ 3$

8. $28 ÷ 4$ 9. $30 ÷ 5$

10. $2\overline{)18}$ 11. $3\overline{)24}$

12. $4\overline{)20}$ 13. $5\overline{)35}$

6. ___8___
7. ___4___
8. ___7___
9. ___6___
10. ___9___
11. ___8___
12. ___5___
13. ___7___

Write the missing number. Then write three more sentences to make a family of facts.

14. $3 × 9 = $ ■   15. $5 × 8 = $ ■

16. $4 × 6 = $ ■   17. $2 × 7 = $ ■

14. $27; 9 × 3 = 27,$ $27 ÷ 3 = 9,$ ___$27 ÷ 9 = 3$___

15. $40; 8 × 5 = 40,$ $40 ÷ 5 = 8,$ ___$40 ÷ 8 = 5$___

16. $24; 6 × 4 = 24,$ $24 ÷ 4 = 6,$ ___$24 ÷ 6 = 4$___

17. $14; 7 × 2 = 14,$ $14 ÷ 2 = 7,$ ___$14 ÷ 7 = 2$___

18. Paula and Jody like to play a computer game. As of this week, their combined scores are 900. Paula's score is 40 points higher than Jody's score. What is each of their scores?

18. **Paula: 470** **Jody: 430**

19. Read this problem. Then answer the questions below.

Susi works in a pet store taking care of the mice. Today she is ordering new cages. There are 36 mice, and there should be no more than 4 mice in each cage.

What does the underlined statement tell you?

a. Susi must get rid of some mice.
b. Susi must find a much bigger cage.
c. Susi must buy more than one cage.

19. ___c___

20. In Item 19, how many cages should Susi order?

20. **At least 9 cages**

21. **Write About Math** When will a family of facts have only 1 multiplication sentence and 1 division sentence?

When the factors are the same. For example, $4 × 4 = 16$ and $16 ÷ 4 = 4$.

The First-Aid Club has 8 kits for members to use.

1. If the club has 40 rolls of tape, how many rolls can go in each kit?

1. ___5 rolls___

2. If the club has 32 special bandages, how many of them should be put in each kit?

2. ___4 bandages___

There are 24 members of the First-Aid Club.

3. If the members work together in 8 groups, how many members will be in each group?

3. ___3 members___

4. If the members work in 6 groups, how many members will be in each group?

4. ___4 members___

5. Write the missing numbers.

■ rolls in all 6 kits

■ ÷ 6 = ■

5. ___18; 18; 3___

Write each quotient.

6. $21 ÷ 3$ 7. $10 ÷ 2$

8. $24 ÷ 4$ 9. $45 ÷ 5$

10. $2\overline{)16}$ 11. $3\overline{)27}$

12. $4\overline{)24}$ 13. $5\overline{)25}$

6. ___7___
7. ___5___
8. ___6___
9. ___9___
10. ___8___
11. ___9___
12. ___6___
13. ___5___

Write the missing number. Then write three more sentences to make a family of facts.

14. $2 × 9 = $ ■   15. $4 × 8 = $ ■

16. $5 × 6 = $ ■   17. $3 × 5 = $ ■

14. $18; 9 × 2 = 18,$ $18 ÷ 2 = 9,$ ___$18 ÷ 9 = 2$___

15. $32; 8 × 4 = 32,$ $32 ÷ 4 = 8,$ ___$32 ÷ 8 = 4$___

16. $30; 6 × 5 = 30,$ $30 ÷ 5 = 6,$ ___$30 ÷ 6 = 5$___

17. $15; 5 × 3 = 15,$ $15 ÷ 3 = 5,$ ___$15 ÷ 5 = 3$___

18. City workers counted a total of 850 cars and trucks using the First Street Bridge on Friday. They counted 50 more cars and trucks in the afternoon than they counted in the morning. How many did they count in the morning and how many in the afternoon?

18. **Morning: 400;** **afternoon: 450**

19. Read this problem.

Pete's teacher asked him to get a new supply of pencils for the class. There are 32 students in the class and each box contains 8 pencils.

What does the underlined statement tell you?

a. Pete can't get a pencil for everyone.
b. Pete must get more than one box of pencils.
c. Pete must find boxes with more pencils.

19. ___b___

20. In Item 19, how many boxes should Pete get?

20. **4 boxes**

21. **Write About Math** How could a family of facts help you solve Item 19? Write the family of facts that goes with the problem.

A family of facts shows the different ways that numbers are related to each other, so it will show how to solve this particular problem. $32 ÷ 8 = 4$, $32 ÷ 4 = 8$, $4 × 8 = 32$, $8 × 4 = 32$

Write each quotient.

1. 42 ÷ 6   2. 6 ÷ 1

3. 45 ÷ 9   4. 64 ÷ 8

5. 0 ÷ 9   6. 56 ÷ 7

7. 6)54   8. 7)35

9. 8)48   10. 9)81

1.	7
2.	6
3.	5
4.	8
5.	0
6.	8
7.	9
8.	5
9.	6
10.	9

Write the letter of the fact that does *not* belong to the family of facts.

11. a. 7 × 7   12. a. 40 ÷ 5
    b. 49 ÷ 7   b. 5 × 8
    c. 42 ÷ 7   c. 8 × 5
                       d. 40 ÷ 4
                       e. 40 ÷ 8

11.	c
12.	d

Divide. Write each quotient and remainder.

13. 23 ÷ 9   14. 70 ÷ 8

15. 61 ÷ 7   16. 58 ÷ 6

13.	2 R 5
14.	8 R 6
15.	8 R 5
16.	9 R 4

Tell whether you would add, subtract, multiply, or divide to solve each problem.

17. Harold bought a box of 24 pencils. He gave an equal number of pencils to each of 6 friends. How many pencils did each friend get?

18. Josie sold 18 packs of seeds. Kelly sold 7 more packs than Josie. How many packs of seeds did Kelly sell?

19. There were 65 boxes of baseball cards on the shelf. How many boxes were left after Wally bought 9 boxes?

20. Solve Item 17.

17.	Divide
18.	Add
19.	Subtract
20.	4 pencils

21. Sara collected 14 pine cones to use in making bird feeders. Each feeder uses 3 pine cones. Choose the most sensible answer for the number of bird feeders Sara can make.

    a. 17 feeders   b. 4 feeders
    c. 5 feeders   d. 11 feeders

21. _____b_____

22. In Item 21, if Sara makes all the bird feeders she can, how many pine cones will be left over?

22. **2 pine cones**

23. **Write About Math** If you divide objects into groups of 6, the greatest number of objects that can be left over is 5. Explain why.

If the remainder is more than 5, there would be another group of 6 objects.

Write each quotient.

1. 54 ÷ 6   2. 8 ÷ 1

3. 54 ÷ 9   4. 56 ÷ 8

5. 0 ÷ 7   6. 63 ÷ 7

7. 6)30   8. 7)28

9. 8)64   10. 9)72

1.	9
2.	8
3.	6
4.	7
5.	0
6.	9
7.	5
8.	4
9.	8
10.	8

Write the letter of the fact that does not belong to the family of facts.

11. a. 7 × 9   12. a. 81 ÷ 9
    b. 42 ÷ 7   b. 9 × 9
    c. 63 ÷ 9   c. 72 ÷ 9
    d. 9 × 7
    e. 63 ÷ 7

11.	b
12.	c

Divide. Write each quotient and remainder.

13. 21 ÷ 4   14. 36 ÷ 8

15. 45 ÷ 7   16. 60 ÷ 9

13.	5, R1
14.	4, R4
15.	6, R3
16.	6, R6

Tell whether you would add, subtract, multiply, or divide to solve each problem.

17. Karla collected 24 shells. Tomas collected 11 more than Karla did. How many shells did Karla and Tomas collect altogether?

18. There were 90 packs of stickers on the shelf. After Jo-Ann bought stickers, there were 78 packs left. How many packs of stickers did Jo-Ann buy?

19. A shipment of 48 goldfish arrived. If Terry put 6 fish in each tank, how many tanks are there?

20. Solve Item 19.

17.	Add
18.	Subtract
19.	Divide
20.	8 tanks

21. The computer lab has 6 computers. All 28 students in Ms. Brown's class go to the lab in groups so that each student can use a computer alone. Choose the most sensible answer for the number of groups of students that will go to the computer lab.

    a. 4 groups   b. 5 groups
    c. 3 groups   d. 10 groups

21. _____b_____

22. In Item 21, one group will have fewer students than the other groups. How many students will be in the smallest group?

22. **4 students**

23. **Write About Math** If you separate objects into groups of 5, what is the greatest number that can be left over? Why?

4; Possible explanation: You cannot have 5 or more left over because they make other groups of 5 objects. So the number left over can be 0, 1, 2, 3, or 4.

Chapter 11 Test

Form A

What fraction names the shaded part?

1. 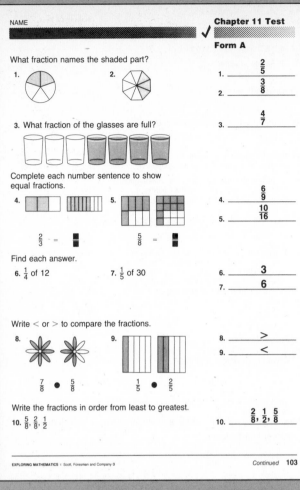   2.

3. What fraction of the glasses are full?

Complete each number sentence to show equal fractions.

4.   5.

$\frac{2}{3} = \blacksquare$ $\frac{5}{8} = \blacksquare$

Find each answer.

6. $\frac{1}{4}$ of 12   7. $\frac{1}{5}$ of 30

Write < or > to compare the fractions.

8.   9.

$\frac{7}{8} \bullet \frac{5}{8}$ $\frac{1}{5} \bullet \frac{2}{5}$

Write the fractions in order from least to greatest.

10. $\frac{5}{8}, \frac{2}{8}, \frac{1}{2}$

1. $\frac{2}{5}$
2. $\frac{3}{8}$
3. $\frac{4}{7}$
4. $\frac{6}{9}$
5. $\frac{10}{16}$
6. 3
7. 6
8. $>$
9. $<$
10. $\frac{2}{8}, \frac{1}{2}, \frac{5}{8}$

Write each decimal.

11. 2 tenths   12. 7 tenths
13. fifty-three hundredths

For each decimal, tell what place the 4 is in.

14. 29.4   15. 45.3   16. 84.6

Write < or > to compare the decimals.

17. 0.5 ● 0.7
18. 0.4 ● 0.36

19. What decimal part of a dollar is one half-dollar?

20. There are four stores in the mall. A record store is at the far left. A bookstore is between the shoe store and the record store. The toy store is at the far right. What does the underlined statement mean?

   a. The store on the right end sells toys.
   b. The toy store has a bookstore on its right.
   c. The toy store is the best store of the five.

21. Write the letter that shows the order of the stores in Item 20, from left to right.

   a. Record store, shoe store, bookstore, toy store
   b. Toy store, shoe store, bookstore, record store
   c. Record store, bookstore, shoe store, toy store

22. **Write About Math** Explain the meaning of each part of the fraction you wrote in Item 1.
Possible answer: The 5 names the equal parts of the circle, and the 2 names the parts that are shaded.

11. 0.2
12. 0.7
13. 0.53
14. Tenths
15. Tens
16. Ones
17. $<$
18. $>$
19. 0.5 or 0.50
20. a
21. c

Chapter 11 Test

Form B

What fraction names the shaded part?

1. 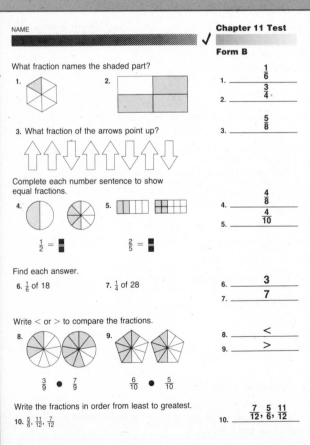   2.

3. What fraction of the arrows point up?

Complete each number sentence to show equal fractions.

4.   5.

$\frac{1}{2} = \blacksquare$ $\frac{2}{5} = \blacksquare$

Find each answer.

6. $\frac{1}{6}$ of 18   7. $\frac{1}{4}$ of 28

Write < or > to compare the fractions.

8.   9.

$\frac{3}{9} \bullet \frac{7}{9}$ $\frac{6}{10} \bullet \frac{5}{10}$

Write the fractions in order from least to greatest.

10. $\frac{5}{6}, \frac{11}{12}, \frac{7}{12}$

1. $\frac{1}{6}$
2. $\frac{3}{4}$
3. $\frac{5}{8}$
4. $\frac{4}{8}$
5. $\frac{4}{10}$
6. 3
7. 7
8. $<$
9. $>$
10. $\frac{7}{12}, \frac{5}{6}, \frac{11}{12}$

Write each decimal.

11. 4 tenths   12. 9 tenths
13. seventy-one hundredths

For each decimal, tell what place the 7 is in.

14. 47.3   15. 75.6   16. 35.7

Write < or > to compare the decimals.

17. 0.8 ● 0.3   18. 0.51 ● 0.6

19. What decimal part of a dollar is one quarter?

20. There are five cars in the lot. The red car is in the center. The blue car is between the red car and the yellow car. The green car is on the right side of the red car. The gray car is on the right side of the green car. Which statement has the same meaning as the underlined statement?

   a. The green car is the newest car.
   b. The red car is on the left side of the green car.
   c. The green car is in the wrong place.

21. Write the letter that shows the order of the cars in Item 20, from left to right.

   a. Yellow car, blue car, red car, green car, gray car
   b. Red car, blue car, yellow car, green car, gray car
   c. Gray car, green car, red car, blue car, yellow car

22. **Write About Math** Explain the meaning of each part of the fraction you wrote in Item 2.
Possible answer: The 4 names the equal parts of the rectangle, and the 3 names the parts that are shaded.

11. 0.4
12. 0.9
13. 0.71
14. Ones
15. Tens
16. Tenths
17. $>$
18. $<$
19. 0.25
20. b
21. a

Chapter 12 Test

Form A

Write each time as minutes before the hour.

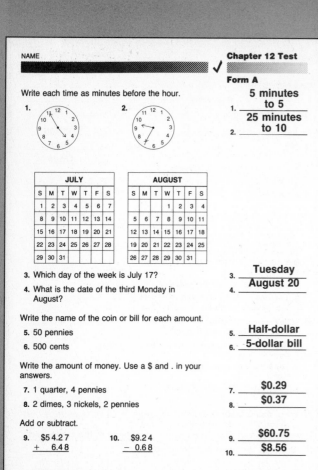

1. _____ 5 minutes to 5

2. _____ 25 minutes to 10

3. Which day of the week is July 17?

4. What is the date of the third Monday in August?

3. _____ Tuesday

4. _____ August 20

Write the name of the coin or bill for each amount.

5. 50 pennies

6. 500 cents

5. _____ Half-dollar

6. _____ 5-dollar bill

Write the amount of money. Use a $ and . in your answers.

7. 1 quarter, 4 pennies

8. 2 dimes, 3 nickels, 2 pennies

7. _____ $0.29

8. _____ $0.37

Add or subtract.

9. $54.27
   + 6.48

10. $9.24
    − 0.68

9. _____ $60.75

10. _____ $8.56

Write the change from $3.00 for a

11. $1.40 box of paints.

12. $0.98 coloring book.

11. _____ $1.60

12. _____ $2.02

13. Which is the better estimate for $3.69 + $0.89?

   a. $4.00   b. $4.50

13. _____ b

14. Work backward to complete the solution of this problem. Complete the number sentences.

   Elton's lunch costs $3 more than Gino's lunch. Gino's lunch costs $2 more than Terri's. If Elton's lunch costs $8, how much did Terri's lunch cost?

   $8 − $■ = $■ $■ − $■ = $■

14. _____ $8 − $3 = $5, $5 − $2 = $3

15. Maggie sold 4 bunches of flowers to Robyn. Later, she sold 3 bunches to Kirk. Altogether, Maggie sold 5 more bunches than she sold to Robyn and Kirk. Which would be the first step in finding how many bunches Maggie sold in all?

   a. 4 + 3 = 7
   b. 4 + 3 − 5 = 2
   c. 4 × 3 = 20

15. _____ a

16. In the problem in Item 15, how many bunches of flowers did Maggie sell in all?

16. _____ 12 bunches

17. **Write About Math** Cara has 6 coins that are together worth $1.00. What coins might she have?

Answers may vary. Possible answer: She might have 3 quarters, 2 dimes, and 1 nickel.

Chapter 12 Test

Form B

Write each time as minutes before the hour.

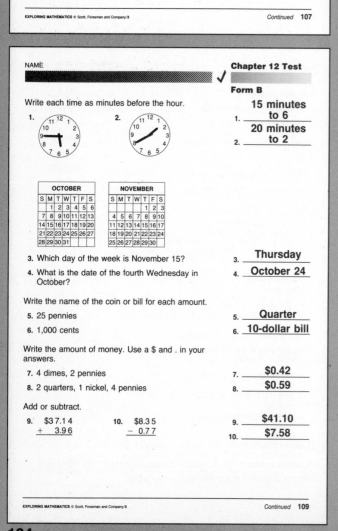

1. _____ 15 minutes to 6

2. _____ 20 minutes to 2

3. Which day of the week is November 15?

4. What is the date of the fourth Wednesday in October?

3. _____ Thursday

4. _____ October 24

Write the name of the coin or bill for each amount.

5. 25 pennies

6. 1,000 cents

5. _____ Quarter

6. _____ 10-dollar bill

Write the amount of money. Use a $ and . in your answers.

7. 4 dimes, 2 pennies

8. 2 quarters, 1 nickel, 4 pennies

7. _____ $0.42

8. _____ $0.59

Add or subtract.

9. $37.14
   + 3.96

10. $8.35
    − 0.77

9. _____ $41.10

10. _____ $7.58

Write the change from $4.00 for a

11. $2.70 model car.

12. $0.59 battery.

11. _____ $1.30

12. _____ $3.41

13. Which is the better estimate for $4.79 + $0.59?

   a. $5.50   b. $6.00

13. _____ a

14. Complete the number sentences by working backward to find the solution.

   A box with 300 crayons, a pad of tracing paper, and 500 sheets of drawing paper cost $7. The crayon box costs $2. The pad of tracing paper costs $3. How much does just the drawing paper cost?

   $7 − $■ = $■ $■ − $■ = $■

14. _____ $7 − $2 = $5, $5 − $3 = $2

   or: $7 − $3 = $4
   $4 − $2 = $2

15. On Monday morning, Tony counted 3 birds at his bird feeder. On Tuesday morning, he counted 7 birds. In the week, Tony counted 6 more birds than he counted Monday and Tuesday mornings. Which would be the first step in finding out how many birds Tony counted in all?

   a. 7 − 3 = 4
   b. 7 + 3 = 10
   c. 7 − 3 + 6 = 4

15. _____ b

16. In the problem in Item 15, how many birds did Tony count in the week?

16. _____ 16 birds

17. **Write About Math** Adam has $2.00 in coins. He has 3 different kinds of coins. What coins might Adam have?

Answers will vary. Possible answer: He might have 1 half dollar, 4 quarters, and 5 dimes.

Chapter 13 Test
Form A

1. Give the standard form for 4 groups of 5 hundreds.

Find each product mentally.

2. 80 × 5   3. 40 × 7

Estimate each product.

Estimates may vary.

4. 32 × 7

5. 6 × 581

6. Find how many are in 5 groups of 37.

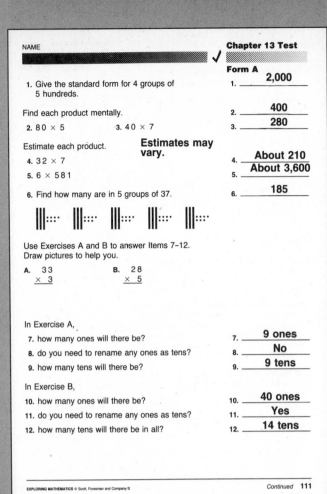

Use Exercises A and B to answer Items 7–12. Draw pictures to help you.

A. 3 3
   × 3

B. 2 8
   × 5

In Exercise A,

7. how many ones will there be?

8. do you need to rename any ones as tens?

9. how many tens will there be?

In Exercise B,

10. how many ones will there be?

11. do you need to rename any ones as tens?

12. how many tens will there be in all?

1. _2,000_
2. _400_
3. _280_
4. _About 210_
5. _About 3,600_
6. _185_

7. _9 ones_
8. _No_
9. _9 tens_
10. _40 ones_
11. _Yes_
12. _14 tens_

Find each product. Draw pictures to help.

13. 7 × 35

14. 4 × 23

15. 5 × 98

16. 6 × 406

17. Elaine planted 15 flower boxes for her building. Each flower box has 2 rows of flowers with 6 flowers in each row. How many flowers did she plant in each box?

18. Fifteen students each drew the same number of pictures for the school fair. Each student drew 3 pictures. Would you add, subtract, multiply, or divide to find how many pictures the students drew?

19. Simon worked the problem in Item 18 and got an answer of 12. Does his answer make sense? Why or why not?

20. Solve the problem in Item 18.

21. **Write About Math** Does Item 17 have too much information? If your answer is yes, tell what information was not needed and why it was not needed.

Yes, it was not necessary to know that Elaine planted 15 flower boxes because the question asks how many she planted in each box.

13. _245_
14. _92_
15. _490_
16. _2,436_
17. _12 flowers_
18. _Multiply_
19. _No, there were more than 12 students._
20. _45 pictures_

Chapter 13 Test
Form B

1. Give the standard form for 8 groups of 2 hundreds.

Find each product mentally.

2. 70 × 6   3. 30 × 7

Estimate each product.

4. 43 × 5

5. 4 × 793

6. Find how many are in 6 groups of 28.

Use Exercises A and B to answer Items 7–12. Draw pictures to help you.

A. 1 2
   × 4

B. 2 3
   × 5

In Exercise A,

7. how many ones will there be?

8. do you need to rename any ones as tens?

9. how many tens will there be?

In Exercise B,

10. how many ones will there be?

11. do you need to rename any ones as tens?

12. how many tens will there be in all?

1. _1,600_
2. _420_
3. _210_
4. _About 200_
5. _About 3,200_
6. _168_

7. _8 ones_
8. _No_
9. _4 tens_
10. _15 ones_
11. _Yes_
12. _11 tens_

Find each product. Draw pictures to help.

13. 6 × 18

14. 3 × 76

15. 4 × 86

16. 5 × 398

17. Jorge made 16 packages of thank-you notes to sell at the school fair. He will sell each package for $0.75. He put 8 note cards in each package. How many note cards did he use?

18. At the class picnic, 7 students have the job of clearing tables. Each student will clear the same number of tables. There are 35 tables. Would you add, subtract, multiply, or divide to find how many tables each one will clear?

19. Laurie worked the problem in Item 18 and got an answer of 42. Does her answer make sense? Why or why not?

20. Solve the problem in Item 18.

21. **Write About Math** In Item 17, is there too much information? If your answer is yes, tell what information was not needed and why it was not needed.

Yes. You do not need to know that each package sells for $0.75 to know how many note cards he used.

13. _108_
14. _228_
15. _344_
16. _1,990_
17. _128 note cards_
18. _Divide_
19. _No, there were fewer than 42 tables._
20. _5 tables_

NAME

Chapter 14 Test
Form A

1. Write two questions to help you gather the necessary data for this problem.

Mrs. Jackson has some quarters to give to her children. Each child will get the same number of quarters. How many quarters will each child get?

How many children does she have? How many quarters does she have?

1. _____

Toys at School Fair

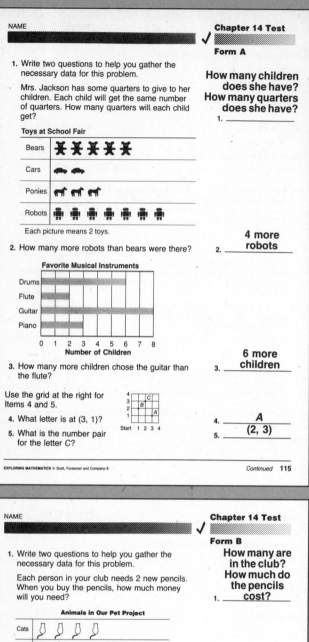

Bears	🐻🐻🐻🐻🐻
Cars	🚗🚗
Ponies	🐎🐎🐎
Robots	🤖🤖🤖🤖🤖🤖🤖

Each picture means 2 toys.

2. How many more robots than bears were there?

2. **4 more robots**

Favorite Musical Instruments

Drums
Flute
Guitar
Piano

0 1 2 3 4 5 6 7 8
Number of Children

3. How many more children chose the guitar than the flute?

3. **6 more children**

Use the grid at the right for Items 4 and 5.

4. What letter is at (3, 1)?

5. What is the number pair for the letter C?

4. **A**
(2, 3)

5. _____

NAME

Chapter 14 Test
Form A *Continued*

6. Tell whether it is certain, possible, or impossible for you to be 25 years old next year.

6. **Impossible**

7. A bowl is filled with black, white, and pink pebbles. There are more pink pebbles than either black or white ones. Which outcome is most likely?

   a. To pick a black pebble
   b. To pick a white pebble
   c. To pick a pink pebble

7. **c**

8. You have a bowl of buttons. There are 10 gray buttons, 5 green ones, and 3 yellow ones. If you take one button without looking, what are you most likely to get?

8. **A gray button**

Color	Tallies	No.
gray	𝍩𝍩	10
green	𝍩	5
yellow	|||	3

9. Make a tally chart for the information in Item 8.

9. _____

10. Look at the graph for Item 3. There were 4 other children who chose the trumpet. How could you show which musical instruments were chosen more often than the trumpet?

    a. Add the total numbers for the bars. Compare that to the number who chose the trumpet.
    b. Add a bar for trumpets to the graph. See which bars are longer than the new one.
    c. Add a bar for trumpets to the graph. See which bars are shorter than the new one.

10. **b**

11. **Write About Math** Look at the grid for Items 4 and 5. Is the number pair (2, 1) correct for point B? Explain why or why not.

No; It should be (1, 2) because the first number means moving to the right and the second number means moving up.

NAME

Chapter 14 Test
Form B

1. Write two questions to help you gather the necessary data for this problem.

Each person in your club needs 2 new pencils. When you buy the pencils, how much money will you need?

How many are in the club? How much do the pencils cost?

1. _____

Animals in Our Pet Project

Cats	🐱🐱🐱
Dogs	🐕🐕🐕🐕🐕🐕🐕🐕
Fish	🐟🐟🐟🐟🐟
Mice	🐭🐭🐭

Each picture means 2 pets.

2. How many more dogs than mice were part of the pet project?

2. **10 more dogs**

Artwork in Class Show

Paper Folding
Drawings
Paintings
Clay Models

0 1 2 3 4 5 6 7 8

3. How many more paintings than clay models were in the class show?

3. **4 more paintings**

Use the grid at the right for Items 4 and 5.

4. What letter is at (1, 3)?

5. What is the number pair for the letter A?

4. **C**
(4, 2)

5. _____

NAME

Chapter 14 Test
Form B *Continued*

In Items 6 and 7, tell whether each is certain, possible, or impossible.

6. You will visit the moon and walk on its surface.

6. **Possible**

7. You will live underwater without needing help to breath.

7. **Impossible**

8. Most of the leaves on a tree are yellow, but some are brown and some are red. Which outcome is most likely?

   a. A brown leaf will fall.
   b. A yellow leaf will fall.
   c. A red leaf will fall.

8. **b**

9. In a bag, there are 15 green plastic clips, 10 orange clips, 5 blue ones, and 5 red ones. If you take one clip without looking, what are you most likely to get?

9. **A green clip**

10. Look at the graph for Item 3. There were 5 pieces of string art in the show, too. How would you show which kind(s) of art had more pieces in the class show than string art?

    a. Add a bar for string art to the graph. See which bars are longer than the new one.
    b. Add a bar for string art to the graph. See which bars are shorter than the new one.
    c. Add the total numbers for the bars. Compare the sum to the number of string art pieces.

10. **a**

11. Which kind(s) of art had more pieces in the class show than string art?

11. **Drawings and paintings**

12. **Write About Math** Look at the grid for Items 4 and 5. If you put point D at (3, 2), would it be next to point A or directly above point B? Explain why.

It would be next to point A; Possible explanation: Both A and D would be 2 units up. A is 4 units to the right and D would be 3 units to the right, so it would be next to A.

Using Multiple-Choice Tests Wit[h]

This book contains multiple-choice test blackline masters for *Exploring Mathematics*. The tests can be used with or without the Computer Management System (CMS). If the tests are scored with CMS, and your optical mark reader, students must use compatible test answer cards or sheets. If you are not scoring with an optical mark reader, students may write their answers directly on the blackline master, or on the answer form provided at the back of the book. Answers with objectives are also provided at the back of the book, and a percentage chart for hand-scoring is on the inside cover.

Two forms, Form C and Form D, can be used as pretests and posttests, or both forms can be used as posttests for different students in one class or in different classes. Because the objectives for each form are parallel, tests are interchangeable. The inventory test can be used at the beginning of the year to assess objectives covered the previous year. These objectives are listed after the answer section at the back of the book. The four cumulative tests cover chapters 1–3, 1–7, 1–11, and 1–15.

A practice item begins each test. Use it to show students how to mark an answer. Students using test answer forms may mark the answer to the practice item in the appropriate place on the form.

Using Scott, Foresman's Computer Management System With *Exploring Mathematics*

This book contains tests in blackline master form for the *Exploring Mathematics Master Objectives Disk Package* that is used with the Scott, Foresman Computer Management System (CMS). Detailed instructions for use of CMS are found in the *Main Program Package*. All the tests are multiple-choice and have three items for each objective tested. If a student responds correctly to 2 out of 3 items for an objective, CMS will evaluate the student as having mastered that objective. This mastery level of 2 out of 3 items is used on all tests. CMS always reports the mastery status for an objective based on the most recent test result. Consult the *Teacher's Guide* in the *Master Objectives Disks Package* for charts identifying the tests that cover each objective.

CMS scores the tests either by keyboard entry or by an optical mark reader that scans answer cards or sheets. Scoring by keyboard can be used whenever a school wants to run CMS without an optical mark reader. This method may be used whenever students are unable to fill out test answer forms.

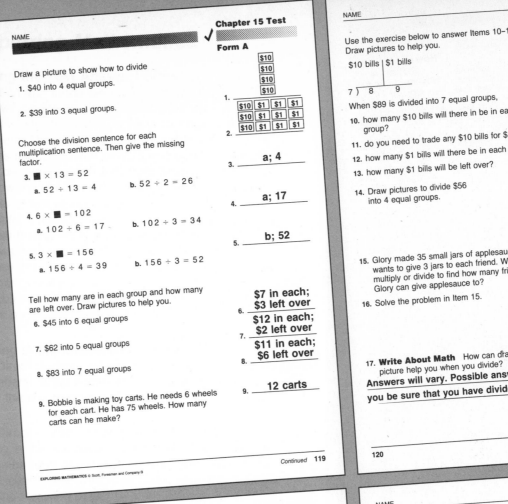

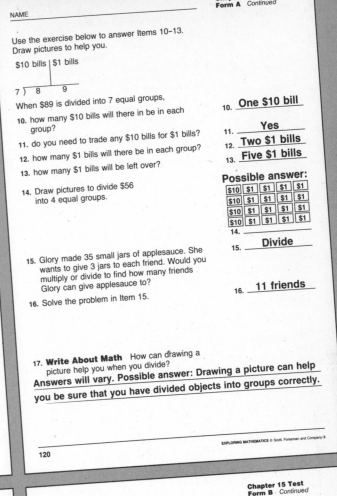

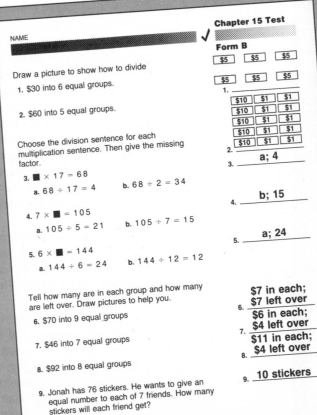

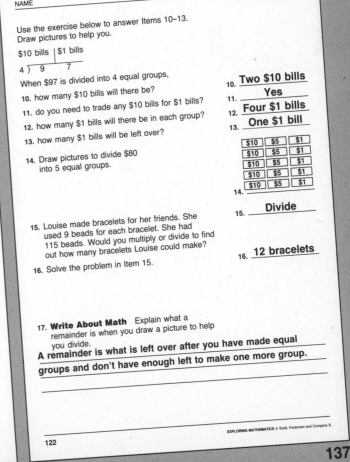

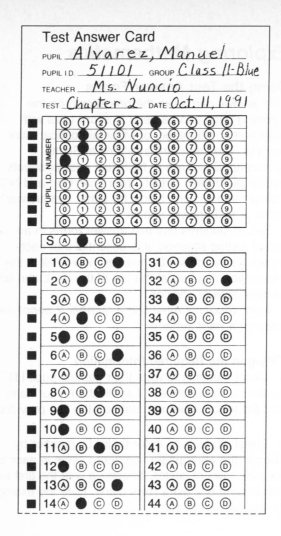

Test Answer Card

PUPIL *Alvarez, Manuel*

PUPIL I.D. *51101* GROUP *Class II-Blue*

TEACHER *Ms. Nuncio*

TEST *Chapter 2* DATE *Oct. 11, 1991*

Description of CMS Reports

The following briefly describes the information available on reports generated by the CMS. For samples of these reports, consult the *Operator's Manual Supplement*.

Pupil List—This is a list of pupils' I.D. information in a class. A list of tests administered to each group in the class to date can also be printed.

Pupil Test Results—This individual pupil's report shows a student's item-by-item responses after a test has been scored. It indicates the student's status of mastery for each objective tested on that test, and tabulates the raw score for each tested objective. Lists of mastered and nonmastered objectives, with prescriptions for remediation, can also be generated.

Group Test Answers—This is a group report that shows item-by-item responses on a test which has just been scored for an entire group. It also gives the total number of students who answered an item incorrectly.

Group Test Results—This group report shows objective-by-objective results for a test that has just been scored. It tells the number of items for each objective each student in the group answered correctly. It also calculates the test percentage score for each student and reports optional letter grades. Objectives mastered on the test by every student can be listed with this report. Nonmastered objectives with prescriptions for remediation and a list of students who did not master the objectives can also be generated.

Group Test Totals—This group report is available any time after a test has been scored, and gives students' scores for an individual test. Students may be ranked alphabetically or by score and listed by name only, I.D. number only, or both. Results on pretests, if given, are reported for comparison with the posttest results.

Pupil Performance (letter home)—This individual pupil's report lists tests taken during a specified period of time. This report may be used as a letter home with places for comments and parent signature. The pupil's score, optional letter grades, and the number of objectives mastered by that pupil are given for each test. Lists of mastered and nonmastered objectives for all objectives attempted to date are also available.

Score Averages—This is a group report that averages test scores and uses teacher-supplied weighting to calculate final scores and optional letter grades. Other tests and other scores can also be included.

Group Status—This group report gives objective mastery information for every objective tested to date or for selected objectives. Mastery is indicated for each objective for all students. A list of objectives mastered by all students is supplied. The average rate of mastery for the group of students reported is calculated, and a list of nonmastered objectives that gave this group the most difficulty is available.

Grade and School Status—These summary reports give average rate of mastery for pupils working at each level in each class and each grade. Lists of objectives that gave students in each grade the most difficulty are available. School averages by level are also reported.

District Reports—These summary reports give the average number of tests administered to each group in each grade and school, determine the average rate of mastery for pupils in each group, and determine the average rate of mastery throughout the district.

Choose the letter of the correct answer.

SAMPLE

Which is the lesser number?

A 54   **B** 31

Add.

1.   7
    +9
                          A 14
                          B 16
                          C 15

2. 8 + 9
                          A 16
                          B 17
                          C 18

3.   7
     3
    +6
                          A 16
                          B 17
                          C 15

Use this graph to answer
Items 4 and 5.

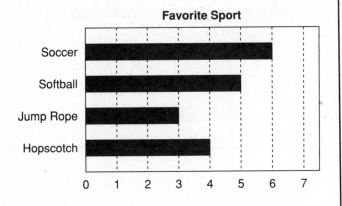

Favorite Sport

4. How many named softball?

   A 6   **B** 3   **C** 5

---

5. Which sport was named by
   6 people?

   A hopscotch
   B soccer
   C jump rope

---

6. How many?

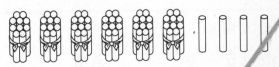

   A 60   **B** 54   **C** 64

---

7. Which is the greater number?

   A 91   **B** 19

---

8. How much?

   A 23¢   **B** 19¢   **C** 28¢

---

9. In what place is the baseball player?

A first   **B** fourth   **C** third

Subtract.

10. 1 5 − 9   **A** 6
B 5
C 24

11.   1 6
  − 8   **A** 7
B 9
C 8

12.   1 8
  − 9   **A** 8
B 9
C 7

13. Tim picked 8 .

He bought 7 more .

How many does he have now?

A 1   **B** 14   **C** 15

14. I put 14 in a bag.

I spent 8 .

How many are left?

A 6   **B** 22   **C** 5

15. What time is it?

A 7:10
B 3:35
C 2:35

16. About how long is the nail?

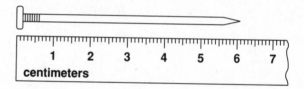

A 7 cm   **B** 5 cm   **C** 6 cm

17. Which is the more sensible measure?

A inches
B feet

Add.

18. 53
    +36

A 23
B 79
C 89

19. 75
    + 8

A 83
B 713
C 73

20. 25
    +35

A 510
B 60
C 70

21. How much?

47¢
+28¢

A 65¢
B 615¢
C 75¢

Subtract.

22. 72
    − 9

A 63
B 77
C 73

23. 86
    −34

A 53
B 52
C 42

24. 92
    −36

A 64
B 66
C 56

25. Janet has 65¢. She spent 29¢. How much does she have left?

A 44¢   B 36¢   C 94¢

26. Juan spent 45¢ for toy animals and 37¢ for a balloon. How much did he spend?

A 8¢   B 72¢   C 82¢

27. How much?

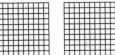

A 254   B 245   C 345

28. Which number comes next?

347, 348, ■

A 346   B 348   C 349

29. Which is true?

A 375 > 357
B 375 < 357

30. How much?

4 one-dollar bills
1 quarter
4 dimes

A $4.65   B $4.45   C $4.55

31. How much is shaded?

A $\frac{4}{1}$ **B** $\frac{3}{4}$ **C** $\frac{1}{4}$

32. Jackie has round and long balloons. What fraction of the balloons are round?

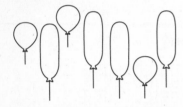

A $\frac{4}{7}$ **B** $\frac{3}{7}$ **C** $\frac{3}{4}$

33. Which two figures have the same shape and size?

A A and D
B A and C
C B and C

34. Name this shape.

A cube
B sphere
C cylinder

35. About how much does a kitten weigh?

A 50 pounds
B 20 pounds
C 2 pounds

36. About how much does this milk glass hold?

A less than 1 liter
B more than 1 liter

Add.

37.　421
　　　+147

A 658
B 568
C 578

38.　429
　　　+258

A 6,717
B 677
C 687

Subtract.

39.　778
　　　−325

A 453
B 493
C 452

40.　968
　　　−529

A 349
B 439
C 449

Date   Score

Choose the letter of the correct answer.

SAMPLE

Add.

$$\begin{array}{r} 5 \\ +6 \\ \hline \end{array}$$

A 1
B 11
C 10
D not given

1. Mrs. Li bought 10 sheets of poster board. How is the number used?

    A to count
    B to label
    C to measure
    D to tell the order

2. Jack used a board 4 feet long in his project. How is the number used?

    A to count
    B to label
    C to measure
    D to tell the order

3. Shayne was 5th in line at the water fountain. How is this number used?

    A to count
    B to label
    C to measure
    D to tell the order

In Items 4–6, use the rule given. Find the missing number.

4.

+5	
1	6
3	■
8	13

A 7
B 8
C 9
D 10

5.

−8	
9	1
16	8
14	■

A 4
B 5
C 6
D 7

6.

+7	
4	11
2	9
9	■

A 15
B 16
C 17
D 18

In Items 7–9, choose the symbol or number that is under the sticker.

7. $7 +$ ☐ $= 11$

    A 4   **B** 5   **C** 3   **D** 6

8. 18 ☐ $9 = 9$

    A +   **B** −   **C** =

9. $6 +$ ☐ $= 11$

    A 4   **B** 17   **C** 5   **D** 18

10. Mr. Jans had 6 cows. He bought 9 more cows. How many cows does he have now?
What are you asked to find?

A the number of cows Mr. Jans has now

B how many more cows Mr. Jans bought than he already had

C the number of cows Mr. Jans had before buying more

D the number of cows Mr. Jans bought

11. What operation would you use to solve this problem?

The pet store has 15 dogs and 9 birds. How many more dogs are there than birds?

A Add.   **B** Subtract.

12. In the last basketball game, Jim shot 16 baskets. He missed 7 of them. How many baskets did he make?

A 10 baskets   **B** 11 baskets

C 9 baskets   **D** 8 baskets

13. Which does *not* belong to the family of facts?

A $6 + 4 = 10$

B $10 - 4 = 6$

C $10 - 6 = 4$

D $10 + 4 = 14$

14. Which set of numbers can Janet use to write a family of facts?

A 4, 5, 9

B 4, 5, 6

C 5, 6, 10

D 4, 8, 11

15. You know that $5 + 4 = 9$. Which of the following is also a member of the family?

A $5 - 4 = 1$

B $9 - 5 = 4$

C $9 + 5 = 14$

D $9 + 4 = 13$

16. Choose the *even* number.

A 37   **B** 23   **C** 9   **D** 36

17. Choose the *odd* number.

A 16

B 12

C 27

D 28

18. Which sum is an *even* number?

A $7 + 5$

B $8 + 3$

C $7 + 6$

D $3 + 6$

EXPLORING MATHEMATICS © Scott, Foresman and Company/3

Use these pictures to solve Items 19–21.

Apples	Bananas	Pears

19. How many more bananas are there than pears?

A 4 more bananas

B 3 more bananas

C 1 more banana

D 13 more bananas

20. How many apples and pears are there in all?

A 12 apples and pears

B 13 apples and pears

C 14 apples and pears

D 9 apples and pears

21. How many more bananas are there than apples?

A 3 more bananas

B 1 more banana

C 4 more bananas

D 2 more bananas

22. Which set of states is listed in alphabetical order?

A Illinois, Oregon, Texas

B Oregon, Texas, Illinois

C Texas, Oregon, Illinois

D Oregon, Illinois, Texas

23. Which set of numbers is in order from least to greatest?

A 22, 11, 5   **B** 5, 22, 11

C 11, 22, 5   **D** 5, 11, 22

24. Which set is in order from largest to smallest?

A horse, mouse, dog

B dog, horse, mouse

C horse, dog, mouse

D mouse, dog, horse

25. Jackie entered 7 in her calculator. Which pattern of pushing three other keys gave a display of 15?

A [−] [3] [=]

B [+] [8] [=]

C [+] [6] [=]

D [−] [8] [=]

26. Dan's secret sequence is [+] [6] [=]. What display will he get if he enters 9?

A 3   **B** 14

C 16   **D** 15

27. Willa's secret sequence is [−] [5] [=]. What display will she get if she enters 7?

A 2   **B** 12

C 13   **D** 3

Choose the letter of the correct answer.

SAMPLE

Add.

```
  5
+ 6
```

  A 1

  B 11

  C 10

  D not given

1. Mrs. Gomez found finger paints in Aisle 3. How is the number used?

  A to count

  B to label

  C to measure

  D to tell the order

2. Winnie used 12 nails in her project. How is the number used?

  A to count

  B to label

  C to measure

  D to tell the order

3. Max rode his bicycle 5 miles. How is this number used?

  A to count

  B to label

  C to measure

  D to tell the order

In Items 4–6, use the rule given. Find the missing number.

4.

−4	
7	3
4	0
11	■

  A 6

  B 8

  C 9

  D 7

5.

+7	
6	■
3	10
5	12

  A 1

  B 13

  C 11

  D 15

6.

−8	
10	2
16	■
13	5

  A 8

  B 12

  C 7

  D 9

In Items 7–9, choose the symbol or number that is under the sticker.

7. 14 − = 5

  A 7   **B** 5   **C** 9   **D** 8

8. 8 [face] 9 = 17

  A +   **B** −   **C** =

9. − 8 = 3

  A 5   **B** 11   **C** 12   **D** 10

10. The school has 12 basketballs. One class checked out 4 basketballs. How many were left?
What are you asked to find?

A the number of basketballs checked out

B the total number of basketballs

C the number of basketballs that were not checked out

D the number of basketballs each class has

11. What operation would you use to solve this problem?

Farmer Ed has 7 cows and 8 goats. How many animals are there in all?

A Add. **B** Subtract.

12. Randi caught 8 fly balls of the 14 balls hit to her. How many balls did she miss?

A 22 balls

B 6 balls

C 14 balls

D 7 balls

13. Which does not belong to the family of facts?

A $3 + 6 = 9$

B $9 - 6 = 3$

C $9 - 3 = 6$

D $9 + 3 = 12$

14. Which set of numbers can Janet use to write a family of facts?

A 6, 7, 8

B 8, 6, 15

C 9, 8, 17

D 1, 2, 4

15. You know that $7 + 8 = 15$. Which of the following is also a member of the family?

A $15 - 9 = 6$

B $15 - 7 = 8$

C $15 - 6 = 9$

D $8 - 7 = 1$

16. Choose the *odd* number.

A 37 **B** 10 **C** 6 **D** 36

17. Choose the *even* number.

A 15

B 45

C 7

D 28

18. Which sum is an *odd* number?

A $7 + 5$

B $9 + 5$

C $7 + 6$

D $7 + 9$

EXPLORING MATHEMATICS © Scott, Foresman and Company/3

Use these pictures to solve Items
19–21.

Oranges	Berries	Pears

19. How many more berries are
there than oranges?

A 4 more berries

B 2 more berries

C 6 more berries

D 3 more berries

20. How many oranges and berries
are there in all?

A 12 oranges and berries

B 14 oranges and berries

C 8 oranges and berries

D 11 oranges and berries

21. How many more berries are
there than pears?

A 4 more berries

B 2 more berries

C 3 more berries

D 6 more berries

22. Which set of numbers is in order
from least to greatest?

A 17, 9, 31

B 31, 17, 9

C 9, 17, 31

D 17, 31, 9

23. Which set of states is listed in
alphabetical order?

A Florida, Idaho, Kansas

B Idaho, Florida, Kansas

C Kansas, Florida, Idaho

D Florida, Kansas, Idaho

24. Which set is in order from
smallest to largest?

A car, tricycle, bicycle

B tricycle, bicycle, car

C bicycle, car, tricycle

D car, bicycle, tricycle

25. Sam entered 8 in his calculator.
Which pattern of pushing three
other keys gave a display of 3?

A [+] [5] [=]

B [−] [3] [=]

C [−] [8] [=]

D [−] [5] [=]

26. Joan's secret sequence is
[−] [9] [=]. What display will she
get if she enters 16?

A 25 **B** 3 **C** 7 **D** 8

27. Dick's secret sequence is
[+] [8] [=]. What display will he
get if he enters 5?

A 3 **B** 13 **C** 12 **D** 14

Choose the letter of the correct answer.

SAMPLE

Which set of numbers is in order from least to greatest?

A 21 9 40

B 9 40 21

C 9 21 40

D 40 21 9

---

1. What is the greatest number of hundreds you can make from 12 tens?

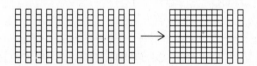

A 2 hundreds

B 1 hundred

C 12 hundreds

D 3 hundreds

---

2. What is the greatest number of hundreds that can be made from 14 tens?

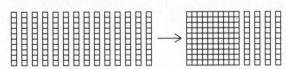

A 1 hundred

B 4 hundreds

C 14 hundreds

D 5 hundreds

---

3. What is the greatest number of hundreds that can be made from 23 tens?

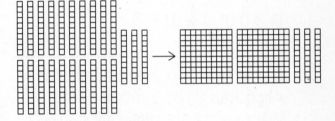

A 3 hundreds

B 5 hundreds

C 23 hundreds

D 2 hundreds

---

4. Stickers come in rolls of 100 stickers and as single stickers. Mr. Jackson bought 6 single stickers and 3 rolls. How many stickers did he buy?

A 9 stickers

B 63 stickers

C 36 stickers

D 306 stickers

---

5. What number is this?

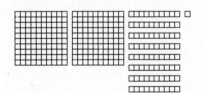

A 182   **B** 281

C 218   **D** 821

---

6. Which is the expanded form of 462?

    A 4 + 60 + 200
    B 200 + 60 + 4
    C 400 + 60 + 2
    D 400 + 20 + 6

7. Ralph has 305 baseball cards. Alice has 312 baseball cards. Who has more baseball cards?

    A Ralph
    B Alice
    C Ralph has the same number of cards as Alice.

Which symbol should be placed in the ●?

8. 267 ● 239

    A =   **B** <   **C** >

9. 780 ● 803

    A >   **B** <   **C** =

10. What numbers are between 209 and 212?

    A 208, 211
    B 210, 213
    C 209, 212
    D 210, 211

11. Which set of numbers is in order from least to greatest?

    A 60   160   75
    B 160   75   60
    C 75   160   60
    D 60   75   160

12. Which set of numbers is in order from least to greatest?

    A 328   436   547
    B 328   547   436
    C 547   436   328
    D 436   547   328

EXPLORING MATHEMATICS © Scott, Foresman and Company/3

Use this table in Items 13–15.

Number Chart

1	2	3	4	5	6	7	8	9	10
11	12	13	14	15	16	17	18	19	20
21	22	23	24	25	26	27	28	29	30
31	32	33	34	35	36	37	38	39	40
41	42	43	44	45	46	47	48	49	50
51	52	53	54	55	56	57	58	59	60
61	62	63	64	65	66	67	68	69	70
71	72	73	74	75	76	77	78	79	80
81	82	83	84	85	86	87	88	89	90
91	92	93	94	95	96	97	98	99	100

13. Begin at 7 and count by twos to 13.

A 7, 8, 10, 13
B 7, 9, 11, 13
C 7, 9, 10, 13
D 7, 8, 11, 13

14. Which set of numbers shows counting by fives?

A 16, 20, 24, 28
B 56, 62, 68, 74
C 35, 40, 45, 50
D 27, 30, 33, 36

15. Which set of numbers shows counting by tens?

A 57, 67, 77, 87
B 57, 68, 79, 90
C 85, 93, 101, 109
D 100, 200, 300, 400

16. Round 342 to the nearest ten.

A 340 **B** 300 **C** 350 **D** 400

17. Round 419 to the nearest hundred.

A 500 **B** 420 **C** 400 **D** 410

18. Round 136 to the nearest ten.

A 100 **B** 140 **C** 200 **D** 130

Use the digits 0, 5, and 8 in Items 19–21.

19. What is the greatest three-digit number you can write?

A 850 **B** 805
C 580 **D** 508

20. What three-digit number can you write where the hundreds digit is 3 less than the ones digit?

A 580 **B** 805
C 850 **D** 508

21. What is the greatest three-digit number less than 600 that you can write?

A 805 **B** 508
C 580 **D** 850

22. Write the number in standard form.

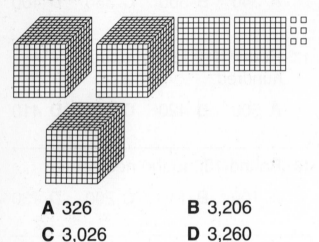

A 326   **B** 3,206

C 3,026   **D** 3,260

23. What is the standard form for $3,000 + 800 + 60 + 3$?

A 3,836   **B** 3,683

C 8,633   **D** 3,863

24. What is the standard form for $6,000 + 300 + 5$?

A 60,305   **B** 635

C 63,005   **D** 6,305

25. Mary has 5,617 pennies and Matthew has 5,538 pennies. Who has more pennies?

A Mary

B Matthew

C Mary and Matthew have an equal amount of pennies.

26. Which symbol should replace ●?

5,6 1 7 ● 5,5 3 8

A >   **B** <   **C** =

27. Which numbers are in order from least to greatest?

A 4,035   2,123   2,045

B 2,123   2,045   4,035

C 2,045   2,123   4,035

D 4,035   2,045   2,123

28. What is sixty thousand in standard form?

A 6,000   **B** 60,000

C 600,000   **D** 60

29. What does the 3 mean in 314,085?

A 3 ten-thousands

B 3 thousands

C 3 hundred-thousands

D 3 hundreds

30. What is three hundred fifty-six thousand, five hundred six in standard form?

A 356,506   **B** 356,560

C 356,056   **D** 365,506

In Items 31–33, choose the most sensible answer.

31. Jack walks to school each day. How far does he walk?

    A 40 blocks

    B 4 blocks

    C 20 blocks

    D 400 blocks

32. How many students are in Ron's third grade class?

    A 25 students

    B 2 students

    C 5 students

    D 250 students

33. Dorothy has 135 marbles in her collection. May has more marbles in her collection than Dorothy. How many marbles does May have?

    A 45 marbles

    B 125 marbles

    C 145 marbles

    D 98 marbles

Date   Score

Choose the letter of the correct answer.

SAMPLE

Which set of numbers is in order from least to greatest?

A 21   9   40

B 9   40   21

C 9   21   40

D 40   21   9

1. What is the greatest number of hundreds you can make from 11 tens?

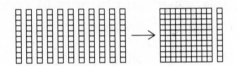

A 1 hundred

B 2 hundreds

C 3 hundreds

D 11 hundreds

2. What is the greatest number of hundreds that can be made from 13 tens?

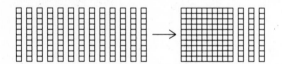

A 1 hundred

B 9 hundreds

C 12 hundreds

D 39 hundreds

3. What is the greatest number of hundreds that can be made from 21 tens?

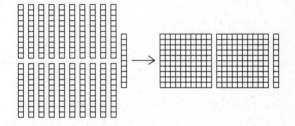

A 3 hundreds

B 2 hundreds

C 23 hundreds

D 5 hundreds

4. Stamps come in rolls of 100 stamps and as single stamps. Mrs. Ross bought 9 single stamps and 2 rolls. How many stamps did she buy?

A 11 stamps

B 209 stamps

C 29 stamps

D 92 stamps

5. What number is this?

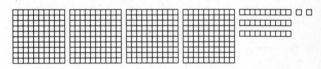

A 432   **B** 234

C 423   **D** 342

6. Which is the expanded form of 317?

   A 3 + 10 + 700
   B 700 + 30 + 1
   C 100 + 30 + 7
   D 300 + 10 + 7

7. Sally has 692 monster stickers. Robert has 407 monster stickers. Who has more monster stickers?

   A Sally
   B Robert
   C Sally has the same number of stickers as Robert.

Which symbol should be placed in the ●?

8. 487 ● 516

   A <   **B** =   **C** >

9. 640 ● 460

   A =   **B** <   **C** >

10. What numbers are between 608 and 611?

    A 609, 610   **B** 607, 610
    C 609, 612   **D** 609, 611

11. Which set of numbers is in order from least to greatest?

    A 234   134   34
    B 34   134   234
    C 134   234   34
    D 34   234   134

12. Which set of numbers is in order from least to greatest?

    A 210   207   201
    B 210   201   207
    C 201   207   210
    D 201   210   207

EXPLORING MATHEMATICS © Scott, Foresman and Company/3

Use this table in Items 13–15.

Number Chart

1	2	3	4	5	6	7	8	9	10
11	12	13	14	15	16	17	18	19	20
21	22	23	24	25	26	27	28	29	30
31	32	33	34	35	36	37	38	39	40
41	42	43	44	45	46	47	48	49	50
51	52	53	54	55	56	57	58	59	60
61	62	63	64	65	66	67	68	69	70
71	72	73	74	75	76	77	78	79	80
81	82	83	84	85	86	87	88	89	90
91	92	93	94	95	96	97	98	99	100

13. Begin at 13 and count by twos to 19.

    A 13, 14, 17, 19

    B 13, 15, 17, 19

    C 13, 15, 16, 19

    D 13, 14, 16, 19

14. Which set of numbers shows counting by fives?

    A 4, 8, 12, 16

    B 13, 16, 19, 22

    C 22, 24, 26, 28

    D 20, 25, 30, 35

15. Which set of numbers shows counting by tens?

    A 45, 50, 60, 70

    B 34, 45, 56, 67

    C 13, 23, 34, 44

    D 62, 72, 82, 92

16. Round 217 to the nearest ten.

    A 210   B 200   C 220   D 300

17. Round 581 to the nearest hundred.

    A 500   B 600   C 580   D 590

18. Round 363 to the nearest ten.

    A 370   B 300   C 400   D 360

Use the digits 2, 4, and 6 in Items 19–21.

19. What is the least three-digit number you can write?

    A 246   B 462

    C 426   D 264

20. What three-digit number can you write where the tens digit is 4 more than the ones digit?

    A 426   B 624

    C 462   D 264

21. What is the greatest three-digit number less than 500 that you can write?

    A 426   B 462

    C 264   D 246

22. Write the number in standard form.

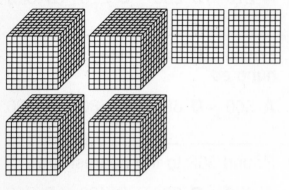

A 402   B 420

C 4,020   D 4,200

23. What is the standard form for 5,000 + 70 + 6?

A 5,760   B 576

C 5,706   D 5,076

24. What is the standard form for 8,000 + 100 + 9?

A 8,109   B 819

C 80,109   D 81,009

25. Nancy has 3,084 marbles. Jim has 3,069 marbles. Who has more marbles?

A Nancy

B Jim

C Nancy and Jim have an equal amount of marbles.

26. Which symbol should replace ●?
3,069 ● 3,084

A =   B >   C <

27. Which numbers are in order from least to greatest?

2 6,123   7,231   7,213

B 6,123   7,213   7,231

C 7,231   7,213   6,123

D 7,213   6,123   7,231

28. What is eighty thousand in standard form?

A 80,000   B 8,000

C 800,000   D 80

29. What is four hundred six thousand, one hundred thirteen in standard form?

A 460,113   B 406,113

C 406,013   D 460,013

30. What does the 5 mean in 153,472?

   A 5 hundred-thousands

   B 5 thousands

   C 5 ten-thousands

   D 5 tens

In Items 31–33, which is the most sensible answer?

31. Willa does sit-ups in the gym each day. How many sit-ups does she do each day?

   A 200,000 sit-ups

   B 20,000 sit-ups

   C 2,000 sit-ups

   D 20 sit-ups

32. Dennis has 352 cards in his collection. Johnny has fewer cards than Dennis. How many cards does Johnny have?

   A 305 cards

   B 355 cards

   C 400 cards

   D 532 cards

33. How many boys in Val's third grade class walk to school?

   A 60 boys

   B 6 boys

   C 30 boys

   D 40 boys

Date   Score

Choose the letter of the correct answer.

SAMPLE

Subtract.

$$\begin{array}{r} 6\,3 \\ -7 \\ \hline \end{array}$$

A 54

B 56

C 66

D not given

1. Lou found 5 shells on Saturday and 8 shells on Sunday. How many shells did Lou find?

   A 12 shells

   B 3 shells

   C 13 shells

   D 2 shells

2. Kim made 12 posters last week and 7 posters this week. How many more posters did Kim make last week than this week?

   A 5 posters

   B 4 posters

   C 18 posters

   D 19 posters

3. Jimmy had 7 baseball cards. He bought 4 more cards. How many cards does Jimmy have now?

   A 3 cards

   B 11 cards

   C 10 cards

   D 2 cards

4.
Tens	Ones
5	17

   Make all the tens you can. How many tens and ones do you have now?

   A 4 tens 7 ones

   B 12 tens 1 one

   C 6 tens 7 ones

   D 6 tens 16 ones

5.
Tens	Ones
9	5

   Trade 1 ten for 10 ones. How many tens and ones do you have now?

   A 9 tens 6 ones

   B 8 tens 5 ones

   C 8 tens 6 ones

   D 8 tens 15 ones

6.
Tens	Ones
5	8

   Trade 1 ten for 10 ones. How many tens and ones do you have now?

   A 4 tens 9 ones

   B 4 tens 18 ones

   C 5 tens 18 ones

   D 5 tens 9 ones

Add.

7.   25
    +43

A 68
B 78
C 58
D not given

8.   37
    +28

A 515
B 65
C 55
D not given

9. On Monday Tamara practiced for 35 minutes. On Tuesday she practiced another 35 minutes. How many minutes did she practice in all?

A 610 minutes
B 60 minutes
C 80 minutes
D 70 minutes

In Items 10–12, add using mental math.

10. 46 + 30

A 66
B 86
C 70
D not given

11. 57 + 28

A 85
B 75
C 715
D not given

12. 69 + 19

A 78
B 718
C 88
D not given

Add.

13.   37
      13
    +25

A 615
B 75
C 65
D not given

14. 45 + 26 + 14

A 75   B 715
C 85   D not given

15. 7 + 18 + 25 + 7

A 57   B 327
C 47   D not given

Subtract.

16.   55
    −18

A 37
B 43
C 47
D not given

17.   97
    −43

A 44
B 45
C 54
D not given

18. A sweater costs $43. It is on sale for $14 off. What is the sale price?

A $57   **B** $29

C $31   **D** $39

In Items 19 and 20, subtract using mental math.

19. 85 − 13   **A** 72

B 78

C 62

D not given

20. 74 − 47   **A** 33

B 37

C 23

D not given

21. Sam's book has 52 pages. He read 19 pages. Use mental math to find how many pages he has left to read.

A 47 pages   **B** 33 pages

C 43 pages   **D** 37 pages

Use front-end estimation in Items 22–24.

22. 57 + 21

A 30   **B** 40   **C** 70   **D** 60

23. 73 − 28

A 90   **B** 30   **C** 60   **D** 50

24. Will the sum 59 + 37 be greater than or less than 100?

A greater than 100

B less than 100

Use the information in this picture for Items 25–27.

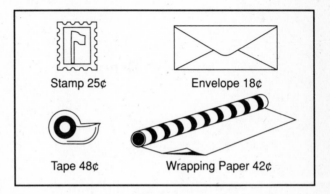

Stamp 25¢   Envelope 18¢

Tape 48¢   Wrapping Paper 42¢

25. You have 85¢. Do you have enough to buy tape and wrapping paper?

A Yes, you have enough.

B No, you do not have enough.

26. You have 50¢. Which two items can you buy?

A tape, envelope

B envelope, stamp

C two tapes

D two wrapping papers

27. You have 90¢. Do you have enough to buy two wrapping papers?

A Yes, you have enough.

B No, you do not have enough.

Date   Score

Choose the letter of the correct answer.

SAMPLE

Subtract.

6 3
− 7

A 54
B 56
C 66
D not given

1. Jan found 12 shells on Monday and 7 shells on Tuesday. How many more shells did Jan find on Monday than on Tuesday?

   A 4 shells
   B 5 shells
   C 19 shells
   D 15 shells

2. Randy made 7 posters last week and 6 posters this week. How many posters did Randy make?

   A 13 posters
   B 1 poster
   C 12 posters
   D 7 posters

3. Roberta had 11 baseball cards. She gave 8 cards to Janet. How many cards does she have left?

   A 19 cards
   B 18 cards
   C 3 cards
   D 4 cards

4.

Tens	Ones
7	13

Make all the tens you can. How many tens and ones do you have now?

   A 8 tens 3 ones
   B 10 tens 1 one
   C 6 tens 3 ones
   D 8 tens 13 ones

5.

Tens	Ones
6	1

Trade 1 ten for 10 ones. How many tens and ones do you have now?

   A 5 tens 10 ones
   B 6 tens 10 ones
   C 5 tens 11 ones
   D 6 tens 11 ones

6.

Tens	Ones
7	5

Trade 1 ten for 10 ones. How many tens and ones do you have now?

   A 7 tens 15 ones
   B 6 tens 6 ones
   C 7 tens 6 ones
   D 6 tens 15 ones

Add.

7. $\begin{array}{r} 31 \\ +57 \\ \hline \end{array}$
    A 88
    B 78
    C 98
    D not given

8. $\begin{array}{r} 45 \\ +45 \\ \hline \end{array}$
    A 90
    B 80
    C 810
    D not given

9. Tim spent 69¢ on a toy horse and 18¢ on a toy monster. How much did he spend in all?

    A 717¢   **B** 77¢
    C 71¢   **D** 87¢

In Items 10–12, add using mental math.

10. $28 + 50$
    A 70
    B 78
    C 88
    D not given

11. $13 + 47$
    A 50
    B 510
    C 60
    D not given

12. $44 + 38$
    A 82
    B 712
    C 72
    D not given

Add.

13. $\begin{array}{r} 29 \\ 36 \\ +21 \\ \hline \end{array}$
    A 716
    B 86
    C 76
    D not given

14. $28 + 17 + 33$
    A 618   **B** 78
    C 68   **D** not given

15. $5 + 17 + 36 + 9$
    A 67   **B** 427
    C 57   **D** not given

Subtract.

16. $\begin{array}{r} 73 \\ -44 \\ \hline \end{array}$
    A 31
    B 39
    C 29
    D not given

17. $\begin{array}{r} 85 \\ -33 \\ \hline \end{array}$
    A 52
    B 25
    C 42
    D not given

18. A jacket costs $54. It is on sale for $18 off. What is the sale price?

A $44   **B** $46

C $72   **D** $36

In Items 19 and 20, subtract using mental math.

19. 6 8 − 3 3

A 25
B 35
C 21
D not given

20. 5 1 − 2 7

A 34
B 36
C 24
D not given

21. Meg had 65 tickets to sell. She sold 28 of them. Use mental math to find how many she has left.

A 33 tickets   **B** 43 tickets
C 47 tickets   **D** 37 tickets

Use front-end estimation in Items 22–24.

22. 3 6 + 2 2

A 40   **B** 20   **C** 10   **D** 50

23. 8 1 − 5 7

A 100   **B** 40   **C** 30   **D** 10

24. Will the sum 6 4 + 2 8 be greater than or less than 100?

A greater than 100

B less than 100

Use the information on the sign for Items 25–27.

| Apple | 33¢ | Banana | 18¢ |
| Pear | 28¢ | Orange | 21¢ |

25. You have 50¢. Do you have enough to buy an apple and a pear?

A Yes, you have enough.

B No, you do not have enough.

26. You have 40¢. Which two items can you buy?

A pear, orange

B apple, banana

C banana, orange

D apple, pear

27. You have 75¢. Do you have enough to buy two apples?

A Yes, you have enough.

B No, you do not have enough.

Choose the letter of the correct answer.

SAMPLE

Add.

$5 + 2$

A 6   **B** 7   **C** 8   **D** not given

1. How is the number 68 used in "Jack weighs 68 pounds"?

   A count   **B** label

   C measure   **D** tell order

2. Tell what number belongs in the box.

   $7 - \blacksquare = 4$

   A 0   **B** 3   **C** 5   **D** 8

Add.

3. $\begin{array}{r} 6 \\ +2 \\ \hline \end{array}$

    A 9

    B 4

    C 7

    D not given

4. $\begin{array}{r} 8 \\ +5 \\ \hline \end{array}$

    A 12

    B 13

    C 14

    D not given

5. Which number belongs in the $\blacksquare$?

   $16 - 8 = \blacksquare$

   A 7   **B** 8   **C** 6   **D** 9

6. Subtract.

   $\begin{array}{r} 15 \\ -\ 7 \\ \hline \end{array}$

   A 7

   B 6

   C 8

   D not given

7. Janet found 8 shells. Bo found 12 shells. How many more shells did Bo find?

   A 4 shells   **B** 20 shells

   C 5 shells   **D** 6 shells

8. Which fact does *not* belong to the family?

   A $15 - 9 = 6$ **B** $9 + 6 = 15$

   C $15 - 6 = 9$ **D** $9 - 6 = 3$

9. Which statement about numbers is true?

   A even + even = odd

   B even + odd = even

   C odd + even = odd

   D odd + odd = odd

10. Which number sentence is true?

    A $35 > 35$ **B** $34 < 21$

    C $51 < 49$ **D** $51 > 49$

11. Use the picture to solve
the problem.

What is the total number of
animals that have four legs?

A 3 animals   **B** 5 animals

C 2 animals   **D** 7 animals

12. Which numbers are written in
order from least to greatest?

A 748   750   806   923

B 750   748   806   923

C 806   923   748   750

D 750   993   806   748

13. Which calculator key sequence
would replace the ⟶ to
change each first number to the
second number?

$$7 \longrightarrow 3$$
$$10 \longrightarrow 6$$
$$5 \longrightarrow 1$$
$$12 \longrightarrow 8$$

A ⊟ 5 ⊜   **B** ⊞ 5 ⊜

C ⊟ 4 ⊜   **D** ⊞ 4 ⊜

14. Which is the same as 45 tens?

A 4 tens 5 ones

B 4 hundreds 5 tens

C 5 hundreds 4 tens

D 45 hundred

15. Which is the hundreds digit
in 671?

A 6   **B** 1   **C** 7

16. Which number sentence is true?

A 312 < 298   **B** 312 < 398

C 312 = 298   **D** 312 > 398

17. Which numbers are written in
order from least to greatest?

A 157   273   398   181

B 398   273   181   157

C 157   181   273   398

D 273   398   181   157

18. Which numbers are written in
order from least to greatest?

A 96   234   105   298   300

B 96   105   234   298   300

C 96   105   234   300   298

D 300   298   234   105   96

19. Round 729 to the
nearest hundred.

A 700   **B** 720

C 800   **D** 730

20. What is the next number when counting by fives?

35 40 45 50 ■

A 60   **B** 65   **C** 70   **D** 55

21. Arrange these digits to match the directions.

1 3 2

The ones digit is the sum of the tens and hundreds digits. The hundreds digit is twice as big as the tens digit.

A 123   **B** 312
C 213   **D** 231

22. Which is the thousands digit in 3,507?

A 5   **B** 3   **C** 0   **D** 7

23. What is the standard form?

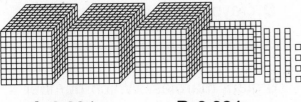

A 2,334   **B** 3,324
C 4,323   **D** 3,234

24. Which number sentence is true?

A 5,956 > 6,012
B 5,012 > 5,956
C 6,012 > 5,956
D 6,003 < 5,123

25. Which is the ten-thousands digit in 573,026?

A 7   **B** 5   **C** 3   **D** 0

26. Which digit is in the hundreds place in 25,640?

A 4   **B** 6   **C** 5   **D** 2

27. Roberta's family goes on a picnic each weekend when the weather is good. Which is the most sensible answer for about how many weekends they have a picnic each year?

A 60 weekends

B 30 weekends

C 2 weekends

D 50 weekends

28. Jan jumped rope 14 times without missing. Robert jumped 6 times without missing. How many more times did Jan jump?

A 20 times   **B** 7 times
C 9 times   **D** 8 times

29. Which is the same as 5 tens 25 ones?

A 7 tens 5 ones

B 6 tens 5 ones

C 30 tens

D 7 tens 15 ones

Add.

30.   3 5
        +4 7

A 72
B 82
C 92
D not given

31.   2 2
           4 7
        +1 8

A 77
B 97
C 717
D not given

32. Subtract.

        8 3
       −1 7

A 66
B 76
C 100
D not given

33. Bert collected 38 pounds and Dorothy collected 47 pounds of newspapers to be recycled. How many pounds did they collect in all?

A 75 pounds   **B** 9 pounds
C 85 pounds   **D** 80 pounds

34. Add using mental math.

        49 + 46

A 85   **B** 95   **C** 87   **D** 97

35. Which is the same as 3?

A 9 − 6   **B** 9 + 6
C 4 + 1   **D** 8 − 4

36. Subtract using mental math.

        93 − 58

A 41   **B** 45   **C** 31   **D** 35

37. Estimate by rounding.

        73 − 27

A about 60   **B** about 50
C about 40   **D** about 100

38. You have 95 cents. Which two school supplies can you buy?

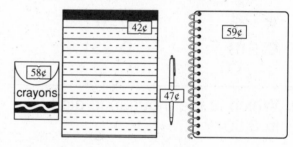

A crayons and pen
B crayons and notebook
C tablet and pen
D crayons and tablet

39. Jackie has 9 agate marbles and 6 giant marbles. Which number sentence could you use to find how many marbles Jackie has in all?

A 9 − 6 = ■
B 9 + 6 = ■
C 15 − 9 = ■
D 15 + 9 = ■

Date   Score

Choose the letter of the correct answer.

SAMPLE
Add.

```
 364
+129
```

A 483
B 493
C 485
D not given

1. How many dimes can you get for 57 pennies?

   A 7 dimes   **B** 6 dimes
   C 5 dimes   **D** not given

2. You have 4 dimes and 36 pennies. After trading pennies for dimes, how many dimes and pennies do you have?

   A 7 dimes, 6 pennies
   B 4 dimes, 6 pennies
   C 3 dimes, 6 pennies
   D 5 dimes, 16 pennies

3.

$	d	p
5	9	15

   Trade as many pennies for dimes and dimes for dollars as you can.
   How many dollars, dimes, and pennies will you have after trading?

   A 5 dollars, 10 dimes, 5 pennies
   B 6 dollars, 1 dime, 5 pennies
   C 5 dollars, 1 dime, 5 pennies
   D 6 dollars, 0 dimes, 5 pennies

In Items 4–6, tell how much in all.

4.

$	d	p
1	3	4
+ 2	5	4

   A $4.88
   B $3.88
   C $3.98
   D not given

5.

$	d	p
2	7	6
+ 1	1	9

   A $3.85
   B $3.95
   C $1.63
   D not given

6.

$	d	p
3	2	5
+ 2	8	7

   A $5.02
   B $5.12
   C $6.02
   D not given

Add.

7.
```
 237
+128
```
   A 365
   B 355
   C 455
   D not given

8.
```
 429
+390
```
   A 719
   B 729
   C 819
   D not given

9. Marty had 646 baseball cards. He got 192 more cards. How many cards does he have in all?

   A 738 cards

   B 838 cards

   C 748 cards

   D 848 cards

Add.

10. $\begin{array}{r} 2,176 \\ +3,951 \end{array}$

   A 6,127

   B 5,027

   C 6,027

   D not given

11. $\begin{array}{r} 4,326 \\ +2,947 \end{array}$

   A 6,263

   B 6,273

   C 7,263

   D not given

12. $\begin{array}{r} 2,896 \\ +578 \end{array}$

   A 2,364

   B 5,364

   C 3,474

   D not given

13. Which of these problems would you use mental math to solve?

   A $\begin{array}{r} 38 \\ +54 \end{array}$

   B $\begin{array}{r} 487 \\ +639 \end{array}$

   C $\begin{array}{r} 8 \\ +9 \end{array}$

14. Which of these problems would you use pencil and paper to solve?

   A $\begin{array}{r} 829 \\ +77 \end{array}$

   B $\begin{array}{r} 30 \\ +40 \end{array}$

   C $\begin{array}{r} 6 \\ +8 \end{array}$

15. Which of these problems would you use a calculator to solve?

   A $\begin{array}{r} 300 \\ +500 \end{array}$

   B $\begin{array}{r} 2,376 \\ +4,855 \end{array}$

   C $\begin{array}{r} 25 \\ +32 \end{array}$

Use this map to solve Items 16–18.

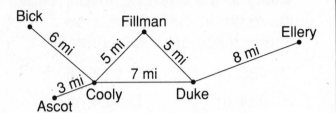

16. What town must you pass through to go the shortest distance from Bick to Duke?

A Ascot   **B** Fillman

C Cooly   **D** Ellery

17. What is the shortest distance from Bick to Duke?

A 13 mi   **B** 34 mi

C 11 mi   **D** 16 mi

18. What is the distance from Ellery to Duke to Fillman?

A 25 mi   **B** 20 mi

C 18 mi   **D** 13 mi

In Items 19–21, subtract to find how much is left.

19.

	$	d	p
Have:	3	7	5
Spend:	1	5	3

A $1.22   **B** $2.22

C $1.12   **D** not given

20.

	$	d	p
Have:	5	6	1
Spend:	2	3	5

A $3.34   **B** $3.36

C $3.24   **D** not given

21.

	$	d	p
Have:	4	1	8
Spend:	2	4	5

A $1.73   **B** $2.73

C $2.33   **D** not given

Subtract.

22.
$$\begin{array}{r} 763 \\ -245 \\ \hline \end{array}$$

A 518
B 522
C 528
D not given

23.
$$\begin{array}{r} 650 \\ -237 \\ \hline \end{array}$$

A 427
B 423
C 413
D not given

24. Alice counted 927 pencils in the school store. Then she sold 355 pencils. How many pencils are left?

    A 632 pencils

    B 672 pencils

    C 532 pencils

    D 572 pencils

Subtract.

25. $\begin{array}{r} 620 \\ -345 \\ \hline \end{array}$ A 275

    B 285

    C 375

    D not given

26. $\begin{array}{r} 507 \\ -259 \\ \hline \end{array}$ A 352

    B 358

    C 248

    D not given

27. The Lee family is driving 700 miles to the Grand Canyon. They have driven 386 miles. How many miles are left to drive?

    A 486 mi   B 314 mi

    C 424 mi   D 324 mi

Subtract.

28. $\begin{array}{r} 8,030 \\ -3,465 \\ \hline \end{array}$ A 4,565

    B 5,435

    C 5,675

    D not given

29. $\begin{array}{r} 6,500 \\ -1,677 \\ \hline \end{array}$ A 5,177

    B 4,833

    C 5,933

    D not given

30. $\begin{array}{r} 7,000 \\ -4,086 \\ \hline \end{array}$ A 3,024

    B 3,086

    C 2,914

    D not given

EXPLORING MATHEMATICS © Scott, Foresman and Company/3

Use the following table to solve
Items 31–33.

Student	Favorite Sport	Number of Baseball Cards	Favorite Kind of Music
Mary	Tennis	123	Country and Western
Mark	Soccer	257	Rock and Roll
Joan	Tennis	415	Rap
Jesse	Soccer	331	Rock and Roll

31. Which student plays tennis and also likes rap music?

   A Jesse

   B Joan

   C Mark

   D Mary

32. Which student has fewer than 300 baseball cards and likes to play soccer?

   A Joan

   B Mark

   C Jesse

   D Mary

33. Which student has the most baseball cards?

   A Mary

   B Jesse

   C Joan

   D Mark

Choose the letter of the correct answer.

SAMPLE

Add.

364
+129

A 483
B 493
C 485
D not given

1. How many dimes can you get for 85 pennies?

A 10 dimes   **B** 9 dimes

C 8 dimes   **D** not given

2. You have 4 dollars and 22 dimes. After trading dimes for dollars, how many dollars and dimes do you have?

A 6 dollars, 2 dimes

B 6 dollars, 20 dimes

C 4 dollars, 2 dimes

D 5 dollars, 21 dimes

3.

$	d	p
2	9	10

Trade as many pennies for dimes and dimes for dollars as you can. How many dollars, dimes, and pennies will you have after trading?

A 2 dollars, 10 dimes, 0 pennies

B 3 dollars, 0 dimes, 0 pennies

C 2 dollars, 0 dimes, 10 pennies

D 3 dollars, 1 dime, 1 penny

In Items 4–6, tell how much in all.

4.

$	d	p
3	0	5
+ 5	2	3

A $9.28
B $8.38
C $8.28
D not given

5.

$	d	p
3	5	8
+ 2	1	7

A $6.65
B $5.65
C $5.55
D not given

6.

$	d	p
4	7	3
+ 1	8	9

A $6.62
B $5.52
C $5.62
D not given

Add.

7.   205
    +637

A 842
B 832
C 932
D not given

8.   582
    +265

A 747
B 757
C 847
D not given

9. Last year there were 753 students in Elm School. There are 191 more students this year. How many students are in Elm School this year?

   A 944 students

   B 844 students

   C 854 students

   D 954 students

Add.

10. $\begin{array}{r} 4{,}268 \\ +1{,}870 \\ \hline \end{array}$ **A** 5,048
   B 5,148
   C 6,038
   D not given

11. $\begin{array}{r} 3{,}627 \\ +5{,}853 \\ \hline \end{array}$ **A** 8,470
   B 8,480
   C 9,480
   D not given

12. $\begin{array}{r} 5{,}578 \\ +986 \\ \hline \end{array}$ **A** 5,454
   B 6,564
   C 8,454
   D not given

13. Which of these problems would you use mental math to solve?

   A $\begin{array}{r} 20 \\ +60 \\ \hline \end{array}$

   B $\begin{array}{r} 38 \\ +49 \\ \hline \end{array}$

   C $\begin{array}{r} 834 \\ +189 \\ \hline \end{array}$

14. Which of these problems would you use pencil and paper to solve?

   A $\begin{array}{r} 9 \\ +7 \\ \hline \end{array}$

   B $\begin{array}{r} 300 \\ +400 \\ \hline \end{array}$

   C $\begin{array}{r} 84 \\ +79 \\ \hline \end{array}$

15. Which of these problems would you use a calculator to solve?

   A $\begin{array}{r} 600 \\ +200 \\ \hline \end{array}$

   B $\begin{array}{r} 4{,}123 \\ +1{,}898 \\ \hline \end{array}$

   C $\begin{array}{r} 21 \\ +67 \\ \hline \end{array}$

Use this map to solve Items 16–18.

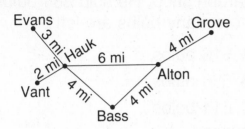

16. What town must you pass through to go the shortest distance from Evans to Bass?

A Vant   **B** Grove

C Alton   **D** Hauk

17. What is the shortest distance from Evans to Bass?

A 7 mi   **B** 13 mi

C 9 mi   **D** 23 mi

18. What is the distance from Hauk to Alton to Grove?

A 18 mi   **B** 23 mi

C 10 mi   **D** 12 mi

In Items 19–21, subtract to find how much is left.

19.

	$	d	p
Have:	6	8	8
Spend:	2	5	0

A $3.38   **B** $4.38

C $4.28   **D** not given

20.

	$	d	p
Have:	4	5	0
Spend:	1	2	5

A $3.35   **B** $3.25

C $2.35   **D** not given

21.

	$	d	p
Have:	5	2	7
Spend:	3	5	5

A $2.32   **B** $2.72

C $1.72   **D** not given

Subtract.

22.
$$
\begin{array}{r} 582 \\ -265 \\ \hline \end{array}
$$

A 323

B 317

C 327

D not given

23.
$$
\begin{array}{r} 753 \\ -416 \\ \hline \end{array}
$$

A 347

B 349

C 343

D not given

24. Sally had 868 stamps in her foreign stamp collection. She gave 475 stamps to a friend. How many stamps does Sally have left?

A 393 stamps

B 413 stamps

C 493 stamps

D 343 stamps

Subtract.

25. 730
−255

A 585

B 475

C 525

D not given

26. 605
−179

A 574

B 536

C 426

D not given

27. George had 900 tulip bulbs in his garden shop. He sold 384 bulbs. How many bulbs are left?

A 516 bulbs

B 626 bulbs

C 614 bulbs

D 526 bulbs

Subtract.

28. 7,040
−4,573

A 2,533

B 3,577

C 2,567

D not given

29. 8,200
−2,766

A 6,566

B 6,544

C 5,434

D not given

30. 5,000
−3,106

A 2,106

B 1,894

C 2,904

D not given

EXPLORING MATHEMATICS © Scott, Foresman and Company/3

Use the following table to solve Items 31–33.

Student	Height	Favorite Animal	Favorite Game
Jill	90 cm	cat	dominoes
Lori	105 cm	dog	dominoes
Mike	98 cm	hamster	checkers
Chris	109 cm	dog	checkers

31. Which student likes to play checkers and also likes hamsters?

   A Jill
   B Lori
   C Chris
   D Mike

32. Which student is taller than 100 centimeters and likes to play dominoes?

   A Lori
   B Chris
   C Jill
   D Mike

33. Which student is tallest?

   A Jill
   B Lori
   C Chris
   D Mike

Choose the letter of the correct answer.

SAMPLE

Choose the most sensible measure for the length of an eraser.

A meter

B kilometer

C centimeter

1.  What time does the clock show?

A 3:20   **B** 3:40

C 4:20   **D** 4:40

2.  What time does the clock show?

A 3:50   **B** 5:10

C 4:10   **D** 4:50

3. 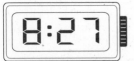 What time does the clock show?

A 27 minutes after 8

B 27 minutes before 8

Use this calendar to answer Items 4–6.

OCTOBER	NOVEMBER	DECEMBER
S M T W T F S		S M T W T F S
1 2 3 4 5		1 2 3 4 5 6 7
6 7 8 9 10 11 12		8 9 10 11 12 13 14
13 14 15 16 17 18 19		15 16 17 18 19 20 21
20 21 22 23 24 25 26		22 23 24 25 26 27 28
27 28 29 30 31		29 30 31

Sun	Mon	Tues	Wed	Thur	Fri	Sat
					1	2
3	4	5	Election 6 Day	7	8	9
10	11	12	13	14	School 15 Play	16
17	18	Band 19 Concert	20	21	22	23
24	25	26	27	Thanksgiving 28 Day	29	30

4. On what day of the week does the band perform in November?

A Tuesday   **B** Monday

C Thursday   **D** Wednesday

5. What happens one week after November 21?

A Election Day

B School Play

C Band Concert

D Thanksgiving Day

6. What is the date of the first Wednesday in December?

A 3   **B** 4   **C** 11   **D** 6

Use this picture for Items 7–9.

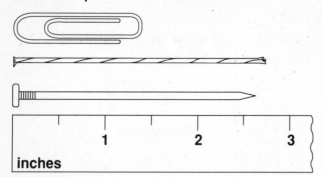

7. What is the length of the string to the nearest inch?

   A $2\frac{1}{2}$ in.　　　　**B** $3\frac{1}{2}$ in.

   C 3 in.　　　　　**D** 4 in.

8. What is the length of the paper clip to the nearest half inch?

   A 1 in.　　　　　**B** $1\frac{1}{2}$ in.

   C 2 in.　　　　　**D** $\frac{1}{2}$ in.

9. What is the length of the nail to the nearest half inch?

   A 2 in.　　　　　**B** $3\frac{1}{2}$ in.

   C $2\frac{1}{2}$ in.　　　　**D** 3 in.

Choose the most sensible unit of measure in Items 10–12.

10. Length of a room

   A foot　　**B** inch　　**C** mile

11. Distance between two cities

   A foot　　**B** yard　　**C** mile

12. Width of a football field

   A inch　　**B** yard　　**C** mile

Use this picture to measure the lines in Items 13–15.

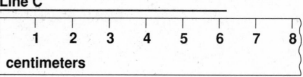

Line A
Line B
Line C

13. Line A to the nearest centimeter

   A 4 cm　　　　**B** 6 cm

   C 5 cm　　　　**D** 7 cm

14. Line B to the nearest centimeter

   A 2 cm　　　　**B** 5 cm

   C 3 cm　　　　**D** 4 cm

15. Line C to the nearest centimeter

   A 4 cm　　　　**B** 7 cm

   C 6 cm　　　　**D** 5 cm

Choose the most sensible unit of measure in Items 16–18.

16. Length of a new pencil

    A centimeter

    B kilometer

    C meter

17. Distance across Texas

    A centimeter

    B meter

    C kilometer

18. Length of a ladder

    A centimeter

    B kilometer

    C meter

Use the story and table for Items 19–21. Sue, Sam, and Tom went to the park. One rode a bike, one rode a skateboard, and one walked.

	Bike	Skateboard	Walked
Sam			
Tom			
Sue			

19. Clue 1: No one's name begins with the same letter as the way they got to the park. This clue tells you:

    A Sam rode a skateboard.

    B Tom rode a skateboard.

    C Sue rode a skateboard.

20. Clue 2: Sue's bike has a flat tire. This clue tells you:

    A Sue rode her bike.

    B Sue did not ride her bike.

    C Sue does not have a bike.

21. Sam didn't walk or ride a skateboard. This clue tells you:

    A Sam rode a bike.

    B Sam rode a skateboard.

    C Sam walked.

Find the perimeter of each figure in Items 22–24.

22.

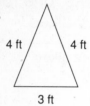

4 ft   4 ft

3 ft

A 8 ft
B 11 ft
C 7 ft
D 12 ft

23.

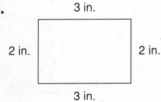

3 in.

2 in.   2 in.

3 in.

A 5 in.
B 8 in.
C 7 in.
D 10 in.

24.

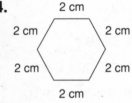

2 cm

2 cm   2 cm

2 cm   2 cm

2 cm

A 6 cm
B 8 cm
C 10 cm
D 12 cm

In Items 25–27, find the area of each figure in square centimeters.

25.

A 12 square centimeters
B 32 square centimeters
C 8 square centimeters
D 10 square centimeters

26.

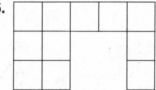

A 20 square centimeters
B 11 square centimeters
C 12 square centimeters
D 44 square centimeters

27.

A 28 square centimeters
B 8 square centimeters
C 12 square centimeters
D 7 square centimeters

In Items 28–30, tell whether you need to find an exact answer or an estimate.

28. Jack plans to make 12 ornaments. He uses 3 feet of ribbon for each ornament. Should he buy a 25-foot or 50-foot roll of ribbon?

   A An estimate is enough.

   B An exact answer is needed.

29. Dorothy wants to make 5 streamers. She wants each streamer to be 18 feet long. Should she buy a 50-foot or 100-foot roll of crepe paper?

   A An exact answer is needed.

   B An estimate is enough.

30. Bill is making a picture frame. He needs 11 inches of wood frame for each side. How much wood frame should Bill buy?

   A An exact answer is needed.

   B An estimate is enough.

Choose the most sensible measure in Items 31–33.

31. Temperature of a hot summer day

   A 38°C

   B 95°C

   C 70°C

32. Temperature of a classroom

   A 20°F

   B 98°F

   C 70°F

33. Temperature for ice skating outdoors

   A 15°C

   B −5°C

   C 20°C

Choose the letter of the correct answer.

SAMPLE

Choose the most sensible measure for the length of an eraser.

A meter

B kilometer

C centimeter

---

1.  What time does the clock show?

   A 4:10   **B** 5:10

   C 4:50   **D** 5:50

---

2.  What time does the clock show?

   A 6:25   **B** 5:25

   C 4:45   **D** 5:45

---

3.  What time does the clock show?

   A 26 minutes before 10

   B 26 minutes after 10

Use this calendar to answer Items 4–6.

NOVEMBER						
S	M	T	W	T	F	S
					1	2
3	4	5	6	7	8	9
10	11	12	13	14	15	16
17	18	19	20	21	22	23
24	25	26	27	28	29	30

DECEMBER

JANUARY						
S	M	T	W	T	F	S
			1	2	3	4
5	6	7	8	9	10	11
12	13	14	15	16	17	18
19	20	21	22	23	24	25
26	27	28	29	30	31	

Sun	Mon	Tues	Wed	Thur	Fri	Sat
1	Ben's 2 birthday	3	4	5	6	7
8	9	10	11	School 12 Play	13	14
15	16	17	Band 18 Concert	19	Winter 20 break	21
22	23	24	25	26	27	28
29	30	31				

4. On what day of the week is the school play in December?

   A Monday   **B** Friday

   C Wednesday   **D** Thursday

5. What happens one week after December 11?

   A School Play

   B Winter break

   C Ben's birthday

   D Band Concert

6. What is the date of the second Friday in January?

   A 3   **B** 8   **C** 10   **D** 13

Use this picture for Items 7–9.

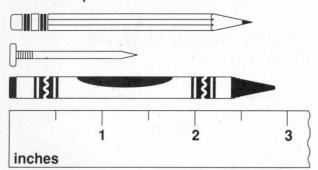

7. What is the length of the crayon to the nearest inch?

A $1\frac{1}{2}$ in.   B 2 in.
C $2\frac{1}{2}$ in.   D 3 in.

8. What is the length of the nail to the nearest half inch?

A 1 in.   B $1\frac{1}{2}$ in.
C 2 in.   D $2\frac{1}{2}$ in.

9. What is the length of the pencil to the nearest half inch?

A 3 in.   B $4\frac{1}{2}$ in.
C $2\frac{1}{2}$ in.   D $3\frac{1}{2}$ in.

Choose the most sensible unit of measure in Items 10–12.

10. Length of a soccer field

A yard   B mile   C inch

11. Distance from New York to Chicago

A foot   B yard   C mile

12. Length of a parking space

A foot   B inch   C mile

Use this picture to measure the lines in Items 13–15.

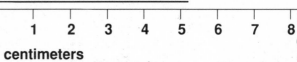

13. Line A to the nearest centimeter

A 3 cm   B 4 cm
C 5 cm   D 6 cm

14. Line B to the nearest centimeter

A 6 cm   B 5 cm
C 4 cm   D 7 cm

15. Line C to the nearest centimeter

A 6 cm   B 4 cm
C 3 cm   D 5 cm

Choose the most sensible unit of measure in Items 16–18.

16. Distance across the United States

   A meter

   B kilometer

   C centimeter

17. Length of your thumb

   A meter

   B kilometer

   C centimeter

18. Length of a car

   A meter

   B kilometer

   C centimeter

Use the story and table for Items 19–21. Joan, Mark, and Sara each play a team sport. One plays baseball, one basketball, and one soccer.

	Baseball	Basketball	Soccer
Joan			
Mark			
Sara			

19. Clue 1: One person's name begins with the same letter as the sport they play. This clue tells you:

   A Joan plays soccer.

   B Mark plays soccer.

   C Sara plays soccer.

20. Clue 2: The girls do not play baseball. This clue tells you:

   A Joan plays baseball.

   B Mark plays baseball.

   C Sara plays baseball.

21. Neither Mark nor Sara play basketball. This clue tells you:

   A Mark plays basketball.

   B Joan plays basketball.

   C Sara plays basketball.

Find the perimeter of each figure in Items 22–24.

22.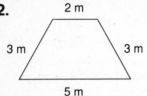

A 13 m
B 14 m
C 10 m
D 11 m

23.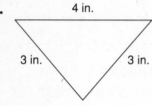

A 14 in.
B 7 in.
C 10 in.
D 13 in.

24.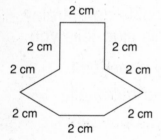

A 16 cm
B 14 cm
C 18 cm
D 12 cm

In Items 25–27, find the area of each figure in square centimeters.

25.

A 24 square centimeters
B 10 square centimeters
C 7 square centimeters
D 6 square centimeters

26.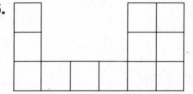

A 48 square centimeters
B 12 square centimeters
C 22 square centimeters
D 13 square centimeters

27.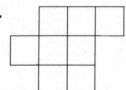

A 9 square centimeters
B 14 square centimeters
C 8 square centimeters
D 32 square centimeters

In Items 28–30, tell whether you need to find an exact answer or an estimate.

28. Willa wants to make 9 hair bows. She uses 2 feet of ribbon for each bow. How much should she buy?

   A An estimate is enough.

   B An exact answer is needed.

29. Johnny wants to make 4 banners. He needs 21 feet of paper for each banner. Should he buy a 50-foot or 100-foot roll of paper?

   A An estimate is enough.

   B An exact answer is needed.

30. Melba is making a picture frame. She needs 9 inches of wood frame for each side. How much wood frame should she buy?

   A An estimate is enough.

   B An exact answer is needed.

Choose the most sensible measure in Items 31–33.

31. Temperature in an air-conditioned room

   A 70°F

   B 100°F

   C 20°F

32. Temperature of a very cold day

   A 80°F

   B −2°F

   C 65°F

33. Temperature of hot soup

   A 5°C

   B 40°C

   C 76°C

Choose the letter of the correct answer.

SAMPLE

How many?

$$4 + 4 + 4$$

A 16   **B** 12   **C** 34   **D** 43

1. Which sentence describes this picture?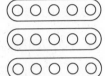

   A $4 + 4 + 4 + 4 = 16$
   B $5 + 5 + 5 + 5 = 20$
   C $10 + 10 = 20$
   D $5 + 5 + 5 = 15$

2. How many?

   $$8 + 8 + 8$$

   A 24   **B** 16
   C 38   **D** 32

3. How many?

   $$10 + 10 + 10 + 10 + 10$$

   A 40   **B** 510
   C 50   **D** 5

4. Which pair of sentences describes this picture?

   ★ ★ ★ ★
   ★ ★ ★ ★
   ★ ★ ★ ★

   A $6 + 6 = 12; 2 \times 6 = 12$
   B $4 + 4 + 4 = 12;$
   $\quad 3 \times 4 = 12$
   C $3 + 3 + 3 = 9; 3 \times 3 = 9$
   D $4 + 4 = 8; 2 \times 4 = 8$

In Items 5 and 6, which addition and multiplication sentences describe the phrase or problem?

5. 6 shelves each with 4 toy dogs

   A $6 + 6 + 6 = 18;$
   $\quad 3 \times 6 = 18$
   B $6 + 6 + 6 + 6 + 6 + 6 = 36;$
   $\quad 6 \times 6 = 36$
   C $4 + 4 + 4 + 4 + 4 = 20;$
   $\quad 5 \times 4 = 20$
   D $4 + 4 + 4 + 4 + 4 + 4 = 24;$
   $\quad 6 \times 4 = 24$

6. Jan bought 3 boxes of pencils. Each box had 8 pencils. How many pencils did she buy?

   A $8 + 8 + 8 + 8 = 32;$
   $\quad 4 \times 8 = 32$
   B $3 + 3 + 3 = 9; 3 \times 3 = 9$
   C $3 + 3 + 3 + 3 = 12;$
   $\quad 4 \times 3 = 12$
   D $8 + 8 + 8 = 24;$
   $\quad 3 \times 8 = 24$

7. Which multiplication sentence describes this array?

☆ ☆ ☆ ☆ ☆
☆ ☆ ☆ ☆ ☆
☆ ☆ ☆ ☆ ☆

A $3 \times 4 = 12$
B $3 \times 4 = 15$
C $3 \times 5 = 15$
D $3 \times 5 = 20$

In Items 8 and 9, make an array to help you find the correct multiplication sentence.

8. 6 rows of 5

A $6 \times 5 = 25$
B $6 \times 5 = 30$
C $5 \times 6 = 36$
D $5 \times 6 = 35$

9. There are 6 eggs in each box. How many eggs are in 3 boxes?

A $2 \times 6 = 18$
B $3 \times 6 = 9$
C $6 \times 3 = 12$
D $3 \times 6 = 18$

Find each product.

10. 3×5

A 15
B 8
C 2
D not given

11. 5×6

A 11
B 1
C 30
D not given

12. The circus has 5 clowns. Each clown holds 8 balloons. How many balloons do the clowns have in all?

A 13 balloons
B 40 balloons
C 45 balloons
D 35 balloons

Find each product.

13. 2×7

A 9
B 14
C 5
D not given

14. 6×2

A 12
B 8
C 14
D not given

15. 2×9

A 11
B 16
C 18
D not given

EXPLORING MATHEMATICS © Scott, Foresman and Company/3

Use this story for Items 16–18. Draw a picture to help you.

Bill put 2 baseballs on the table and 5 basketballs on each of 3 shelves. He put 7 golf balls on the counter.

16. How many basketballs does Bill have?

    A 15 basketballs

    B 10 basketballs

    C 22 basketballs

    D 5 basketballs

17. How many baseballs and basketballs are there?

    A 13 balls

    B 7 balls

    C 10 balls

    D 17 balls

18. How many balls are there altogether?

    A 17 balls

    B 24 balls

    C 22 balls

    D 14 balls

Find each product.

19. 3×8

    A 11

    B 16

    C 24

    D not given

20. 7×3

    A 21

    B 10

    C 18

    D not given

21. Kathy has 3 bags. Each bag has 9 blocks in it. How many blocks does Kathy have?

    A 12 blocks

    B 6 blocks

    C 27 blocks

    D 24 blocks

Find each product.

22. 4×7

    A 11

    B 21

    C 28

    D not given

23. 9×4

    A 35

    B 13

    C 27

    D not given

24. 4×5

    A 20

    B 24

    C 16

    D not given

Use this information for Items 25–27.

A pet shop has 4 cages with 5 birds in each cage. It also has 5 cages with 2 dogs in each cage.

25. Which information is not needed to find how many dogs are in the pet shop?

   A 5 birds

   B 5 cages

   C 2 dogs

26. How many dogs are in the pet shop?

   A 20 dogs

   B 8 dogs

   C 10 dogs

   D 2 dogs

27. How many birds are in the pet shop?

   A 10 birds

   B 5 birds

   C 16 birds

   D 20 birds

Find each product.

28. $\begin{array}{r} 0 \\ \times 5 \\ \hline \end{array}$

   A 0

   B 5

   C 50

   D not given

29. 7×0

   A 7

   B 0

   C 70

   D not given

30. 1×9

   A 10

   B 8

   C 9

   D not given

Choose the letter of the correct answer.

SAMPLE
How many?

$$4 + 4 + 4$$

A 16   **B** 12   **C** 34   **D** 43

---

1. Which sentence describes this picture?

   A $5 + 5 = 10$

   B $3 + 3 + 3 + 3 = 12$

   C $3 + 3 + 3 + 3 + 3 = 15$

   D $6 + 6 = 12$

---

2. How many?

$$7 + 7 + 7 + 7$$

   A 47   **B** 28

   C 35   **D** 21

---

3. How many?

$$100 + 100 + 100 + 100$$

   A 400   **B** 4,100

   C 300   **D** 500

---

4. Which pair of sentences describes this picture?

   A $5 + 5 + 5 = 15;$
   $3 \times 5 = 15$

   B $4 + 4 + 4 + 4 = 16;$
   $4 \times 4 = 16$

   C $5 + 5 + 5 + 5 = 20;$
   $4 \times 5 = 20$

   D $4 + 4 + 4 = 12; 3 \times 4 = 12$

---

5. Which addition and multiplication sentences describe the phrase?

   3 shelves each with 9 toy cats

   A $3 + 3 + 3 + 3 + 3 = 15;$
   $5 \times 3 = 15$

   B $9 + 9 + 9 = 27;$
   $3 \times 9 = 27$

   C $9 + 9 = 18; 2 \times 9 = 18$

   D $3 + 3 + 3 + 3 + 3 + 3 + 3 = 21;$
   $7 \times 3 = 21$

---

6. Which addition and multiplication sentences describe the problem?

Will bought 4 packages of baseball cards. Each package had 6 cards. How many cards did Will buy?

A $4 + 4 + 4 + 4 = 16$;
  $4 \times 4 = 16$

B $4 + 4 + 4 + 4 + 4 = 20$;
  $5 \times 4 = 20$

C $6 + 6 + 6 = 18$;
  $3 \times 6 = 18$

D $6 + 6 + 6 + 6 = 24$;
  $4 \times 6 = 24$

7. Which multiplication sentence describes this array?

X X X X
X X X X
X X X X
X X X X
X X X X

A $5 \times 5 = 20$
B $5 \times 5 = 25$
C $5 \times 4 = 22$
D $5 \times 4 = 20$

In Items 8 and 9, make an array to help you find the correct multiplication sentence.

8. 3 columns of 9

A $3 \times 9 = 28$
B $3 \times 9 = 24$
C $3 \times 9 = 27$
D $3 \times 9 = 36$

9. There are 8 jacks in each bag. How many jacks in 4 bags?

A $8 \times 4 = 12$
B $4 \times 8 = 24$
C $4 \times 8 = 40$
D $4 \times 8 = 32$

Find each product.

10. 5×4

A 9
B 20
C 16
D not given

11. 6×5

A 30
B 11
C 25
D not given

12. Each week has 7 days. How many days in 5 weeks?

A 35 days
B 32 days
C 12 days
D 30 days

13. Find the product.

2×8

A 10
B 16
C 6
D not given

Find each product.

14. 7 × 2

A 16
B 9
C 15
D not given

15. 9 × 2

A 11
B 7
C 16
D not given

Use this story for Items 16–18. Draw a picture to help you.

Hanna put 2 fish in the small tank. She put 4 fish in each of 5 large tanks. She put 9 fish in the wall tank.

16. How many fish are in the large tanks?

A 8 fish
B 10 fish
C 20 fish
D 18 fish

17. How many fish are in all but the wall tank?

A 13 fish
B 22 fish
C 14 fish
D 6 fish

18. How many fish are there altogether?

A 31 fish
B 22 fish
C 27 fish
D 15 fish

Find each product.

19. 3 × 6

A 9
B 3
C 18
D not given

20. 8 × 3

A 24
B 26
C 21
D not given

21. A circus has 3 rings. There are 7 horses in each ring. How many horses are there?

A 20 horses
B 21 horses
C 10 horses
D 24 horses

Find each product.

22. 4 × 8

A 12
B 32
C 34
D not given

23. 6 × 4

A 10
B 2
C 24
D not given

24. 4 × 4

A 8
B 12
C 16
D not given

Use the following information for Items 25–27.

A gift shop has 4 green vases and 5 white vases. Each vase holds 3 roses.

25. Which information is not needed to find how many roses are in the white vases?

A 4 green vases
B 5 white vases
C 3 roses in each vase

26. How many roses are in the white vases?

A 9 roses   **B** 12 roses
C 20 roses   **D** 15 roses

27. How many roses are in the green vases?

A 9 roses
B 12 roses
C 15 roses
D 20 roses

Find each product.

28.   6
     ×0

A 6
B 5
C 0
D not given

29. 9 × 0

A 0
B 9
C 8
D not given

30. 8 × 1

A 9
B 8
C 7
D not given

EXPLORING MATHEMATICS © Scott, Foresman and Company/3

Choose the letter of the correct answer.

SAMPLE

Find the product.

$$3 \times 5$$

A 8   **B** 2

C 15   **D** not given

Find each product.

1.   6
    $\times 4$

        A 10
        B 24
        C 20
        D not given

2. 3×8

        A 24
        B 32
        C 11
        D not given

3. 5×9

        A 36
        B 14
        C 45
        D not given

4.

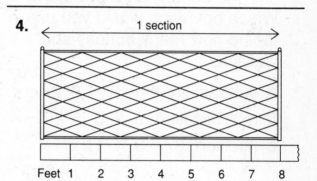

Each section of an iron fence is 8 feet long. Use a number line to find the length of a fence with 4 sections of iron.

   A 12 feet   **B** 36 feet

   C 32 feet   **D** 16 feet

Use a number line to find each product.

5. 6×5

        A 35
        B 30
        C 11
        D not given

6. 9×4

        A 13
        B 27
        C 45
        D not given

7. Carla had 9 buttons. She used 3 of the buttons on a sweater. Which operation would you use to find how many buttons she had left?

A subtraction; $9 - 3 = 6$

B multiplication; $9 \times 3 = 27$

C addition; $9 + 3 = 12$

8. Mac has 9 shells and Jill has 5 shells. How many shells do they have in all?

A 4 shells

B 14 shells

C 45 shells

9. Jack has \$5. Mary has 6 times as much money as Jack. How much does Mary have?

A \$11

B \$1

C \$30

Use a pattern to find each product.

10. 7×7

A 14 **B** 48

C 49 **D** not given

11. 5×5

A 25 **B** 10

C 20 **D** not given

12. 1×1 •

A 2 **B** 1

C 0 **D** not given

13. How much less than 10×7 is 9×7?

A 9 less **B** 10 less

C 7 less **D** 8 less

Find each product.

14. $\begin{array}{r} 9 \\ \times 5 \\ \hline \end{array}$

A 44

B 40

C 14

D not given

15. 8×9

A 72

B 64

C 74

D not given

EXPLORING MATHEMATICS © Scott, Foresman and Company/3

16. The library has 8 tables. There are 6 chairs at each table. How many chairs are there?

   A 14 chairs

   B 49 chairs

   C 48 chairs

   D 36 chairs

Find each product.

17. 8 × 7

   A 64

   B 56

   C 49

   D not given

18. 9 × 6

   A 56

   B 15

   C 63

   D not given

19. What are the next two multiplication facts for 6?

$$
\begin{array}{cccc}
1 & 2 & 3 \\
\times 6 & \times 6 & \times 6 \\
\hline
6 & 12 & 18 \\
\end{array}
\quad \square \quad \square
$$

   A $\begin{array}{c} 4 \\ \times 6 \\ \hline 24 \end{array}$ $\begin{array}{c} 5 \\ \times 6 \\ \hline 30 \end{array}$ **B** $\begin{array}{c} 4 \\ \times 7 \\ \hline 28 \end{array}$ $\begin{array}{c} 4 \\ \times 8 \\ \hline 32 \end{array}$

   C $\begin{array}{c} 5 \\ \times 6 \\ \hline 30 \end{array}$ $\begin{array}{c} 6 \\ \times 6 \\ \hline 36 \end{array}$ **D** $\begin{array}{c} 4 \\ \times 6 \\ \hline 24 \end{array}$ $\begin{array}{c} 4 \\ \times 7 \\ \hline 28 \end{array}$

20. What is the pattern made by the ones digits in the facts for 6?

   A 6, 2, 8, 4, 0   **B** 6, 2, 8

   C 6, 12, 18   **D** 6, 2, 8, 4, 8

21. What is the pattern made by the ones digits in the facts for 4?

   A 4, 8, 12   **B** 4, 8, 2, 6, 0

   C 4, 8   **D** 4, 8, 12, 16

Use the picture of the block tower to help you find each product.

22. 2 × 2 × 3

   A 12

   B 4

   C 6

   D not given

23. 1 × 4 × 5

   A 20

   B 9

   C 10

   D not given

24. 2 × 3 × 4

   A 6

   B 12

   C 8

   D not given

Choose the letter of the correct answer.

SAMPLE

Find the product.

$$3 \times 5$$

A 8   **B** 2
C 15   **D** not given

Find each product.

1. 3
    $\times 6$

A 18
B 15
C 24
D not given

2. 4 × 9

A 13
B 36
C 27
D not given

3. 8 × 5

A 32
B 13
C 45
D not given

4.

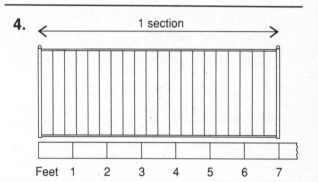

Each section of a redwood slat fence is 7 feet long. Use a number line to find the length of a fence with 4 sections of redwood slats.

A 11 feet   **B** 21 feet
C 24 feet   **D** 28 feet

Use a number line to find each product.

5. 6 × 5

A 30
B 25
C 36
D not given

6. 3 × 7

A 10
B 4
C 21
D not given

7. Kurt has 6 photos on the first page of his album and 5 photos on the second page. Which operation would you use to find how many photos Kurt has in all?

A multiplication; $6 \times 5 = 30$

B subtraction; $6 - 5 = 1$

C addition; $6 + 5 = 11$

8. Jean has 8 shells and Bill has 5 shells. How many more shells does Jean have than Bill?

A 13 shells

B 3 shells

C 40 shells

9. Sam has $6. Willa has 5 times as much money as Sam. How much money does Willa have?

A $30

B $11

C $1

Use a pattern to find each product.

10. 8×8

A 16　　　　**B** 64

C 10　　　　**D** not given

11. 9×9

A 18　　　　**B** 27

C 72　　　　**D** not given

12. 6×6

A 30　　　　**B** 12

C 36　　　　**D** not given

13. How much less than 10×6 is 9×6?

A 6 less　　　　**B** 7 less

C 10 less　　　　**D** 9 less

Find each product.

14. 　9
　　$\times 7$

A 16

B 63

C 64

D not given

15. 9×8

A 17

B 64

C 72

D not given

16. Holly has 7 baskets. She has 6 apples in each basket. How many apples does she have?

    A 42 apples

    B 48 apples

    C 13 apples

    D 36 apples

Find each product.

17. 8 × 6

    A 48

    B 36

    C 64

    D not given

18. 7 × 8

    A 15

    B 48

    C 54

    D not given

19. What are the next two multiplication facts for 5?

    $$\begin{array}{cccc} 1 & 2 & 3 \\ \times 5 & \times 5 & \times 5 \\ \hline 5 & 10 & 15 \end{array} \quad \square \quad \square$$

    A $\begin{array}{cc} 4 & 5 \\ \times 4 & \times 5 \\ \hline 16 & 25 \end{array}$ B $\begin{array}{cc} 4 & 5 \\ \times 5 & \times 5 \\ \hline 20 & 25 \end{array}$

    C $\begin{array}{cc} 3 & 4 \\ \times 5 & \times 5 \\ \hline 15 & 20 \end{array}$ D $\begin{array}{cc} 4 & 4 \\ \times 5 & \times 6 \\ \hline 20 & 24 \end{array}$

20. What is the pattern made by the ones digits in the facts for 5?

    A 5, 10, 15   B 5, 0

    C 5, 10   D 1, 5, 10

21. Start with 5. Use the pattern ADD 3. What are the next two numbers?

     5, □, □

    A 8, 11   B 10, 15

    C 6, 7   D 9, 12

Use the picture of the block tower to help you find each product.

22. 3 × 3 × 3

    A 9

    B 8

    C 27

    D not given

23. 2 × 3 × 3

    A 9

    B 18

    C 6

    D not given

24. 5 × 2 × 3

    A 15

    B 30

    C 10

    D not given

Choose the letter of the correct answer.

SAMPLE

Subtract.

$$\begin{array}{r} 5\,6 \\ -2\,3 \\ \hline \end{array}$$

A 23

B 79

C 33

D not given

1. Use the rule to find the number that is missing in this table.

	+3
6	9
3	6
7	10
5	■

A 2

B 8

C 7

D 9

2. Which number sentence is true?

A 415 < 421   **B** 295 < 239

C 298 > 302   **D** 367 < 293

3. Estimate the sum. First round both numbers to the nearest ten.

$$42 + 49$$

A 80   **B** 100   **C** 90   **D** 70

4. Find $58 + 27$ using mental math.

A 75   **B** 89

C 85   **D** 79

5. What does the digit 6 mean in 360,147?

A 6 thousands

B 6 hundred-thousands

C 6 tens

D 6 ten-thousands

Add.

6.
$$\begin{array}{r} 3\,7 \\ +5\,6 \\ \hline \end{array}$$

A 83

B 93

C 81

D not given

7.
$$\begin{array}{r} 3\,6 \\ +3\,6 \\ \hline \end{array}$$

A 72

B 62

C 81

D not given

8. Subtract.

$$\begin{array}{r} 7\,2 \\ -3\,9 \\ \hline \end{array}$$

A 47

B 33

C 43

D not given

9. Find $46 - 23$ using mental math.

A 13   **B** 29

C 69   **D** 23

10. Add.

$$\begin{array}{r} 477 \\ + 88 \\ \hline \end{array}$$

A 455
B 465
C 565
D not given

11. Use estimation to find out which you can buy if you have 50¢.

14¢ 32¢ 28¢ 41¢ 23¢

A toy car and coloring book
B toy car and balloon
C whistle and coloring book
D balloon and ring

12. Which is the same amount as 3 dollars, 4 dimes, and 13 pennies?

A 3 dollars, 5 dimes, 3 pennies
B 3 dollars, 4 dimes, 3 pennies
C 4 dollars, 4 dimes, 3 pennies
D 4 dollars, 5 dimes, 3 pennies

13. Add.

$$\begin{array}{r} 4,673 \\ + 719 \\ \hline \end{array}$$

A 4,382
B 4,392
C 5,392
D not given

14. Estimate the difference. First round both numbers to the nearest ten.

$$86 - 32$$

A 50 **B** 70 **C** 40 **D** 60

Subtract.

15.
$$\begin{array}{r} 693 \\ -487 \\ \hline \end{array}$$

A 234
B 206
C 176
D not given

16.
$$\begin{array}{r} 752 \\ -317 \\ \hline \end{array}$$

A 435
B 445
C 345
D not given

17.
$$\begin{array}{r} 600 \\ -253 \\ \hline \end{array}$$

A 453
B 347
C 447
D not given

18.
$$\begin{array}{r} 5,028 \\ -1,465 \\ \hline \end{array}$$

A 4,663
B 4,443
C 3,663
D not given

19. Mr. Jinks gave each of the 8 students on his team 4 golf balls. Which number sentence could you use to find how many golf balls he used?

A $8 \times 4 = \blacksquare$ **B** $8 + 4 = \blacksquare$
C $8 - 4 = \blacksquare$ **D** $8 + 8 = \blacksquare$

20. What time is shown on
this clock?

    A 9:30

    B 5:45

    C 5:15

    D 6:45

21. Which date is the fourth Monday
of the month?

JULY						
S	M	T	W	T	F	S
	1	2	3	4	5	6
7	8	9	10	11	12	13
14	15	16	17	18	19	20
21	22	23	24	25	26	27
28	29	30	31			

A July 15   **B** July 8

C July 29   **D** July 22

22. What is the missing number?

There are ■ inches in 1 yard.

A 12   **B** 3   **C** 36   **D** 5,280

23. Choose the most sensible unit of
measure for the length of a shoe.

A centimeters   **B** meters

C kilometers   **D** kiloliters

24. How many students are there in
5 rows of 5 students each?

    A 10 students   **B** 25 students

    C 20 students   **D** 30 students

25. What is the perimeter of
this figure?

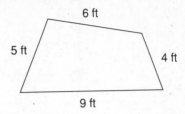

A 22 ft   **B** 26 ft

C 36 ft   **D** 24 ft

26. Which is the same as

$7 + 7 + 7 + 7?$

    A $7 - 4$

    B $7 + 4$

    C 4×7

    D 1×4

Multiply.

27. $\begin{array}{r} 5 \\ \times 6 \\ \hline \end{array}$ **A** 11

     B 30

     C 1

     D not given

28. $\begin{array}{r} 8 \\ \times 4 \\ \hline \end{array}$ **A** 12

     B 28

     C 32

     D not given

29. Which one is *not* correct?

    A $4 \times 0 = 4$

    B $0 + 5 = 5$

    C $1 \times 8 = 8$

    D $4 \times 1 = 4$

Multiply.

30. 3 × 7

    A 10
    B 37
    C 21
    D not given

31.   6
   ×8

    A 48
    B 14
    C 42
    D not given

32.   9
   ×7

    A 54
    B 61
    C 72
    D not given

33.   8
   ×8

    A 63
    B 16
    C 64
    D not given

34. Bryan lined up 7 rows of toy cars. There are 3 cars in each row. How many cars are there?

    A 21 cars   **B** 10 cars
    C 24 cars   **D** 18 cars

35. Rhonda has 33 baseball cards. Mac has 44 cards. How many more cards does Mac have than Rhonda?

    A 77 cards   **B** 17 cards
    C 10 cards   **D** 11 cards

36. A block tower has 4 rows with 5 blocks in each row and 5 layers. How many blocks were used to build the tower?

    A 20 blocks   **B** 100 blocks
    C 25 blocks   **D** 50 blocks

37. Will, Sarah, and Leah each drew a picture of an animal. They drew a cat, a dog, and a rabbit. Neither Will nor Leah drew a rabbit. Will did not draw a cat. Who drew a cat?

    A Sarah
    B Will
    C Leah

38. A yardstick is 3 feet long and 2 inches wide. Lynn measured a rope and found that it was as long as 7 yardsticks. How many feet long was the rope?

    A 21 feet   **B** 10 feet
    C 14 feet   **D** 6 feet

39. Each student has 9 crayons. Which could you use to find how many crayons 5 students have?

    A 9 + 5   **B** 9 − 5
    C 9 × 9   **D** 9 × 5

EXPLORING MATHEMATICS © Scott, Foresman and Company/3

Choose the letter of the correct answer.

SAMPLE

What is this geometric figure?

A square   **B** triangle
C circle   **D** rectangle

1. What shape is a basketball?

   A cube
   B cylinder
   C sphere
   D rectangular prism

2. What is this shape?

   A cube
   B sphere
   C cylinder

3. What is this shape?

   A cube
   B sphere
   C cylinder
   D rectangular prism

4. What is this geometric figure?

   A square   **B** circle
   C rectangle   **D** triangle

5. What is this geometric figure?

   A triangle   **B** pentagon
   C square   **D** circle

6. What is this geometric figure?

   A square   **B** pentagon
   C rectangle   **D** hexagon

7. How many angles are in a triangle?

   A 5 angles   **B** 4 angles
   C 3 angles   **D** 2 angles

8. Is this angle a right angle?

   A yes   **B** no

9. How many angles are in this figure?

A 3 angles   **B** 4 angles
C 6 angles   **D** 5 angles

10. Is the broken line a line of symmetry?

A yes   **B** no

11. Is the broken line a line of symmetry?

A no   **B** yes

12. In which figure is a line of symmetry drawn?

A   **B**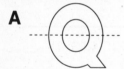

C   **D**

In Items 13–15, decide which figure is congruent to the first figure.

13.

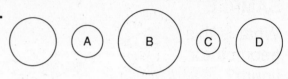

A figure A   **B** figure B
C figure C   **D** figure D

14.

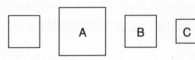

A figure A   **B** figure B
C figure C   **D** figure D

15.

A figure A   **B** figure B
C figure C   **D** figure D

EXPLORING MATHEMATICS © Scott, Foresman and Company/3

Use this graph to answer
Items 16–18.

Favorite Games

Chess	☆ ☆ ☆ ☆ ☆ ☆ ☆
Checkers	☆ ☆ ☆ ☆ ☆ ☆
Dominoes	☆ ☆ ☆ ☆
Computer Games	☆ ☆ ☆ ☆ ☆ ☆ ☆ ☆ ☆

Each ☆ equals one vote.

16. Which game got the most votes?

A chess

B computer games

C checkers

D dominoes

17. How many more students voted for chess than dominoes?

A 7 students

B 4 students

C 2 students

D 3 students

18. Which two games received 11 votes altogether?

A checkers and computer games

B chess and checkers

C dominoes and computer games

D chess and dominoes

19. Find the volume in cubic units.

A 4 cubic units

B 16 cubic units

C 8 cubic units

D 12 cubic units

20. Find the volume in cubic units.

A 8 cubic units

B 4 cubic units

C 12 cubic units

D 16 cubic units

21. Find the volume in cubic units.

A 3 cubic units

B 9 cubic units

C 6 cubic units

D 7 cubic units

In Items 22–24, choose the most sensible customary measure.

22. Drinking glass

A cup   **B** quart

23. Fish tank

A 12 gallons   **B** 12 pints

24. Baby bottle

A 1 gallon   **B** 1 cup

In Items 25–27, choose the most sensible metric measure.

25. Mixing bowl

A 3 L   **B** 3 mL

26. Eyedropper

A 1 L   **B** 1 mL

27. Juice glass

A 150 L   **B** 150 mL

In Items 28 and 29, choose the most sensible customary measure.

28. Weight of a turkey

A 12 ounces   **B** 12 pounds

29. Weight of a child

A 40 pounds   **B** 40 ounces

30. Would you use ounces or pounds to measure the weight of a calculator?

A ounces   **B** pounds

In Items 31–33, choose the most sensible metric measure.

31. Mass of a pencil

A 2 grams   **B** 2 kilograms

32. Mass of a bag of potatoes

A 3 grams   **B** 3 kilograms

33. Mass of a grown man

A 80 kilograms   **B** 80 grams

EXPLORING MATHEMATICS © Scott, Foresman and Company/3

34. Jackie is making an apple salad to serve 12 people. She needs one apple for every 3 servings. How many apples will Jackie need?

A 6 apples   **B** 12 apples

C 4 apples   **D** 3 apples

35. Mrs. Sims needs 42 ounces of tomato paste. It comes in 6-ounce cans. How many cans does she need?

A 7 cans   **B** 8 cans

C 6 cans   **D** 9 cans

36. Keith wants to make a macaroni salad for the class picnic. His recipe uses 12 ounces of macaroni noodles for 8 servings. What information does Keith need to decide the amount of macaroni noodles he will use?

A the cost of a box of macaroni

B how long to cook the noodles

C the date of the picnic

D how many servings he should make

37. A small apple weighs about 2 ounces. About how many small apples weigh 1 pound? (1 pound = 16 ounces)

A 6 apples   **B** 8 apples

C 7 apples   **D** 10 apples

38. What is the correct volume for this box?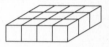

A 3 cubic units

B 4 cubic units

C 12 cubic units

D 10 cubic units

39. Which volume is less than the volume of this box?

A 20 cubic units

B 16 cubic units

C 18 cubic units

D 14 cubic units

Choose the letter of the correct answer.

SAMPLE

What is this geometric figure?

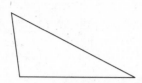

A square   **B** triangle

C circle   **D** rectangle

---

1. What shape is a soccer ball?

    A sphere

    B cylinder

    C cube

    D rectangular prism

---

2. What is this shape?

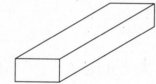

    A cube

    B rectangular prism

    C sphere

    D cylinder

---

3. What is this shape?

    A cube

    B rectangular prism

    C sphere

    D cylinder

---

4. What is this geometric figure?

A square   **B** rectangle

C hexagon   **D** octagon

---

5. What is this geometric figure?

A square   **B** circle

C pentagon   **D** triangle

---

6. What is this geometric figure?

A square   **B** octagon

C pentagon   **D** hexagon

---

7. How many angles are in a square?

A 3 angles   **B** 4 angles

C 5 angles   **D** 2 angles

---

8. How many right angles are in this figure?

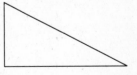

    A 2 right angles

    B 3 right angles

    C 1 right angle

    D 4 right angles

---

9. How many angles are in a circle?

A 0 angles   **B** 2 angles
C 3 angles   **D** 4 angles

10. Is the broken line a line of symmetry?

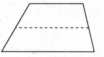

A yes   **B** no

11. Is the broken line a line of symmetry?

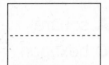

A yes   **B** no

12. In which figure is a line of symmetry drawn?

A 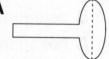   **B**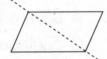

C   **D**

In Items 13–15, decide which figure is congruent to the first figure.

13.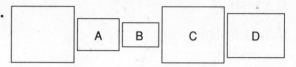

A figure A   **B** figure B
C figure C   **D** figure D

14.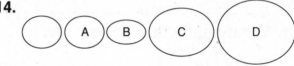

A figure A   **B** figure B
C figure C   **D** figure D

15.

A figure A   **B** figure B
C figure C   **D** figure D

Use this graph to answer
Items 16–18.

Favorite Pets	
Dogs	☆ ☆ ☆ ☆ ☆ ☆ ☆ ☆ ☆
Cats	☆ ☆ ☆ ☆ ☆ ☆ ☆ ☆
Birds	☆ ☆ ☆ ☆ ☆ ☆
Other Animals	☆ ☆ ☆ ☆ ☆

Each ☆ equals one vote.

16. Which pet got the most votes?

A cats

B dogs

C birds

D other animals

17. How many more students voted
for dogs than birds?

A 10 students

B 6 students

C 4 students

D 5 students

18. Which two pets received
14 votes altogether?

A cats and birds

B dogs and other animals

C dogs and cats

D cats and other animals

19. Find the
volume in
cubic units.

A 2 cubic units

B 4 cubic units

C 5 cubic units

D 6 cubic units

20. Find the
volume in
cubic units.

A 4 cubic units

B 12 cubic units

C 8 cubic units

D 16 cubic units

21. Find the
volume in
cubic units.

A 9 cubic units

B 12 cubic units

C 27 cubic units

D 18 cubic units

In Items 22–24, choose the most sensible customary measure.

22. Swimming pool

   A gallon   **B** quart

23. Pail

   A 1 cup   **B** 1 quart

24. Bath tub

   A 40 pints   **B** 40 gallons

In Items 25–27, choose the most sensible metric measure.

25. Carton of milk

   A 2 L   **B** 2 mL

26. Washing machine

   A 80 L   **B** 80 mL

27. Water glass

   A 200 L   **B** 200 mL

In Items 28–29, choose the most sensible customary measure.

28. Weight of a medium-sized dog

   A 30 ounces   **B** 30 pounds

29. Weight of a grown man

   A 175 ounces   **B** 175 pounds

30. Would you use ounces or pounds to measure the weight of a box of cereal?

   A ounces   **B** pounds

In Items 31–33, choose the most sensible metric measure.

31. Mass of a wristwatch

   A 10 kilograms   **B** 10 grams

32. Mass of a television set

   A 40 kilograms   **B** 40 grams

33. Mass of a young girl

   A 20 kilograms   **B** 20 grams

EXPLORING MATHEMATICS © Scott, Foresman and Company/3

34. Jim is making dinner for 8. He is using a recipe that serves 4. If the recipe uses 1 cup of bread crumbs, how many cups should Jim use?

A 1 cup   **B** 8 cups

C 4 cups   **D** 2 cups

35. Mr. Edo is making a vegetable dish that uses 32 ounces of beans. The beans come in 8-ounce boxes. How many boxes does he need?

A 5 boxes   **B** 8 boxes

C 4 boxes   **D** 3 boxes

36. Maria wants to make fruit punch. Her recipe uses 8 ounces of fresh-squeezed lemon juice. What information does Maria need to decide how many lemons she will use?

A the cost per pound of lemons

B how long it will take her to make the punch

C when lemons go on sale

D the number of ounces of juice in each lemon

37. If 1 orange weighs 4 ounces, how many oranges weigh 1 pound?
(1 pound = 16 ounces)

A 4 oranges   **B** 3 oranges

C 5 oranges   **D** 6 oranges

38. What is the correct volume for this box?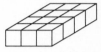

A 10 cubic units

B 3 cubic units

C 12 cubic units

D 4 cubic units

39. Which volume is more than the volume of this box?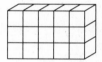

A 12 cubic units

B 16 cubic units

C 15 cubic units

D 10 cubic units

Choose the letter of the correct answer.

SAMPLE

If you have 12 stamps to put in 3 rows, how many stamps are in each row?

A 3 stamps   **B** 4 stamps

C 5 stamps   **D** 2 stamps

1. If you have 15 shells, how many shells go in each of 3 boxes?

   A 4 shells   **B** 6 shells

   C 7 shells   **D** 5 shells

2. If you have 24 shells, how many shells go in each of 4 boxes?

   A 6 shells   **B** 5 shells

   C 7 shells   **D** 8 shells

3. If you have 21 shells, how many shells go in each of 3 boxes?

   A 6 shells   **B** 7 shells

   C 8 shells   **D** 9 shells

4. 10 in all
   2 in each group
   How many groups?

   A 4 groups   **B** 8 groups

   C 5 groups   **D** 6 groups

5. 25 in all
   5 in each group
   How many groups?

   A 20 groups   **B** 4 groups

   C 6 groups   **D** 5 groups

6. 16 in all
   4 in each group
   How many groups?

   A 12 groups   **B** 4 groups

   C 3 groups   **D** 5 groups

In Items 7–9, find the number that will complete the division sentence.

7. 12 in all
   2 groups
   ■ in each group
   $12 \div 2 = $ ■

   A 7   **B** 5   **C** 4   **D** not given

8. 20 in all
   5 in each group
   ■ groups
   $20 \div 5 = $ ■

   A 3   **B** 5   **C** 4   **D** not given

9. 18 in all
   3 groups
   ■ in each group
   $18 \div 3 = $ ■

   A 15   **B** 5   **C** 7   **D** not given

Find each quotient.

10. 1 2 ÷ 2

A 10

B 6

C 4

D not given

11. 2 4 ÷ 3

A 8

B 7

C 9

D not given

12. Carl has 14 pennies. He will put them in 2 equal stacks. How many pennies will be in each stack?

A 7 pennies **B** 6 pennies

C 12 pennies **D** 8 pennies

Find each quotient.

13. 8 ÷ 4

A 3

B 2

C 4

D not given

14. 4)‾1‾6‾

A 5

B 3

C 4

D not given

15. 2 4 ÷ 4

A 6

B 4

C 7

D not given

In Items 16–18, solve each problem by using *Try and Check.*

16. There are 45 math and science books on a shelf. There are 5 more science books than math books. How many science books are there?

A 5 science books

B 20 science books

C 25 science books

D 15 science books

17. Don and Jill have 28 baseball cards. Jill has 10 more cards than Don. How many cards does Jill have?

A 16 cards **B** 19 cards

C 17 cards **D** 18 cards

18. Chris and Leola have 9 magazines between them. Chris has 2 times as many magazines as Leola. How many magazines does Chris have?

A 9 magazines

B 6 magazines

C 3 magazines

D 2 magazines

Find the quotient.

19. 1 5 ÷ 5

A 20

B 10

C 2

D not given

EXPLORING MATHEMATICS © Scott, Foresman and Company/3

Find each quotient.

20. $25 \div 5$

    A 4

    B 6

    C 5

    D not given

21. $5\overline{)40}$

    A 7

    B 8

    C 9

    D not given

22. John wants to buy 15 pairs of socks. The socks are sold 3 pairs to a package. Which number sentence could John use to find how many packages he should buy?

    A $15 + 3 = 18$

    B $15 - 3 = 12$

    C $15 \div 3 = 5$

23. Dorothy has 21 stuffed animals. There are 3 shelves. Which number sentence could you use to find how many animals can be displayed on each shelf?

    A $21 \div 3 = 7$

    B $21 + 3 = 24$

    C $21 - 3 = 18$

24. A bookcase has 8 shelves. Each shelf holds 9 books. Which number sentence could you use to find how many books there are in all?

    A $8 \times 9 = 72$

    B $9 - 8 = 1$

    C $9 + 8 = 17$

25. Which fact belongs to the family of facts with the numbers 3, 4, and 12?

    A $4 - 3 = 1$

    B $4 + 3 = 7$

    C $4 \times 3 = 12$

26. Which number sentence completes the family of facts for $6 \times 6 = 36$?

    A $6 + 6 = 12$

    B $36 \div 6 = 6$

    C $6 - 6 = 0$

27. Which number sentence completes the family of facts for $3 \times 5 = 15$, $5 \times 3 = 15$, and $15 \div 5 = 3$?

    A $15 \div 3 = 5$

    B $5 + 3 = 8$

    C $5 - 3 = 2$

Choose the letter of the correct answer.

SAMPLE

If you have 12 stamps to put in 3 rows, how many stamps are in each row?

A 3 stamps   **B** 4 stamps

C 5 stamps   **D** 2 stamps

---

1. If you have 12 marbles, how many marbles go in each of 3 bags?

   A 3 marbles   **B** 4 marbles

   C 5 marbles   **D** 6 marbles

---

2. If you have 20 marbles, how many marbles go in each of 4 bags?

   A 5 marbles   **B** 6 marbles

   C 4 marbles   **D** 7 marbles

---

3. If you have 18 marbles, how many marbles go in each of 2 bags?

   A 2 marbles   **B** 8 marbles

   C 9 marbles   **D** 6 marbles

---

4. 14 in all
   2 in each group
   How many groups?

   A 6 groups   **B** 8 groups

   C 12 groups   **D** 7 groups

---

5. 18 in all
   6 in each group
   How many groups?

   A 3 groups   **B** 4 groups

   C 2 groups   **D** 5 groups

---

6. 20 in all
   5 in each group
   How many groups?

   A 15 groups   **B** 5 groups

   C 4 groups   **D** 3 groups

In Items 7–9, find the number that will complete the division sentence.

7. 15 in all
   3 groups
   ■ in each group
   $15 \div 3 = ■$

   A 4   **B** 5   **C** 6   **D** not given

8. 21 in all
   7 in each group
   ■ groups
   $21 \div 7 = ■$

   A 3   **B** 4   **C** 2   **D** not given

9. 16 in all
   4 groups
   ■ in each group
   $16 \div 4 = ■$

   A 3   **B** 12   **C** 4   **D** not given

Find each quotient.

10. $10 \div 2$

    A 8

    B 5

    C 4

    D not given

11. $24 \div 3$

    A 21

    B 7

    C 9

    D not given

12. Danny has 21 fish. He will put the same number of fish into each of 3 fishbowls. How many fish will be in each fishbowl?

    A 6 fish   **B** 18 fish

    C 7 fish   **D** 8 fish

Find each quotient.

13. $12 \div 4$

    A 8

    B 3

    C 4

    D not given

14. $20 \div 4$

    A 5

    B 3

    C 4

    D not given

15. $4\overline{)28}$

    A 6

    B 4

    C 7

    D not given

In Items 16–18, solve each problem by using *Try and Check.*

16. There are 52 animal books and poetry books on the shelf. There are 12 more animal books than poetry books. How many poetry books are there?

    A 20 poetry books

    B 12 poetry books

    C 32 poetry books

    D 40 poetry books

17. Jackie and Juan have 26 marbles. Juan has 10 more marbles than Jackie. How many marbles does Juan have?

    A 36 marbles   **B** 16 marbles

    C 6 marbles   **D** 18 marbles

18. Mike and Lynn have 32 marbles together. Lynn has 3 times as many marbles as Mike. How many marbles does Lynn have?

    A 8 marbles

    B 16 marbles

    C 20 marbles

    D 24 marbles

Find the quotient.

19. $20 \div 5$

    A 3

    B 5

    C 4

    D not given

EXPLORING MATHEMATICS © Scott, Foresman and Company/3

Find each quotient.

20. 5$\overline{)35}$

    A 7

    B 6

    C 8

    D not given

21. $45 \div 5$

    A 7

    B 8

    C 6

    D not given

22. Janna wants to buy 12 pairs of socks. The socks are sold 3 pairs to a package. Which number sentence could Janna use to find how many packages she should buy?

    A $12 + 3 = 15$

    B $12 \div 3 = 4$

    C $12 - 3 = 9$

23. Don has 24 model cars. There are 4 shelves. Which number sentence could you use to find how many cars can be displayed on each shelf?

    A $24 - 4 = 20$

    B $24 + 4 = 28$

    C $24 \div 4 = 6$

24. A bookcase has 7 shelves. Each shelf holds 8 books. Which number sentence could you use to find how many books there are in all?

    A $7 + 8 = 15$

    B $8 - 7 = 1$

    C $7 \times 8 = 56$

25. Which fact belongs to the family of facts with the numbers 4, 5, and 20?

    A $20 \div 4 = 5$

    B $5 + 4 = 9$

    C $5 - 4 = 1$

26. Which number sentence completes the family of facts for $49 \div 7 = 7$?

    A $7 - 7 = 0$

    B $7 \times 7 = 49$

    C $7 + 7 = 14$

27. Which number sentence completes the family of facts for $21 \div 3 = 7, 3 \times 7 = 21$, and $21 \div 7 = 3$?

    A $7 + 3 = 10$

    B $7 - 3 = 4$

    C $7 \times 3 = 21$

Choose the letter of the correct answer.

SAMPLE

Find the quotient.

$21 \div 3$

A 6
B 8
C 7
D not given

Find the quotient.

1. $18 \div 6$

A 12
B 3
C 24
D not given

2. $6\overline{)24}$

A 18
B 30
C 4
D not given

3. Jack is putting 48 apples into bags. He will put 6 in each bag. How many bags does Jack need?

A 7 bags
B 42 bags
C 54 bags
D 8 bags

Find the quotient.

4. $7\overline{)21}$

A 14
B 28
C 3
D not given

5. $35 \div 7$

A 28
B 5
C 6
D not given

6. The pet store has 49 birds. There are 7 birds in each cage. How many bird cages are there?

A 42 cages
B 7 cages
C 6 cages
D 8 cages

Find the quotient.

7. $24 \div 8$

A 3
B 4
C 16
D not given

8. $8\overline{)40}$

A 6
B 32
C 5
D not given

9. Tina hiked 64 miles in 8 days. She hiked the same number of miles each day. How many miles did she hike each day?

A 7 miles
B 8 miles
C 9 miles
D 6 miles

Find the quotient.

10. $27 \div 9$

   A 4
   B 18
   C 3
   D not given

11. $9\overline{)45}$

   A 4
   B 36
   C 6
   D not given

12. $63 \div 9$

   A 7
   B 6
   C 8
   D not given

13. Which number sentence is a member of the family of facts for this picture?

   A $12 - 4 = 8$ **B** $12 \div 4 = 3$
   C $3 + 4 = 7$ **D** $12 - 3 = 9$

14. Which pair of number sentences is a family of facts for this picture?

   A $3 + 3 = 6$ **B** $3 - 3 = 0$
       $6 - 3 = 3$ $3 \times 3 = 9$
   C $9 \div 3 = 3$ **D** $3 \times 3 = 9$
       $9 - 6 = 3$ $9 \div 3 = 3$

15. Find the missing numbers for this pair of number sentences.

$$3 \times 9 = \blacksquare$$
$$27 \div 3 = \blacksquare$$

   A 27, 9   **B** 27, 3
   C 27, 24   **D** 27, 30

16. Jack arranged his stamps on pages. On each page, he made 5 rows with 4 in each row. Which operation is best to use to find how many stamps are on each page?

   A subtraction; $5 - 4 = 1$
   B multiplication; $5 \times 4 = 20$
   C division; $5 \div 4 = 1$
   D addition; $5 + 4 = 9$

17. There are 36 flowers in 4 vases. Each vase has the same number of flowers. Which operation is best to use to find how many flowers are in each vase?

   A division; $36 \div 4 = 9$
   B addition; $36 + 4 = 40$
   C multiplication; $36 \times 4 = 144$
   D subtraction; $36 - 4 = 32$

18. There are 5 rose bushes with 6 buds on each bush. How many rosebuds are there?

   A 30 rosebuds   **B** 11 rosebuds
   C 36 rosebuds   **D** 25 rosebuds

Find the quotient.

19. 8 ÷ 1

A 0
B 9
C 8
D not given

20. 0 ÷ 4

A 4
B 0
C 3
D not given

21. Marty has 5 hats and 5 pins. He puts the same number of pins on each hat. How many pins can he put on each hat?

A 1 pin
B 2 pins
C 4 pins
D 5 pins

Divide. Find each quotient and remainder.

22. 16 ÷ 5

A 3, remainder 1
B 1, remainder 3
C 4, remainder 4
D not given

23. 14 ÷ 4

A 2, remainder 3
B 4, remainder 2
C 3, remainder 2
D not given

24. 17 ÷ 3

A 6, remainder 1
B 5, remainder 1
C 2, remainder 5
D not given

In Items 25–27, draw a picture to help you solve the problem.

25. Chris has 17 cents. Each bolt costs 5 cents. What is the greatest number of bolts Chris can buy?

A 5 bolts
B 3 bolts
C 4 bolts
D 2 bolts

26. There are 38 people to play a game. Only 6 people can sit at each table. How many tables will be needed?

A 5 tables
B 6 tables
C 8 tables
D 7 tables

27. Karen is packing 50 glasses into boxes. She packs 8 glasses into each box. How many glasses will be in the box that is not full?

A 6 glasses
B 7 glasses
C 2 glasses
D 4 glasses

Date   Score

Choose the letter of the correct answer.

SAMPLE

Find the quotient.

$21 \div 3$

- **A** 6
- **B** 8
- **C** 7
- **D** not given

Find the quotient.

1. $6\overline{)12}$

- **A** 6
- **B** 18
- **C** 2
- **D** not given

2. $24 \div 6$

- **A** 18
- **B** 4
- **C** 30
- **D** not given

3. There are 54 cans of juice. Each package has 6 cans. How many packages are there?

- **A** 9 packages
- **B** 10 packages
- **C** 8 packages
- **D** 7 packages

Find the quotient.

4. $28 \div 7$

- **A** 3
- **B** 5
- **C** 4
- **D** not given

5. $7\overline{)42}$

- **A** 7
- **B** 8
- **C** 9
- **D** not given

6. There are 7 days in a week. How many weeks are there in 56 days?

- **A** 8 weeks
- **B** 9 weeks
- **C** 7 weeks
- **D** 6 weeks

Find the quotient.

7. $56 \div 8$

- **A** 9
- **B** 7
- **C** 8
- **D** not given

8. $8\overline{)48}$

- **A** 7
- **B** 8
- **C** 6
- **D** not given

9. Joe hiked 40 miles in 8 days. He hiked the same number of miles each day. How many miles did he hike each day?

- **A** 4 miles
- **B** 6 miles
- **C** 7 miles
- **D** 5 miles

Find each quotient.

10. $36 \div 9$

    A 4
    B 3
    C 27
    D not given

11. $54 \div 9$

    A 45
    B 7
    C 6
    D not given

12. $9\overline{)72}$

    A 7
    B 8
    C 6
    D not given

13. Which number sentence is a member of the family of facts for this picture?

☆ ☆ ☆ ☆ ☆
☆ ☆ ☆ ☆ ☆
☆ ☆ ☆ ☆ ☆
☆ ☆ ☆ ☆ ☆

    A $5 \times 4 = 20$
    B $5 + 4 = 9$
    C $20 - 5 = 15$
    D $20 \div 10 = 2$

14. Which pair of number sentences is a family of facts for this picture?

☆ ☆ ☆ ☆
☆ ☆ ☆ ☆
☆ ☆ ☆ ☆
☆ ☆ ☆ ☆

  A $4 + 4 = 8$ **B** $4 - 4 = 0$
     $8 - 4 = 4$ $0 + 4 = 4$

  C $4 \times 4 = 16$ **D** $4 \times 4 = 16$
     $16 - 4 = 12$ $16 \div 4 = 4$

15. Find the missing numbers for this pair of number sentences.

$$7 \times 6 = \blacksquare$$
$$42 \div 6 = \blacksquare$$

  A 42, 6   **B** 42, 7
  C 42, 36   **D** 42, 48

16. Janet put 6 rows of stamps with 5 stamps in each row on a page in her stamp book. Which operation is best to use to find how many stamps are on each page?

    A subtraction; $6 - 5 = 1$
    B multiplication; $6 \times 5 = 30$
    C division; $6 \div 5 = 1$
    D addition; $6 + 5 = 11$

17. There are 32 jacks in 4 bags. Each bag has the same number of jacks. Which operation is best to use to find how many jacks are in each bag?

    A division; $32 \div 4 = 8$
    B addition; $32 + 4 = 36$
    C multiplication; $32 \times 4 = 128$
    D subtraction; $32 - 4 = 28$

18. There are 6 boxes of pencils with 8 pencils in each box. How many pencils are there?

  A 14 pencils   **B** 56 pencils
  C 42 pencils   **D** 48 pencils

Find the quotient.

19. 7 ÷ 1

    A 8
    B 7
    C 6
    D not given

20. 0 ÷ 5

    A 5
    B 4
    C 0
    D not given

21. Mary has 4 letters and 4 stamps. She wants to put the same number of stamps on each letter. How many stamps can she put on each letter?

    A 1 stamp   **B** 2 stamps
    C 3 stamps   **D** 4 stamps

Divide. Find each quotient and remainder.

22. 14 ÷ 3

    A 2, remainder 4
    B 4, remainder 2
    C 5, remainder 1
    D not given

23. 9 ÷ 2

    A 3, remainder 1
    B 4, remainder 2
    C 1, remainder 4
    D not given

24. 19 ÷ 6

    A 1, remainder 3
    B 3, remainder 2
    C 3, remainder 1
    D not given

In Items 25–27, draw a picture to help you solve the problem.

25. Amy has 21 cents. Each picture card costs 5 cents. What is the greatest number of cards Amy can buy?

    A 4 cards   **B** 1 card
    C 5 cards   **D** 3 cards

26. There are 34 students going on a field trip. Only 5 students can ride in each car. How many cars will be needed?

    A 6 cars   **B** 7 cars
    C 4 cars   **D** 5 cars

27. In Item 26, how many students will ride in the car that is not full?

    A 6 students   **B** 5 students
    C 4 students   **D** 3 students

Choose the letter of the correct answer.

SAMPLE

Which fraction names the shaded part?

A $\frac{1}{6}$

B $\frac{5}{6}$

C $\frac{6}{6}$

D $\frac{3}{6}$

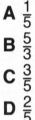

1. Which fraction names the shaded part?

A $\frac{1}{2}$

B $\frac{1}{4}$

C $\frac{1}{3}$

D $\frac{3}{1}$

2. Which fraction names the shaded part?

A $\frac{3}{6}$

B $\frac{6}{3}$

C $\frac{3}{3}$

D $\frac{3}{7}$

3. Which fraction names the shaded part?

A three fourths

B three thirds

C three fifths

D four thirds

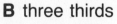

4. What fraction of these figures are circles?

A $\frac{3}{3}$

B $\frac{6}{3}$

C $\frac{3}{6}$

D $\frac{1}{5}$

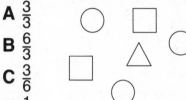

5. What fraction of the marbles are white?

A $\frac{1}{5}$

B $\frac{5}{3}$

C $\frac{3}{5}$

D $\frac{2}{5}$

6. What fraction of the balls are round?

A $\frac{4}{6}$

B $\frac{1}{6}$

C $\frac{2}{6}$

D $\frac{6}{4}$

7. Which number sentence shows equal fractions?

A $\frac{1}{3} = \frac{2}{4}$

B $\frac{1}{2} = \frac{2}{4}$

C $\frac{1}{2} = \frac{3}{4}$

D $\frac{1}{4} = \frac{1}{2}$

8. Which number sentence shows equal fractions?

A $\frac{5}{8} = \frac{3}{4}$

B $\frac{5}{8} = \frac{4}{3}$

C $\frac{6}{8} = \frac{3}{4}$

D $\frac{6}{8} = \frac{4}{4}$

9. Which number sentence shows equal fractions?

A $\frac{1}{6} = \frac{1}{2}$

B $\frac{2}{6} = \frac{1}{2}$

C $\frac{4}{6} = \frac{1}{2}$

D $\frac{3}{6} = \frac{1}{2}$

Find the number.

10. $\frac{1}{2}$ of 6

A 3

B 2

C 1

D 4

11. $\frac{1}{3}$ of 15

A 4

B 5

C 6

D 3

12. $\frac{1}{6}$ of 36

A 7

B 5

C 4

D 6

Use this information and the strategy *Try and Check* to solve Items 13–15.

The rodeo had horses and people in its parade. Jean counted a total of 26 feet.

13. If there are 5 people, how many horses are there?

A 3 horses

B 4 horses

C 5 horses

D 16 horses

14. If there are 3 horses, how many people are there?

A 7 people

B 5 people

C 10 people

D 14 people

15. If there are 3 people, how many horses are there?

A 10 horses

B 6 horses

C 7 horses

D 5 horses

EXPLORING MATHEMATICS © Scott, Foresman and Company/3

Complete each number sentence.

16. $\frac{3}{5}$ ● $\frac{2}{5}$

   A =   **B** <   **C** >

17. $\frac{1}{4}$ ● $\frac{1}{3}$

   A >   **B** <   **C** =

18. Five of the 12 club members are girls. Seven are boys. Compare the fraction that are girls with the fraction that are boys.

$$\frac{5}{12} \bullet \frac{7}{12}$$

   A <   **B** >   **C** =

Use the fraction bars to order the fractions from least to greatest.

$\frac{1}{2}$		$\frac{1}{2}$	

$\frac{1}{3}$	$\frac{1}{3}$	$\frac{1}{3}$

$\frac{1}{4}$	$\frac{1}{4}$	$\frac{1}{4}$	$\frac{1}{4}$

$\frac{1}{6}$	$\frac{1}{6}$	$\frac{1}{6}$	$\frac{1}{6}$	$\frac{1}{6}$	$\frac{1}{6}$

$\frac{1}{10}$	$\frac{1}{10}$	$\frac{1}{10}$	$\frac{1}{10}$	$\frac{1}{10}$	$\frac{1}{10}$	$\frac{1}{10}$	$\frac{1}{10}$	$\frac{1}{10}$	$\frac{1}{10}$

19. $\frac{1}{3}, \frac{1}{2}, \frac{1}{4}$

   A $\frac{1}{2}, \frac{1}{3}, \frac{1}{4}$

   B $\frac{1}{2}, \frac{1}{4}, \frac{1}{3}$

   C $\frac{1}{4}, \frac{1}{3}, \frac{1}{2}$

   D $\frac{1}{4}, \frac{1}{2}, \frac{1}{3}$

20. $\frac{3}{10}, \frac{3}{4}, \frac{2}{10}$

   A $\frac{3}{4}, \frac{2}{10}, \frac{3}{10}$

   B $\frac{3}{10}, \frac{2}{10}, \frac{3}{4}$

   C $\frac{2}{10}, \frac{3}{4}, \frac{3}{10}$

   D $\frac{2}{10}, \frac{3}{10}, \frac{3}{4}$

21. $\frac{1}{6}, \frac{1}{3}, \frac{5}{6}$

   A $\frac{1}{6}, \frac{5}{6}, \frac{1}{3}$

   B $\frac{1}{6}, \frac{1}{3}, \frac{5}{6}$

   C $\frac{1}{3}, \frac{5}{6}, \frac{1}{6}$

   D $\frac{1}{3}, \frac{1}{6}, \frac{5}{6}$

22. What is the decimal for $\frac{5}{10}$?

   A 0.5

   B 0.510

   C 5.10

   D 0.51

23. What is the decimal for $\frac{4}{10}$?

   A 4.10

   B 0.41

   C 0.410

   D 0.4

24. What is the decimal for eight tenths?

  A 810

  B 0.8

  C 8.10

  D 0.81

Tell what place the 4 is in.

25. 14.7

  A tens

  B ones

  C tenths

26. 61.4

  A tens

  B ones

  C tenths

27. 45.3

  A tens

  B ones

  C tenths

28. What is the decimal for $2\frac{27}{100}$?

  A 22.7

  B 2.27

  C 0.227

  D 227

29. What is the decimal for four and 6 hundredths?

  A 4.06

  B 406

  C 4.6

  D 46

30. There are 100 students on the playground. Thirty-one of the students are third graders. What decimal shows the part of the group that are third graders?

  A 31

  B 3.1

  C 0.31

  D 0.031

Complete each number sentence.

31. 0.3 ● 0.03

  A >   **B** <   **C** =

32. 1.09 ● 1.19

  A >   **B** <   **C** =

33. 31.2 ● 30.19

  A =   **B** <   **C** >

Use this drawing or use *Try and Check* to solve Items 34–36.

Jan ate 0.2 of the pizza. Jack ate 0.3 of the pizza. Dad ate the rest of the pizza.

34. What part of the pizza did Jan and Jack eat?

A 0.3 of the pizza

B 0.5 of the pizza

C 0.2 of the pizza

D 0.4 of the pizza

35. What part of the pizza did Dad eat?

A 0.5 of the pizza

B 0.2 of the pizza

C 0.3 of the pizza

D 0.6 of the pizza

36. What decimal shows the part of the pizza eaten by Jan, Jack, and Dad?

A 0.5

B 1.0

C 0.3

D 0.2

37. A nickel is what part of a dollar?

A 0.01

B 0.5

C 0.05

D 0.50

38. What will the meter show when the car travels another tenth of a mile?

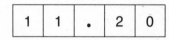

A 21.20

B 12.20

C 11.21

D 11.30

39. About how long is this pencil to the nearest centimeter?

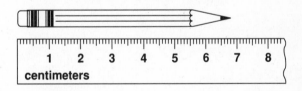

A 8 cm

B 10 cm

C 6 cm

D 7 cm

Date   Score

Choose the letter of the correct answer.

SAMPLE

Which fraction names the shaded part?

A $\frac{1}{6}$

B $\frac{5}{6}$

C $\frac{6}{6}$

D $\frac{3}{6}$

1. Which fraction names the shaded part?

A $\frac{4}{1}$

B $\frac{1}{4}$

C $\frac{1}{3}$

D $\frac{1}{5}$

2. Which fraction names the shaded part?

A $\frac{3}{5}$

B $\frac{5}{3}$

C $\frac{3}{3}$

D $\frac{3}{2}$

3. Which fraction names the shaded part?

A five eighths

B five sevenths

C five thirds

D five fifths

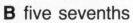

4. What fraction in this set of figures are triangles?

A $\frac{3}{9}$

B $\frac{4}{9}$

C $\frac{4}{4}$

D $\frac{9}{4}$

5. What fraction of the balls are round?

A $\frac{1}{3}$

B $\frac{3}{3}$

C $\frac{3}{2}$

D $\frac{2}{3}$

6. What fraction of the marbles are white?

A $\frac{4}{7}$

B $\frac{3}{7}$

C $\frac{5}{7}$

D $\frac{7}{4}$

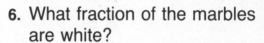

7. Which number sentence shows equal fractions?

A $\frac{1}{2} = \frac{3}{4}$

B $\frac{2}{6} = \frac{2}{3}$

C $\frac{1}{3} = \frac{2}{6}$

D $\frac{1}{3} = \frac{1}{6}$

8. Which number sentence shows equal fractions?

A $\frac{4}{8} = \frac{2}{4}$

B $\frac{4}{8} = \frac{1}{4}$

C $\frac{1}{8} = \frac{1}{4}$

D $\frac{1}{8} = \frac{2}{4}$

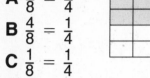

9. Which number sentence shows equal fractions?

A $\frac{1}{12} = \frac{1}{6}$

B $\frac{2}{12} = \frac{1}{6}$

C $\frac{2}{12} = \frac{5}{6}$

D $\frac{10}{12} = \frac{1}{6}$

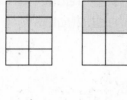

Find the number.

10. $\frac{1}{2}$ of 8

A 2
B 6
C 4
D 8

11. $\frac{1}{4}$ of 12

A 4
B 5
C 6
D 3

12. $\frac{1}{7}$ of 42

A 6
B 7
C 5
D 8

Use this information and the strategy *Try and Check* to solve Items 13–15.

The circus parade has both clowns and elephants. Janet counted a total of 30 feet.

13. If there are 7 clowns, how many elephants are there?

A 16 elephants
B 4 elephants
C 8 elephants
D 14 elephants

14. If there are 6 elephants, how many clowns are there?

A 6 clowns
B 2 clowns
C 3 clowns
D 12 clowns

15. If there are 5 clowns, how many elephants are there?

A 10 elephants
B 20 elephants
C 5 elephants
D 15 elephants

Complete each number sentence.

16. $\frac{2}{6} \bullet \frac{3}{6}$

    A >   **B** <   **C** =

17. $\frac{3}{6} \bullet \frac{1}{2}$

    A <   **B** >   **C** =

18. A recipe calls for $\frac{2}{3}$ cup of oil and $\frac{1}{3}$ cup of water. Compare the amounts of oil and water.

$$\frac{2}{3} \bullet \frac{1}{3}$$

    A >   **B** <   **C** =

Use the fraction bars to order the fractions from least to greatest.

$\frac{1}{2}$		$\frac{1}{2}$		

$\frac{1}{3}$		$\frac{1}{3}$		$\frac{1}{3}$

$\frac{1}{4}$	$\frac{1}{4}$	$\frac{1}{4}$	$\frac{1}{4}$

$\frac{1}{5}$	$\frac{1}{5}$	$\frac{1}{5}$	$\frac{1}{5}$	$\frac{1}{5}$

$\frac{1}{8}$	$\frac{1}{8}$	$\frac{1}{8}$	$\frac{1}{8}$	$\frac{1}{8}$	$\frac{1}{8}$	$\frac{1}{8}$	$\frac{1}{8}$

19. $\frac{1}{4}, \frac{1}{3}, \frac{1}{5}$

    A $\frac{1}{3}, \frac{1}{5}, \frac{1}{4}$

    B $\frac{1}{4}, \frac{1}{5}, \frac{1}{3}$

    C $\frac{1}{3}, \frac{1}{4}, \frac{1}{5}$

    D $\frac{1}{5}, \frac{1}{4}, \frac{1}{3}$

20. $\frac{1}{2}, \frac{1}{4}, \frac{3}{4}$

    A $\frac{1}{2}, \frac{3}{4}, \frac{1}{4}$

    B $\frac{1}{4}, \frac{1}{2}, \frac{3}{4}$

    C $\frac{1}{4}, \frac{3}{4}, \frac{1}{2}$

    D $\frac{3}{4}, \frac{1}{2}, \frac{1}{4}$

21. $\frac{1}{2}, \frac{1}{4}, \frac{3}{8}$

    A $\frac{1}{2}, \frac{3}{8}, \frac{1}{4}$

    B $\frac{1}{4}, \frac{1}{2}, \frac{3}{8}$

    C $\frac{3}{8}, \frac{1}{4}, \frac{1}{2}$

    D $\frac{1}{4}, \frac{3}{8}, \frac{1}{2}$

---

22. What is the decimal for $\frac{7}{10}$?

    A 0.7

    B 0.71

    C 0.710

    D 7.10

---

23. What is the decimal for $\frac{9}{10}$?

    A 0.91

    B 910

    C 9.10

    D 0.9

24. What is the decimal for five tenths?

    A 510

    B 0.5

    C 5.10

    D 0.51

Tell what place the 7 is in.

25. 12.7

    A tens

    B ones

    C tenths

26. 37.2

    A tens

    B ones

    C tenths

27. 71.4

    A tens

    B ones

    C tenths

28. What is the decimal for $1\frac{35}{100}$?

    A 135

    B 0.135

    C 1.35

    D 13.5

29. What is the decimal for fifteen and eight hundredths?

    A 1.508

    B 158

    C 15.8

    D 15.08

30. There are 100 students on the playground. Thirty-seven are third graders. What decimal shows the part of the group that are third graders?

    A 37

    B 3.7

    C 0.037

    D 0.37

Complete each number sentence.

31. 0.05 ● 0.5

    A <   **B** >   **C** =

32. 0.86 ● 0.18

    A =   **B** <   **C** >

33. 11.1 ● 10.06

    A <   **B** >   **C** =

EXPLORING MATHEMATICS © Scott, Foresman and Company/3

Use this drawing or use *Try and Check* to solve Items 34–36.

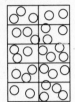

Mom ate 0.1 of the pizza. Doug ate 0.4 of the pizza. Dad ate the rest of the pizza.

34. What part of the pizza did Mom and Doug eat?

A 0.1 of the pizza

B 0.5 of the pizza

C 0.4 of the pizza

D 0.6 of the pizza

35. What part of the pizza did Dad eat?

A 0.5 of the pizza

B 0.1 of the pizza

C 0.4 of the pizza

D 0.6 of the pizza

36. What decimal shows the part of the pizza eaten by Mom, Dad, and Doug?

A 0.5

B 0.1

C 1.0

D 0.4

37. A penny is what part of a dollar?

A 0.1

B 0.01

C 1.0

D 1.1

38. What will the meter show when the car travels another tenth of a mile?

2	7	.	8	0

A 37.80

B 28.80

C 27.81

D 27.90

39. About how long is this pencil to the nearest centimeter?

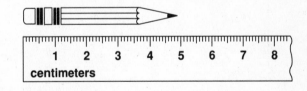

A 6 cm

B 10 cm

C 5 cm

D 4 cm

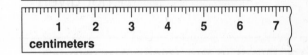
Choose the letter of the correct answer.

SAMPLE

Add.

$\begin{array}{r} 145 \\ +432 \end{array}$

A 577
B 677
C 517
D not given

---

1. Which number sentence is true?

A 437 > 485
B 107 > 207
C 258 < 268
D 369 < 319

---

2. Add.

$\begin{array}{r} 532 \\ +174 \end{array}$

A 706
B 696
C 596
D not given

---

3. Subtract.

$\begin{array}{r} 673 \\ -369 \end{array}$

A 314
B 304
C 204
D not given

---

4. What time is shown on this clock?

A 1:35
B 3:35
C 2:35
D 2:25

---

5. What is the length of this line segment to the nearest centimeter?

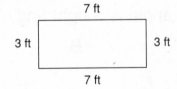

A 4 cm   **B** 7 cm
C 5 cm   **D** 6 cm

---

6. Find the perimeter of the figure below?

7 ft

3 ft   3 ft

7 ft

A 10 ft   **B** 14 ft
C 20 ft   **D** 21 ft

---

7. Clarice filled 5 rows of her stamp album with 7 stamps in each row. How many stamps did she put in her album in all?

A 12 stamps   **B** 7 stamps
C 35 stamps   **D** 28 stamps

---

8. Multiply.

$\begin{array}{r} 7 \\ \times 8 \end{array}$

A 15
B 56
C 63
D not given

---

9. Multiply.

   6
×9

A 54

B 48

C 56

D not given

10. What is the missing number?

$1 \times$ $= 7$
$2 \times$ ■ $= 14$
$3 \times$ ■ $= 21$
$4 \times$ ■ $= 28$

A 6

B 8

C 9

D 7

11. Which angle is a right angle?

A

B

C

D

12. Which of the following should be measured in liters?

A a glass of juice

B water in a swimming pool

C a carton of milk

D an eyedropper of water

13. Which one is not a member of the family of facts?

A $6 \times 3 = 18$ **B** $18 \div 3 = 6$

C $6 + 3 = 9$ **D** $3 \times 6 = 18$

14. Jack is three times as old as his sister Pat. Two years ago, he was 4 times as old as Pat. Use *Try and Check* to find how old they are now.

A Jack is 18. Pat is 6.

B Jack is 12. Pat is 6.

C Jack is 6. Pat is 18.

D Jack is 10. Pat is 4.

15. Janet needs 12 poster boards. She wants the same number in each of 3 colors. Which number sentence could you use to find the number of each color of poster board Janet should buy?

A ■ $+ 3 = 12$

B ■ $\times 3 = 12$

C $12 -$ ■ $= 3$

D ■ $\div 12 = 3$

16. Multiply.

4×8

A 40

B 36

C 30

D not given

17. Divide.

$40 \div 5$

A 9

B 8

C 7

D not given

Divide.

18. $30 \div 6$

A 5
B 4
C 6
D not given

19. $4\overline{)36}$

A 8
B 7
C 9
D not given

20. $7\overline{)56}$

A 6
B 7
C 9
D not given

21. $8\overline{)48}$

A 7
B 6
C 5
D not given

22. $27 \div 3$

A 9
B 7
C 24
D not given

23. $54 \div 9$

A 6
B 5
C 7
D not given

24. $0 \div 7$

A 7
B 0
C 1
D not given

25. $42 \div 5$

A 9 R3
B 2 R8
C 8 R2
D not given

26. Raul arranged the nickels he had saved in piles of 5 each. If he had saved 35 nickels, how many piles were there?

A 175 piles   **B** 7 piles
C 30 piles   **D** 8 piles

27. Which fact has only 2 number sentences in its family?

A $49 \div 7 = 7$
B $7 \times 6 = 42$
C $36 \div 4 = 9$
D $4 \times 7 = 28$

28. Lynn has 48 stuffed animals. She lined them up in 6 rows with the same number of animals in each row. What should you do to find how many there are in each row?

A subtract
B multiply
C divide

29. The class is going on a field trip. Each car can carry 5 students. How many cars are needed for 28 students?

A 23 cars   **B** 6 cars

C 5 cars   **D** 33 cars

30. What fraction names the shaded part?

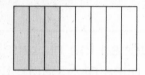

A $\frac{1}{2}$ **B** $\frac{5}{8}$ **C** $\frac{3}{8}$ **D** $\frac{3}{5}$

31. Find the missing number.

$$\frac{2}{3} = \frac{\blacksquare}{15}$$

A 10   **B** 5   **C** 15   **D** 8

32. Mary Ann has 15 books. She gave $\frac{1}{5}$ of them to her sister. How many books did she give to her sister?

A 8 books   **B** 3 books

C 5 books   **D** 1 book

33. Which decimal means the same as $\frac{54}{100}$?

A 5.4   **B** 54.0

C 0.054   **D** 0.54

34. The sum of Dorothy and Ron's ages is 15. Ron is 3 years older than Dorothy. Which correctly describes their ages?

A Dorothy, 6; Ron, 9

B Dorothy, 9; Ron, 6

C Dorothy, 10; Ron, 5

D Dorothy, 5; Ron, 10

35. Which number sentence is true?

A $4.06 > 4.6$

B $0.7 > 0.8$

C $4.5 < 4.52$

D $0.37 < 0.35$

36. John and his little sister Sue both walk to school. It takes John 4 times as long as his sister. It takes his sister 12 minutes to walk to school. Which number sentence could you use to find how long it takes John?

A $12 + 4 = \blacksquare$

B $4 \times 12 = \blacksquare$

C $12 \div 4 = \blacksquare$

D $12 - 4 = \blacksquare$

Choose the letter of the correct answer.

SAMPLE

What is this amount of money?

A 35¢   **B** 50¢   **C** 40¢   **D** 45¢

---

1. What time is shown on this clock?

   A 6:00   **B** 7:00
   C 12:00   **D** 12:35

---

2. What time is shown on this clock?

   A 3:18   **B** 2:18
   C 4:15   **D** 3:20

---

3. What time is shown on this clock?

   A 24 minutes before 10

   B 6 minutes before 7

   C 24 minutes before 11

   D 6 minutes before 8

Use this calendar to answer Items 4–6.

APRIL							MAY							JUNE						
S	M	T	W	T	F	S	S	M	T	W	T	F	S	S	M	T	W	T	F	S
						1		1	2	3	4	5	6						1	2	3
2	3	4	5	6	7	8	7	8	9	10	11	12	13	4	5	6	7	8	9	10
9	10	11	12	13	14	15	14	15	16	17	18	19	20	11	12	13	14	15	16	17
16	17	18	19	20	21	22	21	22	23	24	25	26	27	18	19	20	21	22	23	24
23/30	24	25	26	27	28	29	28	29	30	31				25	26	27	28	29	30	

JULY							AUGUST							SEPTEMBER						
S	M	T	W	T	F	S	S	M	T	W	T	F	S	S	M	T	W	T	F	S
						1		1	2	3	4	5							1	2
2	3	4	5	6	7	8	6	7	8	9	10	11	12	3	4	5	6	7	8	9
9	10	11	12	13	14	15	13	14	15	16	17	18	19	10	11	12	13	14	15	16
16	17	18	19	20	21	22	20	21	22	23	24	25	26	17	18	19	20	21	22	23
23/30	24/31	25	26	27	28	29	27	28	29	30	31			24	25	26	27	28	29	30

OCTOBER							NOVEMBER							DECEMBER						
S	M	T	W	T	F	S	S	M	T	W	T	F	S	S	M	T	W	T	F	S
1	2	3	4	5	6	7				1	2	3	4						1	2
8	9	10	11	12	13	14	5	6	7	8	9	10	11	3	4	5	6	7	8	9
15	16	17	18	19	20	21	12	13	14	15	16	17	18	10	11	12	13	14	15	16
22	23	24	25	26	27	28	19	20	21	22	23	24	25	17	18	19	20	21	22	23
29	30	31					26	27	28	29	30			24/31	25	26	27	28	29	30

4. What day of the week is July 27?

   A Tuesday   **B** Wednesday
   C Thursday   **D** Saturday

5. How many Mondays are in May?

   A 3 Mondays   **B** 4 Mondays
   C 6 Mondays   **D** 5 Mondays

6. What is the last Friday in April?

   A April 28   **B** April 30
   C April 29   **D** April 21

7. Jan left home at 2:25. It took her 15 minutes to walk to Sally's house. Then it took Jan and Sally 10 minutes to walk to the library. What time did they get to the library?

A 2:40

B 2:35

C 2:50

D 3:00

8. Dan spends 15 minutes on the school bus and 5 minutes walking to get from school to home. If he leaves school at 3:15, what time will he get home?

A 3:20

B 3:35

C 2:55

D 3:30

9. John got to David's house at 3:05. He waited for David for 25 minutes. Then it took them 10 minutes to ride their bikes to the park. What time did they get to the park?

A 3:40

B 3:30

C 3:45

D 3:50

10. Name this coin.

A quarter

B nickel

C dime

D half dollar

11. What is the value of this coin?

A $0.01   **B** $0.10

C $0.05   **D** $0.25

12. What is the value of this bill?

A 5¢   **B** $5.00

C 50¢   **D** $50.00

13. What is this amount of money?

A 85¢   **B** $1.85

C 90¢   **D** $1.35

14. How much is 5 dollars, 2 nickels, and 4 pennies?

A $5.24

B $5.42

C $5.34

D $5.14

15. How much is 1 half dollar, 2 quarters, 1 dime, and 2 pennies?

A $1.21

B $1.22

C $1.12

D $3.12

Add or subtract.

16. $1.35
    + 3.77

A $4.12

B $5.12

C $5.02

D not given

17. $9.67
    − 3.58

A $6.09

B $6.19

C $5.19

D not given

18. $5.00
    − 2.29

A $3.81

B $3.29

C $3.71

D not given

19. You gave the clerk $5.00 for a yo-yo costing $2.75. How much change will you get?

A $3.35   B $3.25

C $2.25   D $2.75

20. You gave the clerk $10.00 for a game costing $6.98. How much change will you get?

A $4.12   B $3.02

C $4.02   D $3.12

21. Lauren bought a soccer ball for $11.94. She gave the clerk $20.00. How much change did she get?

A $31.94   B $9.06

C $9.94   D $8.06

In Items 22–24, solve each problem by working backward.

22. Dorothy bought 2 books for $3 each and a magazine for $1.50. Her change was 50¢. How much did she give the salesperson?

A $7.00   **B** $5.00
C $3.00   **D** $8.00

23. Juan worked 20 hours in 3 days. He worked 8 hours on Day 1 and 5 hours on Day 2. How many hours did he work on Day 3?

A 17 hours   **B** 7 hours
C 33 hours   **D** 12 hours

24. Willie made $18 in 3 weeks repairing bicycles. He made $6 in Week 1 and $7 in Week 3. How much did he make in Week 2?

A $13   **B** $12
C $5   **D** $11

Give the best estimate of the sum.

25. $1.31 + $2.78 + $4.90

A $9   **B** $10
C $7   **D** $8

26. $1.43 + $0.91 + $1.58

A $5   **B** $2
C $3   **D** $4

27. $3.85 + $6.25 + $1.15

A $10   **B** $13
C $11   **D** $12

Choose the letter of the correct answer.

SAMPLE

What is this amount of money?

A 35¢   **B** 50¢   **C** 40¢   **D** 45¢

---

1. What time is shown on this clock?

A 2:00   **B** 12:00
C 3:00   **D** 12:15

---

2. What time is shown on this clock?

A 7:20   **B** 4:35
C 7:25   **D** 7:23

---

3. What time is shown on this clock?

A 5 minutes before 10
B 5 minutes before 9
C 11 minutes before 10
D 11 minutes before 11

Use this calendar to answer Items 4–6.

JANUARY							FEBRUARY							MARCH						
S	M	T	W	T	F	S	S	M	T	W	T	F	S	S	M	T	W	T	F	S
		1	2	3	4	5						1	2						1	2
6	7	8	9	10	11	12	3	4	5	6	7	8	9	3	4	5	6	7	8	9
13	14	15	16	17	18	19	10	11	12	13	14	15	16	10	11	12	13	14	15	16
20	21	22	23	24	25	26	17	18	19	20	21	22	23	17	18	19	20	21	22	23
27	28	29	30	31			24	25	26	27	28			24/31	25	26	27	28	29	30

APRIL							MAY							JUNE						
S	M	T	W	T	F	S	S	M	T	W	T	F	S	S	M	T	W	T	F	S
	1	2	3	4	5	6				1	2	3	4							1
7	8	9	10	11	12	13	5	6	7	8	9	10	11	2	3	4	5	6	7	8
14	15	16	17	18	19	20	12	13	14	15	16	17	18	9	10	11	12	13	14	15
21	22	23	24	25	26	27	19	20	21	22	23	24	25	16	17	18	19	20	21	22
28	29	30					26	27	28	29	30	31		23/30	24	25	26	27	28	29

JULY							AUGUST							SEPTEMBER						
S	M	T	W	T	F	S	S	M	T	W	T	F	S	S	M	T	W	T	F	S
	1	2	3	4	5	6					1	2	3	1	2	3	4	5	6	7
7	8	9	10	11	12	13	4	5	6	7	8	9	10	8	9	10	11	12	13	14
14	15	16	17	18	19	20	11	12	13	14	15	16	17	15	16	17	18	19	20	21
21	22	23	24	25	26	27	18	19	20	21	22	23	24	22	23	24	25	26	27	28
28	29	30	31				25	26	27	28	29	30	31	29	30					

4. What day of the week is April 12?

A Thursday   **B** Friday
C Saturday   **D** Sunday

5. How many Wednesdays are in June?

A 5 Wednesdays
B 7 Wednesdays
C 3 Wednesdays
D 4 Wednesdays

6. What is the last Friday in July?

A July 27   **B** July 29
C July 26   **D** July 19

7. Bill left home at 1:10. It took him 10 minutes to walk to Bob's house. Then it took Bill and Bob 15 minutes to walk to the store. What time did they get to the store?

   A 1:35
   B 1:25
   C 1:20
   D 1:45

8. Shirley has a 20-minute train ride and a 5-minute walk from the train station to the shopping center. If the train leaves the station at 10:15, what time will she get to the shopping center?

   A 10:30
   B 10:40
   C 9:50
   D 10:45

9. At 4:05 José started his homework. It took him 20 minutes to do his math homework and 15 minutes to do his reading. What time did he finish his homework?

   A 4:45
   B 4:25
   C 4:40
   D 4:35

10. Name this coin.

    A half dollar   **B** quarter
    C dime   **D** nickel

11. What is the value of this coin?

    A $0.01   **B** $0.50
    C $0.25   **D** $0.05

12. What is the value of this bill?

    A 100¢   **B** $10.00
    C 10¢   **D** $1.00

13. What is this amount of money?

    A $1.91   **B** 86¢
    C 91¢   **D** 81¢

14. How much is 7 dollars, 5 dimes, and 1 penny?

A $7.26

B $7.01

C $7.15

D $7.51

15. How much is 2 half dollars, 1 quarter, and 3 pennies?

A $1.28

B $2.13

C $1.03

D $2.28

Add or subtract.

16. $2.75
    + 5.65

A $7.30

B $8.40

C $7.40

D not given

17. $12.26
    − 5.93

A $7.33

B $7.73

C $6.33

D not given

18. $10.00
    − 3.69

A $6.31

B $7.69

C $7.31

D not given

19. You gave the clerk $5.00 for some flowers costing $3.25. How much change will you get?

A $2.25   B $1.75

C $2.75   D $1.85

20. You gave the clerk $10.00 for a game costing $5.49. How much change will you get?

A $4.61   B $5.49

C $5.51   D $4.51

21. Denise bought a backpack for $14.97. She gave the clerk $20.00. How much change did she get?

A $6.03   B $6.97

C $5.03   D $5.97

In Items 22–24, solve each problem by working backward.

22. Phil bought 2 toy cars for $3 each and a yo-yo for $1.25. His change was 75¢. How much did he give the salesperson?

A $8.00   **B** $7.00

C $5.00   **D** $6.00

23. Juanita worked 17 hours in 3 days. She worked 5 hours on Day 1 and 7 hours on Day 2. How many hours did she work on Day 3?

A 12 hours   **B** 5 hours

C 10 hours   **D** 4 hours

24. Chris spent $19 on school supplies during the first 3 weeks of school. She spent $9 in Week 1 and $6 in Week 2. How much did she spend in Week 3?

A $10   **B** $13

C $15   **D** $4

Give the best estimate of the sum.

25. $2.25 + $3.88 + $1.09

A $6   **B** $9

C $7   **D** $8

26. $2.39 + $3.41 + $0.75

A $6   **B** $7

C $5   **D** $8

27. $2.19 + $5.63 + $4.91

A $11   **B** $13

C $12   **D** $14

EXPLORING MATHEMATICS © Scott, Foresman and Company/**3**

Choose the letter of the correct answer.

SAMPLE

Find the product.

6×40

A 24

B 240

C 2,400

D not given

---

1. What is the standard form for 8 tens?

A 8   B 800

C 80   D 8,000

---

2. What is the standard form for 7 hundreds?

A 700   B 70

C 7   D 7,000

---

3. What is the standard form for 3 groups of 4 hundreds?

A 120   B 1,200

C 12   D 12,000

Find the product mentally.

4. 7×30

A 210

B 21

C 2,100

D not given

---

5. 400×4

A 16

B 160

C 16,000

D not given

---

6. 23×100

A 23

B 230

C 2,300

D not given

Estimate by using rounded numbers.

7. 5×18

A 10

B 100

C 1,000

D 50

---

8. 3×475

A 1,500

B 150

C 15

D 1,200

---

9. 520×6

A 3,600

B 300

C 30

D 3,000

---

10. Find how many are in 4 groups of 32.

A 120   B 160
C 128   D 122

11. Find how many are in 3 groups of 12.

A 15   B 36
C 32   D 312

12. The Pet Shoppe has 3 tanks. There are 18 fish in each tank. How many fish are there?

A 54 fish   B 60 fish
C 38 fish   D 36 fish

Multiply.

13.
$$\begin{array}{r} 17 \\ \times\ 5 \\ \hline \end{array}$$

A 55
B 85
C 75
D not given

14.
$$\begin{array}{r} 49 \\ \times\ 2 \\ \hline \end{array}$$

A 78
B 88
C 100
D not given

15.
$$\begin{array}{r} 14 \\ \times\ 7 \\ \hline \end{array}$$

A 88
B 78
C 98
D not given

16. Jack planted 5 rows of plants. He put 21 plants in each row. Each plant costs $3. What information is not needed to find how many plants were planted?

A Each plant costs $3.
B There are 21 plants.
C There are 5 rows.
D All the information is needed.

17. The Pet Shoppe sold 6 dogs and 4 cats each day for 5 days. How many dogs were sold?

A 30 dogs   B 50 dogs
C 44 dogs   D 20 dogs

18. Baseball cards come in packages of 5 each. Each child will be given 4 cards. How many cards are in 15 packages?

A 300 cards   B 60 cards
C 75 cards   D 135 cards

Multiply.

19. 41
× 8

A 320

B 328

C 408

D not given

20. 35
× 6

A 190

B 180

C 200

D not given

21. 87
× 5

A 435

B 405

C 425

D not given

In Items 22–24, choose the operation you should use and the correct answer for the problem.

22. The 45 third graders are going on a field trip. Each car can take 5 students. How many cars will be needed?

A addition; 50 cars

B subtraction; 40 cars

C division; 9 cars

D multiplication; 225 cars

23. Jackie has 358 baseball cards. Bill has 179 baseball cards. How many more cards does Jackie have?

A addition; 537 more cards

B subtraction; 179 more cards

C subtraction; 289 more cards

D addition; 437 more cards

24. Melba has 24 pages in her stamp collection. There are 6 stamps on each page. How many stamps are in her collection?

A addition; 30 stamps

B multiplication; 144 stamps

C division; 4 stamps

D subtraction; 18 stamps

Multiply.

25. 221
×   6

A 1,226

B 1,426

C 1,326

D not given

26. 408
×   5

A 2,200

B 2,040

C 4,020

D not given

27. 234
×   4

A 846

B 826

C 836

D not given

Date   Score

Choose the letter of the correct answer.

SAMPLE

Find the product.

6 × 4 0
- **A** 24
- **B** 240
- **C** 2,400
- **D** not given

1. What is the standard form for 6 tens?
   - **A** 6
   - **B** 60
   - **C** 600
   - **D** 6,000

2. What is the standard form for 9 hundreds?
   - **A** 9
   - **B** 9,000
   - **C** 90
   - **D** 900

3. What is the standard form for 6 groups of 2 hundreds?
   - **A** 120
   - **B** 12
   - **C** 1,200
   - **D** 12,000

Find the product mentally.

4. 7 × 4 0
   - **A** 280
   - **B** 2,800
   - **C** 28
   - **D** not given

5. 3 0 0 × 8
   - **A** 240
   - **B** 2,400
   - **C** 24
   - **D** not given

6. 1 8 × 1 0 0
   - **A** 180
   - **B** 1,800
   - **C** 18
   - **D** not given

Estimate by using rounded numbers.

7. 7 × 2 1
   - **A** 140
   - **B** 14
   - **C** 1,400
   - **D** 210

8. 6 × 2 1 9
   - **A** 12
   - **B** 120
   - **C** 1,800
   - **D** 1,200

9. 3 8 0 × 9
   - **A** 360
   - **B** 3,600
   - **C** 36
   - **D** 2,700

10. Find how many are in 3 groups of 53.

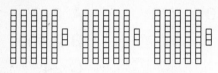

A 180   B 150

C 159   D 153

11. Find how many are in 2 groups of 31.

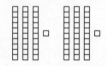

A 30   B 62

C 33   D 52

12. Juanita's stamp book has 25 pages. There are 6 stamps on each page. How many stamps are there?

A 150 stamps   B 120 stamps

C 125 stamps   D 180 stamps

Multiply.

13.
$$\begin{array}{r} 14 \\ \times\ 6 \\ \hline \end{array}$$

A 74
B 64
C 84
D not given

14.
$$\begin{array}{r} 38 \\ \times\ 2 \\ \hline \end{array}$$

A 86
B 66
C 40
D not given

15.
$$\begin{array}{r} 18 \\ \times\ 5 \\ \hline \end{array}$$

A 60
B 90
C 50
D not given

16. Wanda bought 4 boxes of crayons. Each box costs 50¢. There are 16 crayons in each box. What information is not needed to find how many crayons in all?

A Each box costs 50¢.

B There are 16 crayons in each box.

C Wanda bought 4 boxes of crayons.

D All the information is needed.

17. The Johnsons sold 3 cheese pizzas and 7 meat pizzas each week for 6 weeks. How many cheese pizzas did they sell?

A 21 cheese pizzas

B 60 cheese pizzas

C 18 cheese pizzas

D 42 cheese pizzas

18. Jacks come in bags of 8 jacks each. Each child will be given 5 jacks. How many jacks are in 10 bags?

A 40 jacks   B 50 jacks

C 80 jacks   D 130 jacks

Multiply.

19.   72
       × 4

A 288
B 280
C 218
D not given

20.   47
       × 5

A 215
B 205
C 225
D not given

21.   95
       × 3

A 275
B 285
C 270
D not given

In Items 22–24, choose the operation you should use and the correct answer for the problem.

22. A game board has 64 squares. There are 8 rows of squares. How many squares are in each row?

A addition; 72 squares
B multiplication; 512 squares
C division; 8 squares
D subtraction; 56 squares

23. John has 415 marbles. Diane has 227 marbles. How many marbles do they have together?

A subtraction; 212 marbles
B addition; 632 marbles
C subtraction; 188 marbles
D addition; 642 marbles

24. There are 12 sheets of each of 6 colors of construction paper. How many sheets of construction paper are there?

A multiplication; 72 sheets
B division; 2 sheets
C addition; 18 sheets
D subtraction; 6 sheets

Multiply.

25.   352
       × 4

A 1,208
B 1,408
C 1,308
D not given

26.   307
       × 6

A 1,842
B 222
C 2,042
D not given

27.   145
       × 6

A 640
B 840
C 870
D not given

Choose the letter of the correct answer.

SAMPLE

Class Favorite Games

Game	Tally of Votes
Monopoly	JHT IIII
Battle	JHT II
Old Maid	JHT JHT
Scrabble	III

Which game received the most votes?

A Monopoly   **B** Battle

C Old Maid   **D** Scrabble

1. From how many people should you collect data to find out the favorite sport of third graders at your school?

   A all of the third graders

   B one other third grader besides myself

   C Only my own opinion is necessary.

Use the following information for Items 2 and 3.

The parents club wants to serve two flavors of frozen yogurt to the students at the school picnic. They have four flavors from which to choose: vanilla, chocolate, cherry, and strawberry.

2. Who should they ask to help them decide which two flavors to buy?

   A the members of one family

   B twenty to thirty students

   C one first grader, one third grader, and one fifth grader

   D two teachers

3. What is the best question for them to ask?

   A Do you like chocolate frozen yogurt?

   B Do you like vanilla or cherry frozen yogurt?

   C Which is your favorite flavor of frozen yogurt?

   D Do you like vanilla, chocolate, cherry, or strawberry frozen yogurt best?

4. Keith asked, "How many people are in your family?" He recorded this data:

3 5 4 4 6 5 4 3
5 4 4 3 4 6 5 2

Number of Family Members

Number of Members	Tally	Number
2		
3		
4		
5		
6		

What should appear in the tally column of Keith's tally chart for 4 members in a family?

A III

B IIII

C ⅃⊦⊦Ⳁ

D ⅃⊦⊦Ⳁ I

Use this tally of data to answer Items 5 and 6.

Votes for Class President

Name	Tally
Bea	⅃⊦⊦Ⳁ III
John	⅃⊦⊦Ⳁ I
Raye	⅃⊦⊦Ⳁ IIII
Kyle	IIII

5. How many votes did Bea get?

A 8 votes **B** 6 votes
C 10 votes **D** 4 votes

6. How many more votes did Raye get than Bea?

A 4 votes **B** 6 votes
C 1 vote **D** 3 votes

Use this pictograph to answer Items 7–9.

Favorite Pet

Bird	☺ ☺ ☺
Dog	☺ ☺ ☺ ☺ ☺ ☺
Cat	☺ ☺ ☺ ☺
Other Animal	☺ ☺ ☺

Each ☺ stands for 2 children.

7. Which pet got the most votes?

A cat
B dog
C bird
D other animals

8. How many children chose a cat?

A 11 children
B 5 children
C 8 children
D 6 children

9. How many children chose an animal that was not a bird, dog, or cat?

A 3 children **B** 5 children
C 4 children **D** 6 children

Use this bar graph to answer Items 10–12.

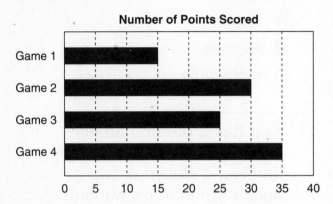

Number of Points Scored

10. What was the least number of points scored in any one game?

   A 15 points   **B** 25 points
   C 35 points   **D** 30 points

11. How many points were scored in Game 1?

   A 5 points   **B** 20 points
   C 10 points   **D** 15 points

12. In which game were 25 points scored?

   A Game 1   **B** Game 2
   C Game 3   **D** Game 4

Use this information for Items 13–15.

Grades 3, 4, and 5 collected old newspapers for recycling. Grade 3 collected 20 pounds in Week 1 and 40 pounds in Week 2. Grade 5 collected 10 pounds in Week 1 and 45 pounds in Week 2. Grade 4 collected 15 pounds in Week 1 and 35 pounds in Week 2.

13. Which numbers complete the table for Grade 4?

	Week 1	Week 2
Grade 3	20 pounds	40 pounds
Grade 4	■ pounds	■ pounds
Grade 5	10 pounds	45 pounds

   A 15; 45   **B** 10; 45
   C 15; 35   **D** 10; 35

14. How long should you make the bar for Grade 5 in this graph?

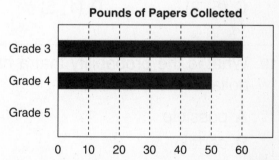

Pounds of Papers Collected

   A from 0 to 45   **B** from 0 to 35
   C from 0 to 10   **D** from 0 to 55

15. Which grade collected the most newspapers?

   A Grade 4

   B Grade 3

   C Grade 5

Use this grid for Items 16–18.

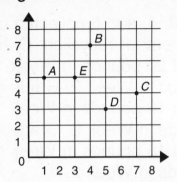

16. Which point is located at (5, 3)?

A point D   **B** point C
C point B   **D** point E

17. Which point is located at (7, 4)?

A point A   **B** point B
C point C   **D** point D

18. What is the number pair for point A?

A (3, 2)   **B** (5, 1)
C (5, 3)   **D** (1, 5)

19. What is the probability that a half dollar is worth 50¢?

A possible
B certain
C impossible

20. What is the probability that the sun will shine tomorrow?

A possible
B certain
C impossible

21. What is the probability you will have two birthdays in one year?

A certain
B possible
C impossible

22. A jar has 2 green marbles, 4 white marbles, and 6 orange marbles. If Robyn draws a marble from the jar without looking, which color marble will she most likely draw?

A green
B orange
C white

Use this information to answer Items 23 and 24.

A bag contains 5 red, 1 white, and 3 green marbles. Pick a marble without looking.

23. Which color marble is most likely to be drawn?

A red
B white
C green

24. Which color marble is least likely to be drawn?

A red
B green
C white

Use this spinner
to answer Items 25–27.

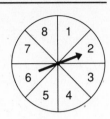

25. How many possible outcomes
are there?

 A 4 outcomes

 B 6 outcomes

 C 8 outcomes

 D 7 outcomes

26. Which number will be impossible
to spin?

 A 1

 B 9

 C 4

 D 7

27. How many outcomes involve
spinning an even number?

 A 1 outcome

 B 8 outcomes

 C 6 outcomes

 D 4 outcomes

Choose the letter of the correct answer.

SAMPLE

Class Favorite Games	
Game	Tally of Votes
Monopoly	ⅢⅢ IIII
Battle	ⅢⅢ II
Old Maid	ⅢⅢ ⅢⅢ
Scrabble	III

Which game received the most votes?

A Monopoly   **B** Battle
C Old Maid   **D** Scrabble

---

1. From how many people should you collect data to find out the favorite zoo animal of the third graders at your school?

   A at least 20 students
   B one other third grader besides myself
   C Only my own opinion is necessary.

Use this information for Items 2 and 3.

A third-grade teacher is taking her class on a picnic. They can eat hamburgers, hot dogs, or cold chicken.

2. Who should the teacher ask to help her decide how much of each food to order for the picnic?

   A two other teachers
   B one boy and one girl in the class
   C a person who works at the zoo
   D each member of the class

3. What is the best question for her to ask?

   A Where would you like to eat?
   B Which would you like to eat— a hot dog, a hamburger, or cold chicken?
   C Do you want to go to the picnic?
   D Would you like to eat a hamburger at the picnic?

4. Jennifer asked several friends, "Did you read the book, 'Miss Nelson is Missing'"? She recorded this data:

yes no no yes yes yes
no no no yes yes no
yes yes no yes yes yes

Answer	Tally	Number
yes		
no		

What should appear in the tally column of Jennifer's tally chart for yes?

A ЖНТ   **B** ЖНТ ll

C ЖНТ ЖНТ   **D** ЖНТ ЖНТ l

Use this tally of data to answer Items 5 and 6.

Votes for Class Treasurer

Name	Tally
Jake	llll
Lana	ЖНТ ЖНТ l
Emma	ЖНТ lll
Ryan	ЖНТ

5. How many votes did Emma get?

A 4 votes   **B** 8 votes

C 11 votes   **D** 5 votes

6. How many more votes did Lana get than Jake?

A 7 votes   **B** 4 votes

C 6 votes   **D** 3 votes

Use this pictograph to answer Items 7–9.

Favorite Pet

Dog	☺ ☺ ☺ ☺
Bird	☺ ☺ ☺
Cat	☺ ☺ ☺ ☺ ☺
Other Animal	☺ ☺ ☺ ☺

Each ☺ stands for 2 children.

7. Which pet got the most votes?

A bird

B dog

C cat

D other animal

8. How many children chose a bird?

A 3 children

B 6 children

C 9 children

D 8 children

9. How many children chose a dog?

A 4 children

B 8 children

C 6 children

D 10 children

EXPLORING MATHEMATICS © Scott, Foresman and Company/3

Use this bar graph to answer
Items 10–12.

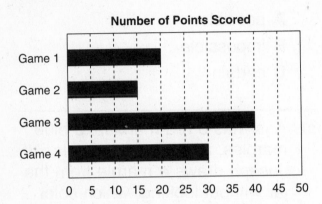

Number of Points Scored

10. What was the most number of
points scored in any one game?

A 15 points B 20 points

C 40 points D 30 points

11. How many points were scored in
Game 2?

A 10 points B 20 points

C 15 points D 25 points

12. In which game were 20 points
scored?

A Game 1 B Game 2

C Game 3 D Game 4

Use this information for Items 13–15.

Jim, Mary, and Juan ran two races
for charity. Jim ran 4 miles in Race 1
and 6 miles in Race 2. Juan ran
6 miles in Race 1 and 7 miles in
Race 2. Mary ran 5 miles in Race 2
and 4 miles in Race 1.

13. Which numbers complete
the table?

	Race 1	Race 2
Jim	4 miles	6 miles
Mary	4 miles	5 miles
Juan	■ miles	■ miles

A 7; 6 B 6; 7

C 2; 4 D 4; 2

14. How long should you make the
bar for Jim in this graph?

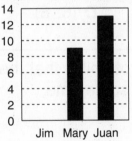

Miles Run in Two Races

A from 0 to 4

B from 0 to 6

C from 0 to 9

D from 0 to 10

15. Who ran the most miles for the
two races?

A Jim   B Mary   C Juan

Use this grid for Items 16–18.

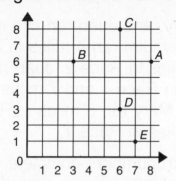

16. Which point is located at (3, 6)?

A point B   **B** point C

C point D   **D** point E

17. Which point is located at (6, 8)?

A point A   **B** point B

C point C   **D** point D

18. What is the number pair for point E?

A (5, 4)   **B** (1, 7)

C (7, 1)   **D** (6, 8)

19. What is the probability that the sun will shine some time next year?

A certain

B impossible

C possible

20. What is the probability that you will pet a puppy today?

A certain

B impossible

C possible

21. What is the probability that a quarter is worth 5¢?

A possible

B impossible

C certain

22. A jar has 5 red marbles, 3 blue marbles, and 4 green marbles. If Joseph draws a marble from the jar without looking, which color marble will he most likely draw?

A blue

B green

C red

Use this information to answer Items 23 and 24.

A box contains 3 triangles, 2 squares, and 6 circles. Pick a shape from the box without looking.

23. Which shape is most likely to be drawn?

A circle

B triangle

C square

24. Which shape is least likely to be drawn?

A triangle

B square

C circle

Use this spinner
to answer Items 25–27.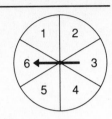

25. How many possible outcomes
are there?

   A 1 outcome

   B 6 outcomes

   C 3 outcomes

   D 4 outcomes

26. Which number will be impossible
to spin?

   A 3

   B 1

   C 5

   D 0

27. How many outcomes involve
spinning an odd number?

   A 1 outcome

   B 0 outcomes

   C 3 outcomes

   D 2 outcomes

Date   Score

Choose the letter of the correct answer.

SAMPLE

Willie has $30. How many $5 baseball cards can he buy?

A 5 cards   **B** 7 cards

C 6 cards   **D** 8 cards

1. Divide $36 into 3 equal groups. How many $10 bills and $1 bills will you use?

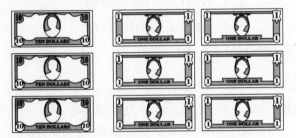

A six $10 bills, three $1 bills

B three $10 bills, six $1 bills

C one $10 bill, two $1 bills

D nine $1 bills

2. How many $10 bills and $1 bills are in each group if $32 is divided into 2 equal groups?

A 1 $10 bill, 6 $1 bills

B 3 $10 bills, 2 $1 bills

C 6 $10 bills, 1 $1 bill

D 1 $10 bill, 1 $1 bill

3. Divide $65 into 5 equal groups.

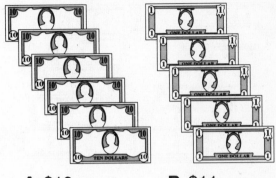

A $10   **B** $11

C $13   **D** $15

In Items 4–6, match the multiplication sentence with the related division sentence.

4. ■ × 4 = 64

   A 64 ÷ 2 = 32

   B 64 ÷ 8 = 8

   C 64 ÷ 4 = 16

5. ■ × 6 = 96

   A 96 ÷ 8 = 12

   B 96 ÷ 6 = 16

   C 96 ÷ 4 = 24

6. 3 × ■ = 45

   A 45 ÷ 3 = 15

   B 45 ÷ 9 = 5

   C 45 ÷ 5 = 9

How much money is in each group and how much is left over?

7. Divide $75 into 6 equal groups.

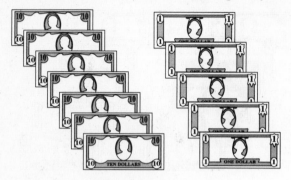

A $10, $5 left over

B $11, $3 left over

C $12, $1 left over

D $12, $3 left over

8. Divide $40 into 3 equal groups.

A $12 with $2 left over

B $3 with $13 left over

C $13 with $1 left over

D not given

9. Divide $98 into 8 equal groups.

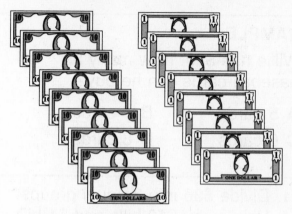

A $12 with $2 left over

B $12 with $4 left over

C $11 with $9 left over

D not given

10. Jake has $23. If he buys as many $4 baseball cards as he can, how much money will he have left over?

A $2   B $3

C $4   D $1

11. After school, 19 students formed 6-person teams. How many teams can be formed?

A 4 teams   B 5 teams

C 2 teams   D 3 teams

12. Mrs. Wilkes wants to take 32 children to an exhibition soccer game. She can put only 5 children in a car. How many cars will she need?

A 6 cars	**B** 8 cars
C 7 cars	**D** 5 cars

Divide.

13. $66 ÷ 4
A $16 R $3
B $16
C $16 R $1
D not given

14. $73 ÷ 3
A $21
B $24 R $1
C $24 R $3
D not given

15. $60 ÷ 7
A $8 R $6
B $8 R $5
C $8 R $4
D not given

16. Janet made $27 in 9 hours. Which operation should you use to find how much she was paid each hour?

A subtraction; $18
B division; $3
C addition; $36
D multiplication; $243

17. Jack has 6 fish. Mary has 3 times as many fish. Which operation should you use and which answer is correct for how many fish Mary has?

A multiplication; 18 fish
B addition; 9 fish
C division; 2 fish
D subtraction; 3 fish

18. In our class, 15 students walk to school and 3 ride the bus. Which operation should you use and which answer is correct for how many more students walk to school than ride the bus?

A addition; 18 students
B division; 5 students
C multiplication; 45 students
D subtraction; 12 students

Choose the letter of the correct answer.

SAMPLE

Willie has $30. How many $5 baseball cards can he buy?

A 5 cards   **B** 7 cards

C 6 cards   **D** 8 cards

---

1. Divide $48 into 4 equal groups. How many $10 bills and $1 bills will be in each group?

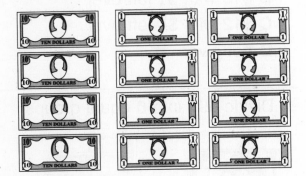

A one $10 bill, two $1 bills

B one $10 bill, one $1 bill

C two $10 bills, one $1 bill

D eleven $1 bills

---

2. How many $10 bills and $1 bills are in each group if $42 is divided into 3 equal groups?

A 4 $10 bills, 1 $1 bill

B 1 $10 bill, 4 $1 bills

C 1 $10 bill, 2 $1 bills

D 2 $10 bills, 4 $1 bills

---

3. Divide $64 into 4 equal groups.

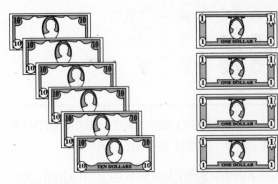

A $11   **B** $10

C $13   **D** $16

In Items 4–6, match the multiplication sentence with the related division sentence.

4. ■ × 5 = 80

   A 80 ÷ 8 = 10
   B 80 ÷ 4 = 20
   C 80 ÷ 5 = 16

5. 6 × ■ = 90

   A 90 ÷ 9 = 10
   B 90 ÷ 6 = 15
   C 90 ÷ 5 = 18

6. ■ × 4 = 72

   A 72 ÷ 4 = 18
   B 72 ÷ 3 = 24
   C 72 ÷ 8 = 9

How much money is in each group and how much is left over?

7. Divide $58 into 4 equal groups.

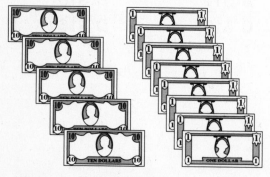

   A $13, $2 left over
   B $12, $9 left over
   C $14, $4 left over
   D $14, $2 left over

8. Divide $88 into 7 equal groups.

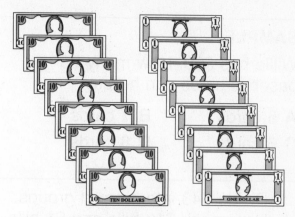

   A $12 with $6 left over
   B $13 with $1 left over
   C $12 with $4 left over
   D not given

---

9. Divide $95 into 6 equal groups.

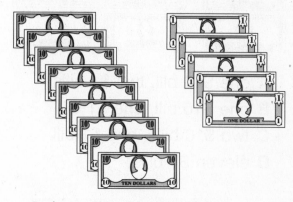

   A $15 with $5 left over
   B $15 with $4 left over
   C $15 with $3 left over
   D not given

---

10. Janice has $17. If she buys as many $3 toy cars as she can, how much money will she have left over?

   A $2   **B** $5   **C** $3   **D** $4

11. On Saturday, the 27 children at Janet's party formed as many 5-person groups as they could. How many 5-person groups were formed?

A 4 groups   **B** 6 groups
C 5 groups   **D** 7 groups

12. Mr. Lee is planning cars to take 30 girl scouts to camp. He can put only 4 girls in a car. How many cars will be needed?

A 7 cars   **B** 8 cars
C 9 cars   **D** 6 cars

Divide.

13. $48 ÷ 5
A $8 R $3
B $9 R $2
C $8 R $1
D not given

14. $75 ÷ 4
A $16 R $1
B $19
C $18 R $3
D not given

15. $76 ÷ 3
A $15 R $1
B $25 R $2
C $26 R $2
D not given

16. Will earned $21 in 7 hours. Which operation should you use to find how much he was paid each hour?

A addition; $128
B multiplication; $147
C division; $3
D subtraction; $14

17. Marie has 5 fish. Tim has 4 times as many fish. Which operation should you use and which answer is correct for how many fish Tim has?

A multiplication; 20 fish
B addition; 9 fish
C multiplication; 25 fish
D subtraction; 1 fish

18. In our class, 14 students have pet cats and 7 have pet dogs. Which operation should you use and which answer is correct for how many more students have pet cats than dogs?

A addition; 21 students
B subtraction; 7 students
C division; 2 students
D multiplication; 98 students

Choose the letter of the correct answer.

SAMPLE

Divide.

$$8 \div 4$$

A 4   **B** 3

C 2   **D** not given

---

1. Which calculator sequence would replace the ⟶ to change each first number to the second number?

    12 ⟶ 3
    15 ⟶ 6
    10 ⟶ 1
    16 ⟶ 7

    A ⊕ 8 ⊜
    B ⊖ 9 ⊜
    C ⊕ 9 ⊜
    D ⊖ 8 ⊜

---

2. Which numbers are written in order from least to greatest?

    A 379   397   419

    B 397   379   419

    C 379   419   397

    D 419   397   379

---

3. Round 64 to the nearest ten.

    A 70   **B** 50   **C** 65   **D** 60

---

4. Add.

    $$\begin{array}{r} 647 \\ +137 \\ \end{array}$$

    A 774
    B 874
    C 884
    D not given

---

5. Subtract.

    $$\begin{array}{r} 545 \\ -362 \\ \end{array}$$

    A 283
    B 183
    C 223
    D not given

---

6. There are 5 children. Each child has 8 pencils. How many pencils are there in all?

    A 32 pencils   **B** 13 pencils

    C 3 pencils   **D** 40 pencils

---

7. Multiply.

    $$\begin{array}{r} 9 \\ \times 5 \\ \end{array}$$

    A 45
    B 42
    C 14
    D not given

---

8. How many blocks are there in a block tower that has 2 rows with 3 blocks in each row and 5 layers?

    A 25 blocks   **B** 10 blocks

    C 30 blocks   **D** 24 blocks

---

9. Multiply.

    $$\begin{array}{r} 7 \\ \times 8 \\ \end{array}$$

    A 15
    B 56
    C 63
    D not given

---

10. Which is the length of this line segment to the nearest inch?

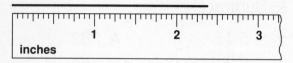

A 2 inches   **B** 4 inches
C 3 inches   **D** 1 inch

11. How many angles are there in this figure?

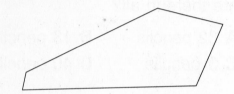

A 3 angles   **B** 1 angle
C 5 angles   **D** 4 angles

12. Which letter has a line of symmetry?

A P   **B** E
C N   **D** G

13. The weight of which item should be measured in ounces?

A a TV   **B** a person
C a pig   **D** an apple

Divide.

14. $5\overline{)35}$ **A** 9
            B 5
            C 6
            D not given

15. $63 \div 9$ **A** 6
            B 8
            C 7
            D not given

16. $18 \div 18$ **A** 1
            B 0
            C 18
            D not given

17. What is the remainder when you divide 43 by 5?

A 3   **B** 8
C 5   **D** not given

18. What fraction of the figure is shaded?

A $\frac{1}{6}$ **B** $\frac{1}{11}$
C $\frac{6}{5}$ **D** $\frac{5}{6}$

19. Find $\frac{1}{4}$ of 24.

A 4   **B** 96
C 6   **D** 12

20. There are 9 players on the team. Four of them are fielders. What fraction stands for the fielders in the group?

A $\frac{9}{4}$ **B** $\frac{4}{9}$
C $\frac{9}{5}$ **D** $\frac{5}{9}$

21. Which sentence is true?

A $\frac{5}{12} > \frac{7}{12}$ **B** $\frac{5}{10} < \frac{3}{10}$

C $\frac{1}{6} > \frac{1}{5}$ **D** $\frac{1}{2} > \frac{1}{3}$

---

22. Which fraction means the same as 0.4?

A $\frac{4}{10}$ **B** $\frac{0}{4}$

C $\frac{1}{4}$ **D** $\frac{4}{1}$

---

23. Which number sentence is true?

A $3.23 > 3.32$ **B** $2.6 < 2.06$

C $3.42 > 3.4$ **D** $5.32 > 6.02$

---

24. Which decimal means the same as $\frac{57}{100}$?

A 0.57   **B** 5.7

C 0.057   **D** 57.0

---

25. Sean and April leave school at 3:15 and walk 12 minutes to April's house. Then Sean walks home from April's house in 9 minutes. What time is it when Sean gets home?

A 3:18   **B** 3:36

C 9:12   **D** 12:15

---

26. What time is shown on this clock?

A 5 minutes after 4

B 5 minutes before 4

C 5 minutes after 5

D 5 minutes before 5

---

27. Find the amount of money.
1 half dollar, 5 dimes, 4 nickels

A $1.20   **B** $0.95

C $1.15   **D** $1.25

---

28. Add.

$$\begin{array}{r} \$13.46 \\ + \quad 9.74 \\ \hline \end{array}$$

A $22.10

B $22.20

C $23.20

D not given

---

29. What is the change from $10 when you buy a ball for $6.75?

A $0.25   **B** $3.25

C $4.25   **D** $4.75

---

30. Which is the best estimate for 619×5?

A 3,000   **B** 3,500

C 300   **D** 350

Multiply.

31. 26
× 3

A 29
B 68
C 78
D not given

32. 271
× 4

A 884
B 1,084
C 1,094
D not given

33. What number is shown by the following tally marks?

JHT   JHT
JHT   JHT
JHT   JHT
III

A 23   **B** 3   **C** 63   **D** 33

Study the graph. Then answer the question.

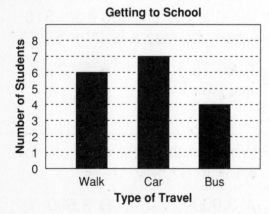

Getting to School

34. How many students walk to school?

A 6 students   **B** 7 students
C 4 students   **D** 5 students

35. There are 8 granola bars in a package. How many packages should be bought so that everyone in a group of 90 gets a granola bar?

A 10 packages   **B** 11 packages
C 12 packages   **D** 9 packages

36. Four students earned $52 doing yard work. They split the money equally. Should you *add, subtract, multiply,* or *divide* to find how much each student earned?

A add   **B** subtract
C multiply   **D** divide

37. There are 16 people in 4 cars on a trip. There are the same number of people in each car. The trip will take 3 hours if the drivers travel at 50 miles an hour. What is the key idea in finding how many miles they will travel?

A They will travel for 3 hours at 50 miles an hour, so you can divide.

B They will travel for 3 hours at 50 miles an hour, so you can multiply.

C There are 16 people in 4 cars, so you can multiply.

D There are 16 people in 4 cars, so you can divide.

Answer Form for
Multiple-Choice Tests

Student _____   **Date** _____

Name of Test _____   **Score** _____

Sample   (A) (B) (C) (D)

1. (A) (B) (C) (D)   21. (A) (B) (C) (D)   41. (A) (B) (C) (D)
2. (A) (B) (C) (D)   22. (A) (B) (C) (D)   42. (A) (B) (C) (D)
3. (A) (B) (C) (D)   23. (A) (B) (C) (D)   43. (A) (B) (C) (D)
4. (A) (B) (C) (D)   24. (A) (B) (C) (D)   44. (A) (B) (C) (D)
5. (A) (B) (C) (D)   25. (A) (B) (C) (D)   45. (A) (B) (C) (D)

6. (A) (B) (C) (D)   26. (A) (B) (C) (D)   46. (A) (B) (C) (D)
7. (A) (B) (C) (D)   27. (A) (B) (C) (D)   47. (A) (B) (C) (D)
8. (A) (B) (C) (D)   28. (A) (B) (C) (D)   48. (A) (B) (C) (D)
9. (A) (B) (C) (D)   29. (A) (B) (C) (D)   49. (A) (B) (C) (D)
10. (A) (B) (C) (D)   30. (A) (B) (C) (D)   50. (A) (B) (C) (D)

11. (A) (B) (C) (D)   31. (A) (B) (C) (D)   51. (A) (B) (C) (D)
12. (A) (B) (C) (D)   32. (A) (B) (C) (D)   52. (A) (B) (C) (D)
13. (A) (B) (C) (D)   33. (A) (B) (C) (D)   53. (A) (B) (C) (D)
14. (A) (B) (C) (D)   34. (A) (B) (C) (D)   54. (A) (B) (C) (D)
15. (A) (B) (C) (D)   35. (A) (B) (C) (D)   55. (A) (B) (C) (D)

16. (A) (B) (C) (D)   36. (A) (B) (C) (D)   56. (A) (B) (C) (D)
17. (A) (B) (C) (D)   37. (A) (B) (C) (D)   57. (A) (B) (C) (D)
18. (A) (B) (C) (D)   38. (A) (B) (C) (D)   58. (A) (B) (C) (D)
19. (A) (B) (C) (D)   39. (A) (B) (C) (D)   59. (A) (B) (C) (D)
20. (A) (B) (C) (D)   40. (A) (B) (C) (D)   60. (A) (B) (C) (D)

Answers for Multiple-Choice Tests

Inventory Test

SAMPLE B

Grade 2

Objective (See page 312.)

Obj.	Item	Ans.
20	1.	B
17	2.	B
19	3.	A
23	4.	C
23	5.	B
25	6.	C
27	7.	A
32	8.	C
30	9.	B
38	10.	A
34	11.	C
38	12.	B
41	13.	C
41	14.	A
44	15.	C
53	16.	C
55	17.	B
67	18.	C
65	19.	A
68	20.	B
69	21.	C
76	22.	A
77	23.	B
78	24.	C
80	25.	B
80	26.	C
88	27.	B
91	28.	C
92	29.	A
104	30.	A
107	31.	C
110	32.	B
117	33.	B
120	34.	A
127	35.	C
123	36.	A
128	37.	B
130	38.	C
132	39.	A
133	40.	B

Chapter 1 Form C

SAMPLE B

Objective

Obj.	Item	Ans.
1	1.	A
	2.	C
	3.	D
2	4.	B
	5.	C
	6.	B
3	7.	A
	8.	B
	9.	C
4	10.	A
	11.	B
	12.	C
5	13.	D
	14.	A
	15.	B
6	16.	D
	17.	C
	18.	A
7	19.	B
	20.	D
	21.	C
8	22.	A
	23.	D
	24.	C
9	25.	B
	26.	D
	27.	A

Chapter 1 Form D

SAMPLE B

Objective

Obj.	Item	Ans.
1	1.	B
	2.	A
	3.	C
2	4.	D
	5.	B
	6.	A
3	7.	C
	8.	A
	9.	B
4	10.	C
	11.	A
	12.	B
5	13.	D
	14.	C
	15.	B
6	16.	A
	17.	D
	18.	C
7	19.	A
	20.	B
	21.	D
8	22.	C
	23.	A
	24.	B
9	25.	D
	26.	C
	27.	B

Chapter 2 Form C

SAMPLE C

Objective

Obj.	Item	Ans.
10	1.	B
	2.	A
	3.	D
11	4.	D
	5.	B
	6.	C
12	7.	B
	8.	C
	9.	B
13	10.	D
	11.	D
	12.	A
14	13.	B
	14.	C
	15.	A
15	16.	A
	17.	C
	18.	B
16	19.	A
	20.	B
	21.	A
17	22.	B
	23.	D
	24.	D
18	25.	A
	26.	A
	27.	C
19	28.	B
	29.	C
	30.	A
20	31.	B
	32.	A
	33.	C

Chapter 2 Form D

SAMPLE C

Objective

Obj.	Item	Ans.
10	1.	A
	2.	A
	3.	B
11	4.	B
	5.	A
	6.	D
12	7.	A
	8.	A
	9.	C
13	10.	A
	11.	B
	12.	C
14	13.	B
	14.	D
	15.	D
15	16.	C
	17.	B
	18.	D
16	19.	A
	20.	C
	21.	B
17	22.	D
	23.	D
	24.	A

Chapter 3 Form C

SAMPLE B

Objective

Obj.	Item	Ans.
21	1.	C
	2.	A
	3.	B
22	4.	C
	5.	D
	6.	B
23	7.	A
	8.	B
	9.	D
24	10.	D
	11.	A
	12.	C
25	13.	B
	14.	C
	15.	A
26	16.	C
	17.	C
	18.	B
27	19.	A
	20.	D
	21.	B
28	22.	C
	23.	D
	24.	B
29	25.	B
	26.	B
	27.	A

Chapter 3 Form D

SAMPLE B

Objective

Obj.	Item	Ans.
21	1.	B
	2.	A
	3.	C
22	4.	A
	5.	C
	6.	D
23	7.	A
	8.	A
	9.	D
24	10.	B
	11.	C
	12.	A
25	13.	B
	14.	B
	15.	A
26	16.	C
	17.	A
	18.	D
27	19.	B
	20.	C
	21.	D
28	22.	D
	23.	C
	24.	B
29	25.	B
	26.	C
	27.	A

Cumulative Test Chapters 1–3

SAMPLE B

Objective

Obj.	Item	Ans.
1	1.	C
3	2.	B
2	3.	D
2	4.	B
5	5.	B
2	6.	C
4	7.	A
5	8.	D
6	9.	C
12	10.	D
7	11.	B
13	12.	A
13	13.	C
10	14.	B
11	15.	A
12	16.	B
13	17.	C
13	18.	B
14	19.	A
15	20.	D
16	21.	C
17	22.	B
17	23.	D
18	24.	C
19	25.	A
19	26.	B
20	27.	B
21	28.	D
22	29.	A
23	30.	B
25	31.	D
26	32.	A
23	33.	C
24	34.	B
21	35.	A
27	36.	D
28	37.	C
29	38.	C
21	39.	B

EXPLORING MATHEMATICS © Scott, Foresman and Company/3

26	8.	B
27	9.	D
32	10.	C
29	11.	B
30	12.	A
33	13.	C
28	14.	D
37	15.	B
37	16.	A
38	17.	B
39	18.	D
53	19.	A
41	20.	B
42	21.	D
44	22.	C
45	23.	A
54	24.	B
48	25.	D
52	26.	C
55	27.	B
59	28.	C
61	29.	A
62	30.	C
62	31.	A
62	32.	D
65	33.	C
64	34.	A
64	35.	D
69	36.	B
47	37.	C
60	38.	A
64	39.	D

Chapter 8
Form C

SAMPLE   B
Objective

70	1.	C
	2.	A
	3.	C
71	4.	C
	5.	D
	6.	B
72	7.	C
	8.	B
	9.	C
73	10.	A
	11.	A
	12.	D
74	13.	D
	14.	B
	15.	A
75	16.	B
	17.	D
	18.	D
76	19.	C
	20.	D
	21.	B
77	22.	A
	23.	A
	24.	B

78	25.	A
	26.	B
	27.	B
79	28.	B
	29.	A
	30.	A
80	31.	A
	32.	B
	33.	A
81	34.	C
	35.	A
	36.	D
82	37.	B
	38.	C
	39.	D

Chapter 8
Form D

SAMPLE   B
Objective

70	1.	A
	2.	B
	3.	D
71	4.	D
	5.	A
	6.	D
72	7.	B
	8.	C
	9.	A
73	10.	A
	11.	B
	12.	D
74	13.	C
	14.	A
	15.	C
75	16.	B
	17.	C
	18.	A
76	19.	D
	20.	B
	21.	C
77	22.	A
	23.	B
	24.	B
78	25.	A
	26.	A
	27.	B
79	28.	B
	29.	B
	30.	A
80	31.	B
	32.	A
	33.	A
81	34.	D
	35.	C
	36.	D
82	37.	A
	38.	C
	39.	B

Chapter 9
Form C

SAMPLE   B
Objective

83	1.	D
	2.	A
	3.	B
84	4.	C
	5.	D
	6.	B
85	7.	D
	8.	C
	9.	D
86	10.	B
	11.	A
	12.	A
87	13.	B
	14.	C
	15.	A
88	16.	C
	17.	B
	18.	B
89	19.	D
	20.	C
	21.	B
90	22.	C
	23.	A
	24.	A
91	25.	C
	26.	B
	27.	A

Chapter 9
Form D

SAMPLE   B
Objective

83	1.	B
	2.	A
	3.	C
84	4.	D
	5.	A
	6.	C
85	7.	B
	8.	A
	9.	C
86	10.	B
	11.	D
	12.	C
87	13.	B
	14.	A
	15.	C
88	16.	A
	17.	D
	18.	D
89	19.	C
	20.	A
	21.	D
90	22.	B
	23.	C
	24.	C

91	25.	A
	26.	B
	27.	C

Chapter 10
Form C

SAMPLE   C
Objective

92	1.	B
	2.	C
	3.	D
93	4.	C
	5.	B
	6.	B
94	7.	A
	8.	C
	9.	B
95	10.	C
	11.	D
	12.	A
96	13.	B
	14.	D
	15.	A
97	16.	B
	17.	A
	18.	A
98	19.	C
	20.	B
	21.	A
99	22.	A
	23.	C
	24.	D
100	25.	B
	26.	D
	27.	C

Chapter 10
Form D

SAMPLE   C
Objective

92	1.	C
	2.	B
	3.	A
93	4.	C
	5.	D
	6.	A
94	7.	B
	8.	C
	9.	D
95	10.	A
	11.	C
	12.	B
96	13.	A
	14.	D
	15.	B

97	16.	B
	17.	A
	18.	D
98	19.	B
	20.	C
	21.	A
99	22.	B
	23.	D
	24.	C
100	25.	A
	26.	B
	27.	C

Chapter 11
Form C

SAMPLE   B
Objective

101	1.	C
	2.	A
	3.	A
102	4.	C
	5.	C
	6.	A
103	7.	B
	8.	C
	9.	D
104	10.	A
	11.	B
	12.	D
105	13.	B
	14.	A
	15.	D
106	16.	C
	17.	B
	18.	A
107	19.	C
	20.	D
	21.	B
108	22.	A
	23.	D
	24.	B
109	25.	B
	26.	C
	27.	A
110	28.	B
	29.	A
	30.	C
111	31.	A
	32.	B
	33.	C
112	34.	B
	35.	A
	36.	B
113	37.	C
	38.	D
	39.	D

EXPLORING MATHEMATICS © Scott, Foresman and Company/3

Chapter 11 Form D

SAMPLE B
Objective

Obj.	#	Ans.
101	1.	B
	2.	A
	3.	A
102	4.	B
	5.	D
	6.	A
103	7.	C
	8.	A
	9.	B
104	10.	C
	11.	D
	12.	A
105	13.	B
	14.	C
	15.	C
106	16.	B
	17.	C
	18.	A
107	19.	D
	20.	B
	21.	D
108	22.	A
	23.	D
	24.	B
109	25.	C
	26.	B
	27.	A
110	28.	C
	29.	D
	30.	D
111	31.	A
	32.	C
	33.	B
112	34.	B
	35.	A
	36.	C
113	37.	B
	38.	D
	39.	C

Cumulative Test Chapters 1–11

SAMPLE A
Objective

Obj.	#	Ans.
12	1.	C
32	2.	A
37	3.	B
41	4.	C
45	5.	D
48	6.	C
55	7.	C
62	8.	B
62	9.	A
68	10.	D
72	11.	B
78	12.	C
91	13.	C
91	14.	A
88	15.	B
59	16.	D
89	17.	B
92	18.	A
87	19.	C
93	20.	D
94	21.	B
86	22.	A
95	23.	A
98	24.	B
99	25.	C
97	26.	B
96	27.	A
97	28.	C
100	29.	B
101	30.	C
103	31.	A
104	32.	B
110	33.	D
112	34.	A
111	35.	C
97	36.	B

Chapter 12 Form C

SAMPLE C
Objective

Obj.	#	Ans.
114	1.	B
	2.	A
	3.	C
115	4.	C
	5.	D
	6.	A
116	7.	C
	8.	B
	9.	A
117	10.	A
	11.	B
	12.	B
118	13.	A
	14.	D
	15.	C
119	16.	B
	17.	A
	18.	D
120	19.	C
	20.	B
	21.	D
121	22.	D
	23.	B
	24.	C
122	25.	A
	26.	D
	27.	C

Chapter 12 Form D

SAMPLE C
Objective

Obj.	#	Ans.
114	1.	C
	2.	D
	3.	A
115	4.	B
	5.	D
	6.	C
116	7.	A
	8.	B
	9.	C
117	10.	A
	11.	D
	12.	B
118	13.	C
	14.	D
	15.	A
119	16.	B
	17.	C
	18.	A
120	19.	B
	20.	D
	21.	C
121	22.	A
	23.	B
	24.	D
122	25.	C
	26.	A
	27.	B

Chapter 13 Form C

SAMPLE B
Objective

Obj.	#	Ans.
123	1.	C
	2.	A
	3.	B
124	4.	A
	5.	D
	6.	C
125	7.	B
	8.	A
	9.	D
126	10.	C
	11.	B
	12.	A
127	13.	B
	14.	D
	15.	C
128	16.	A
	17.	A
	18.	C
129	19.	B
	20.	D
	21.	A
130	22.	C
	23.	B
	24.	B

Chapter 13 Form D

SAMPLE B
Objective

Obj.	#	Ans.
123	1.	B
	2.	D
	3.	C
124	4.	A
	5.	B
	6.	B
125	7.	A
	8.	D
	9.	B
126	10.	C
	11.	B
	12.	A
127	13.	C
	14.	D
	15.	B
128	16.	A
	17.	C
	18.	A
129	19.	A
	20.	D
	21.	B
130	22.	C
	23.	D
	24.	A
131	25.	B
	26.	A
	27.	C

Chapter 14 Form C

SAMPLE C
Objective

Obj.	#	Ans.
132	1.	A
	2.	B
	3.	D
133	4.	D
	5.	A
	6.	C
134	7.	B
	8.	C
	9.	D
135	10.	A
	11.	D
	12.	C
136	13.	C
	14.	D
	15.	B
137	16.	A
	17.	C
	18.	D

Chapter 14 Form D

SAMPLE C
Objective

Obj.	#	Ans.
131	25.	C
	26.	B
	27.	D
132	1.	A
	2.	D
	3.	B
133	4.	D
	5.	B
	6.	A
134	7.	C
	8.	B
	9.	B
135	10.	C
	11.	C
	12.	A
136	13.	B
	14.	D
	15.	C
137	16.	A
	17.	C
	18.	C
138	19.	B
	20.	A
	21.	C
139	22.	B
	23.	A
	24.	C
140	25.	C
	26.	B
	27.	D

(Chapter 14 Form D, continued)

Obj.	#	Ans.
138	19.	A
	20.	C
	21.	B
139	22.	C
	23.	A
	24.	B
140	25.	B
	26.	D
	27.	C

Chapter 15 Form C

SAMPLE C
Objective

Obj.	#	Ans.
141	1.	B
	2.	A
	3.	C
142	4.	C
	5.	B
	6.	A
143	7.	D
	8.	C
	9.	A
144	10.	B
	11.	D
	12.	C

145	**13.**	D		106	**21.**	D
	14.	B		108	**22.**	A
	15.	C		111	**23.**	C
146	**16.**	B		110	**24.**	A
	17.	A		116	**25.**	B
	18.	D		41	**26.**	D
				118	**27.**	A
				119	**28.**	C

Chapter 15
Form D

				120	**29.**	B
				125	**30.**	A
				127	**31.**	C
SAMPLE		C		131	**32.**	B
Objective				133	**33.**	D
141	**1.**	A		135	**34.**	A
	2.	B		144	**35.**	C
	3.	D		146	**36.**	D
142	**4.**	C		146	**37.**	B
	5.	B
	6.	A
143	**7.**	D
	8.	C
	9.	A
144	**10.**	A
	11.	C
	12.	B
145	**13.**	D
	14.	C
	15.	D
146	**16.**	C
	17.	A
	18.	B

Cumulative Test
Chapters 1–15

SAMPLE		C
Objective		
9	**1.**	B
13	**2.**	A
15	**3.**	D
32	**4.**	D
37	**5.**	B
55	**6.**	D
55	**7.**	A
69	**8.**	C
67	**9.**	B
43	**10.**	A
72	**11.**	C
73	**12.**	B
79	**13.**	D
89	**14.**	D
95	**15.**	C
98	**16.**	A
99	**17.**	A
101	**18.**	D
104	**19.**	C
102	**20.**	B

310

Using Management Forms

This assessment handbook contains three types of management forms to help with record-keeping:

- forms for individualizing
- class record forms
- a percent table for scoring tests

Forms for Individualizing

The forms for individualizing can be used to analyze the test results of an individual student, assess the student's strengths and weaknesses, make individualized assignments, and keep a record of work completed.

	Inventory Test Form for Individualizing	Chapter Form for Individualizing	Cumulative Tests Form for Individualizing
When to use	Beginning of school year	After each chapter	After each quarter
Number of forms	1 for each grade	10 for Kindergarten 14 for Grades 1 and 2 15 for Grades 3–8	1 for each grade
Record results from	Multiple-Choice Inventory Test	Pupil Edition Review/Test A and B Test Forms C and D Test Forms Alternative Assessments	Multiple-Choice Cumulative Tests
Number of objectives covered	Key objectives from previous grade (1–8) Preschool objectives for Kindergarten	All objectives	Key objectives for chapters covered to date at grade level
Review options	Reteaching from previous grade (1–8) Reteaching for Kindergarten Review in back of student text (3–8) Listed with objective on form	In student text (3–8) More Practice Reteaching In Workbooks/BLM (K–8) Practice Reteaching Enrichment	In student text (3–8) More Practice Reteaching In Workbooks/BLM (K–8) Practice Reteaching Enrichment

Class Test Record Form

This two-page form may be used for recording chapter test scores and cumulative test scores for the whole class for an entire year.

Percent Table for Scoring Tests

This table can be used to convert a raw test score to a percentage score for any test containing up to 53 items.

Grade 3 Inventory Test Form for Individualizing

Student Name _____

See page 61 for scoring.

Grade 2 Objectives	Inventory Test		Review
	Item	✔ if correct	Grade 2 Reteaching
17 Use doubles and doubles plus 1 facts to find sums through 18.	2		R16
19 Add three numbers with sums of 18 or less. (See Grade 3, Review p. 543.)	3		R19
20 Add on from 7 or 8 to find sums through 18.	1		R20
23 Solve problems by using data from a bar graph.	4, 5		R23
25 Find the number of tens and ones and write the numbers through 99 in standard form. (See Grade 3, Review p. 539.)	6		R25
27 Given two numbers through 99, identify which is greater and which is less. (See Grade 3, Review p. 540.)	7		R27
30 Use ordinal numbers through twentieth to identify positions of objects. (See Grade 3, Review p. 536.)	9		R30
32 Identify amounts of money through 99¢ by counting on from the coin of greatest value.	8		R32
34 Use a doubles fact for addition to solve a related subtraction fact.	11		R34
38 Use related subtraction facts to find differences from 15 through 18.	10, 12		R38
41 Solve problems by choosing an operation.	13, 14		R14
44 Identify time to the hour and to 5-minute intervals. (See Grade 3, Review p. 545.)	15		R42
53 Measure lengths of objects to the nearest centimeter. (See Grade 3, Review p. 548.)	16		R52
55 Solve problems by choosing a sensible measure.	17		R55
65 Determine whether or not a trade is needed. Add one- and two-digit numbers.	19		R64
67 Determine whether or not a trade is needed. Add two-digit numbers.	18		R66
68 Add two-digit numbers. (See Grade 3, Review p. 542.)	20		R68
69 Add money amounts to find two-digit sums.	21		R69
76 Subtract one-digit numbers from two-digit numbers.	22		R75
77 Subtract two-digit numbers. (See Grade 3, Review p. 544.)	23		R77
78 Subtract two-digit numbers. (See Grade 3, Review p. 544.)	24		R78
80 Solve problems by choosing an operation.	25, 26		R80
88 Identify how many hundreds, tens, and ones. Write numbers through 999.	27		R88
91 Order numbers from 900 to 999 using a chart.	28		R91

EXPLORING MATHEMATICS © Scott, Foresman and Company/3

Student Name _____

See page 61 for scoring.

Grade 2 Objectives	Inventory Test		Review
	Item	✔ if correct	Grade 2 Reteaching
92 Compare three-digit numbers using greater than and less than symbols.	29		R92
104 Count and write amounts of money through $4.99.	30		R104
107 Identify halves, thirds, and fourths of a region by determining the number of equal parts and the number of colored parts.	31		R107
110 Use pictures to identify fractions of a set.	32		R110
117 Identify shapes that have the same size and shape.	33		R117
120 Name geometric solids. Explore the relationship between solids and plane shapes.	34		R120
123 Estimate whether a container holds more than or less than 1 liter.	36		R123
127 Solve problems involving measurement by using logical reasoning.	35		R127
128 Add one-, two-, and three-digit numbers. Trade ones for tens when necessary.	37		R128
130 Add three-digit numbers. Trade ones for tens or tens for hundreds if necessary.	38		R130
132 Subtract three-digit numbers. Trade tens for ones when necessary.	39		R132
133 Subtract three-digit numbers. Trade hundreds for tens when necessary.	40		R133

Grade 3 Chapter 1 Form for Individualizing

Student Name _____

	Date	Score
Pretest		
Posttest		

(handwritten note overlapping table: "ODP 170-6440")

Using Basic Facts

Objectives	Text Pages	Review/Test in PE — Item Numbers	Forms A & B — Item Numbers	Forms C & D — Item Numbers	Alternate Assessment	Independent Study		Supplements R	Supplements E
1 Identify uses of numbers.	4–5	1	1	1, 2, 3				1	1
2 Use basic addition and subtraction facts to find sums and differences.	6–7	2	2	4, 5, 6				2	2
3 Find missing numbers and operation signs in addition and subtraction facts.	8–9	3, 4, 5, 6, 7	3, 4, 5, 6, 7	7, 8, 9				3	3
4 Solve problems by using a problem-solving guide.	10–11	15, 16	15, 16	10, 11, 12				4	4
5 Use families of facts to solve problems.	12–15	8, 17	8, 17	13, 14, 15		Set D, p. 29	Set D, p. 31	5	5
6 Identify even and odd numbers.	18–19	9, 10, 11	9, 10, 11	16, 17, 18		Set E, p. 29	Set E, p. 31	6	6
7 Solve problems by using data from pictures.	20–21	12	12	19, 20, 21				7	7
8 Order events correctly.	22–23	13	13	22, 23, 24		Set F, p. 29	Set F, p. 31	8	8
9 Solve problems by finding patterns.	24–25	14	14	25, 26, 27				9	9

314

Grade 3 Chapter 2 Form for Individualizing

Student Name _____

See page 61 for scoring.

	Date	Score
Pretest		
Posttest		

Place Value

Objectives	Text Pages	Review/Test in PE — Item Numbers	Test Records — Forms A & B — Item Numbers	Test Records — Forms C & D — Item Numbers	Test Records — Alternative Assessment	Review Options — Independent Study — Reteaching	Review Options — Independent Study — More Practice	Review Options — Supplements P	Review Options — Supplements R	Review Options — Supplements E
10 Use place-value materials to understand hundreds.	36–39	1, 2	1, 2, 3, 4	1, 2, 3		Set A, p. 66	Set A, p. 68	10	10	10
11 Write digits in the proper sequence for pictured hundreds, tens, and ones, and numbers through 999 in standard and expanded form.	40–41	4	8	4, 5, 6		Set B, p. 66	Set B, p. 68	11	11	11
12 Compare numbers less than 1,000 using < and >.	42–43	7, 15	11, 12	7, 8, 9		Set C, p. 66	Set C, p. 68	12	12	12
13 Order three-digit numbers.	44–45	9	14	10, 11, 12		Set D, p. 66	Set D, p. 68	13	13	13
14 Find patterns in a number chart.	46–47	10	15, 16	13, 14, 15		Set E, p. 67	Set E, p. 69	14	14	14
15 Round numbers to the nearest ten and nearest hundred.	48–49	11, 12	17, 18	16, 17, 18		Set F, p. 67	Set F, p. 69	15	15	15
16 Solve problems by using logical reasoning.	52–53	13	19, 22	19, 20, 21				16	16	16
17 Write numbers through 9,999 in standard form.	54–57	3	5, 6	22, 23, 24		Set G, p. 67	Set G, p. 69	17	17	17
18 Compare and order numbers less than 9,999.	58–59	8	13, 21	25, 26, 27		Set H, p. 67	Set H, p. 69	18	18	18
19 Write numbers and give place value for numbers through 999,999.	60–61	5, 6, 16	7, 9, 10	28, 29, 30		Set I, p. 67	Set I, p. 69	19	19	19
20 Solve problems by choosing sensible answers.	62–63	14	20	31, 32, 33				20	20	20

See page 61 for scoring.

Student Name _____

	Date	Score
Pretest		
Posttest		

Two-Digit Addition and Subtraction

Objectives	Text Pages	Review/Test in PE — Item Numbers	Test Records — Item Numbers (Forms A & B)	Forms A & B	Item Numbers (Forms C & D)	Forms C & D	Alternative Assessment	Independent Study — Reteaching	Independent Study — More Practice	Supplements P	Supplements R	Supplements E
21 Solve problems by choosing addition or subtraction facts.	74–75	18, 20	18, 20		1, 2, 3					21	21	21
22 Rename numbers by changing ones to tens and tens to ones.	76–79	1, 2, 3, 4	1, 2, 3, 4		4, 5, 6			Set A, p. 98	Set A, p. 100	22	22	22
23 Add 2-digit numbers with and without renaming ones as tens.	80–81	5, 6, 7	5, 6, 7		7, 8, 9			Set B, p. 98	Set B, p. 100	23	23	23
24 Use mental math strategies to find the sum of two numbers.	82–83	8	8		10, 11, 12			Set C, p. 98	Set C, p. 100	24	24	24
25 Add three or four numbers of one and two digits whose sums do not exceed 99.	84–85	9, 10	9, 10		13, 14, 15			Set D, p. 98	Set D, p. 101	25	25	25
26 Subtract numbers with up to two digits, renaming tens as ones.	88–89	11, 12, 13	11, 12, 13		16, 17, 18			Set E, p. 99	Set E, p. 101	26	26	26
27 Use mental math strategies to find the difference between two numbers.	90–91	14, 15	14, 15		19, 20, 21			Set F, p. 99	Set F, p. 101	27	27	27
28 Estimate the sum or difference between two numbers.	92–93	16, 17, 21	16, 17, 21		22, 23, 24			Set G, p. 99	Set G, p. 101	28	28	28
29 Solve addition problems by using estimation.	94–95	19	19		25, 26, 27					29	29	29

Grade 3 Chapter 4 Form for Individualizing

Student Name _____

Three- and Four-Digit Addition and Subtraction

See page 61 for scoring.

	Date	Score
Pretest		
Posttest		

Objectives	Text Pages	Review/Test in PE — Item Numbers	Forms A & B — Item Numbers	Forms C & D — Item Numbers	Alternative Assessment	Reteaching	More Practice	Supplements P	Supplements R	Supplements E
30 Use pennies, dimes, and dollars to rename.	110–113	1	1, 2	1, 2, 3		Set A, p. 142	Set A, p. 144	30	30	30
31 Explore three-digit addition using dollars, dimes, and pennies.	114–117	2	3	4, 5, 6		Set B, p. 142	Set B, p. 144	31	31	31
32 Add three-digit numbers with one renaming.	118–119	4, 5	5, 6	7, 8, 9		Set C, p. 142	Set C, p. 144	32	32	32
33 Add three- and four-digit numbers with more than one renaming.	120–121	6	7, 8	10, 11, 12		Set D, p. 142	Set D, p. 144	33	33	33
34 Choose a method of computation from among paper and pencil, mental math, and calculator.	122–123	11, 12, 13	15, 16, 17	13, 14, 15		Set E, p. 143	Set E, p. 145	34	34	34
35 Solve problems by using data from pictures.	124–125	14	18	16, 17, 18				35	35	35
36 Explore three-digit subtraction using dollars, dimes, and pennies.	126–128	3	4	19, 20, 21		Set F, p. 143	Set F, p. 145	36	36	36
37 Subtract three-digit numbers with one renaming.	132–133	7	9, 12	22, 23, 24		Set G, p. 143	Set G, p. 145	37	37	37
38 Subtract three-digit numbers with up to two renamings involving zeros.	134–135	8	10, 11,	25, 26, 27		Set H, p. 143	Set H, p. 145	38	38	38
39 Subtract three- and four-digit numbers with three renamings involving zeros.	136–137	9, 10, 17	13, 14, 21	28, 29, 30		Set I, p. 143	Set I, p. 145	39	39	39
40 Solve problems by using data from tables.	138–139	15, 16	19, 20	31, 32, 33				40	40	40

Test Records includes Review/Test in PE, Forms A & B, Forms C & D, and Alternative Assessment. *Review Options* includes Independent Study (Reteaching, More Practice) and Supplements (P, R, E).

Grade 3 Chapter 5 Form for Individualizing

Student Name _____

See page 61 for scoring.

	Date	Score
Pretest		
Posttest		

Time, Measurement, and Geometry

Objectives	Text Pages	Test Records: Review/Test in PE — Item Numbers	Test Records: Forms A & B — Item Numbers	Test Records: Forms C & D — Item Numbers	Test Records: Alternative Assessment	Review Options: Independent Study — Reteaching	Review Options: Independent Study — More Practice	Supplements P	Supplements R	Supplements E
41 Tell time to the nearest minute using standard and digital clocks.	150–153	1, 2	1, 2	1, 2, 3		Set A, p. 178	Set A, p. 180	41	41	41
42 Read and interpret a three-month calendar.	154–155	3	3, 4	4, 5, 6		Set B, p. 178	Set B, p. 180	42	42	42
43 Measure objects to the nearest inch and half inch.	156–157	4	5, 6	7, 8, 9		Set C, p. 178	Set C, p. 180	43	43	43
44 Choose an appropriate customary unit of length using inch, foot, yard, or mile.	158–159	5, 14	7, 8, 18	10, 11, 12		Set D, p. 178	Set D, p. 180	44	44	44
45 Measure objects to the nearest centimeter and decimeter.	160–161	4	9, 10	13, 14, 15		Set E, p. 179	Set E, p. 181	45	45	45
46 Choose an appropriate metric unit of length using centimeter, meter, or kilometer.	164–165	6	9, 10	16, 17, 18		Set F, p. 179	Set F, p. 181	46	46	46
47 Solve problems by making tables.	166–167	11, 12, 13	15, 16, 17	19, 20, 21				47	47	47
48 Find perimeters.	168–169	7	11	22, 23, 24		Set G, p. 179	Set G, p. 181	48	48	48
49 Find areas by counting square units.	170–171	8	12	25, 26, 27				49	49	49
50 Solve problems by deciding whether an estimate is enough.	172–173	10	14	28, 29, 30				50	50	50
51 Choose an appropriate temperature using degrees Celsius or degrees Fahrenheit.	174–175	9	13	31, 32, 33		Set H, p. 179	Set H, p. 181	51	51	51

Grade 3 Chapter 6 Form for Individualizing

Student Name _____

See page 61 for scoring.

	Date	Score
Pretest		
Posttest		

Multiplication Concepts

Objectives	Text Pages	Test Records — Review/Test in PE — Item Numbers	Test Records — Forms A & B — Item Numbers	Test Records — Forms C & D — Item Numbers	Alternative Assessment	Review Options — Independent Study — Reteaching	Review Options — Independent Study — More Practice	Supplements P	Supplements R	Supplements E
52 Join groups of equal size.	186–187	1	1, 2, 3			Set A, p. 212	Set A, p. 214	52	52	52
53 Write and solve addition and multiplication sentences.	188–191	2	4, 5, 6			Set B, p. 212	Set B, p. 214	53	53	53
54 Use arrays to find products.	192–193	3	7, 8, 9			Set C, p. 212	Set C, p. 214	54	54	54
55 Find products using 5 as a factor.	194–195	4, 10	10, 11, 12			Set D, p. 212	Set D, p. 215	55	55	55
56 Find products using 2 as a factor.	196–197	5, 6, 7	13, 14, 15			Set E, p. 213	Set E, p. 215	56	56	56
57 Solve problems by drawing pictures.	200–201	16, 19	16, 17, 18					57	57	57
58 Find products using 3 as a factor.	202–203	8, 9	19, 20, 21			Set F, p. 213	Set F, p. 215	58	58	58
59 Find products using 4 as a factor.	204–205	11	22, 23, 24			Set G, p. 213	Set G, p. 215	59	59	59
60 Solve problems with too much information.	206–207	17, 18	25, 26, 27					60	60	60
61 Find products using zero or 1 as a factor.	208–209	12, 13, 14, 15	28, 29, 30			Set H, p. 213	Set H, p. 215	61	61	61

Student Name _____

See page 61 for scoring.

	Date	Score
Pretest		
Posttest		

Multiplication Facts

Objectives	Text Pages	Test Records: Item Numbers	Review/Test in PE: Item Numbers	Forms A & B: Item Numbers	Forms C & D	Alternative Assessment	Independent Study: Reteaching	Independent Study: More Practice	Supplements: P	Supplements: R	Supplements: E
62 Write products for multiplication facts using 6 through 9 as factors.	220–221	2, 3, 5, 7, 10, 13		2, 3, 5, 7, 10, 13	1, 2, 3		Set A, p. 242	Set A, p. 244	62	62	62
63 Write multiplication facts with 6 through 9 using a number line.	222–223	1		1	4, 5, 6		Set B, p. 242	Set B, p. 244	63	63	63
64 Solve problems by choosing addition, subtraction, or multiplication.	224–225	16, 17, 18, 19		16, 17, 18, 19	7, 8, 9				64	64	64
65 Use patterns to multiply.	226–227	20		20	10, 11, 12		Set C, p. 242	Set C, p. 244	65	65	65
66 Use tens to multiply with 9.	230–231	6, 11, 12		6, 11, 12	13, 14, 15		Set D, p. 242	Set D, p. 244	66	66	66
67 Find products with 6, 7, 8, or 9 as a factor.	232–235	4, 8, 9		4, 8, 9	16, 17, 18		Set E, p. 243	Set E, p. 245	67	67	67
68 Solve problems by finding patterns.	236–237	14		14	19, 20, 21				68	68	68
69 Find products of three factors using volume models.	238–239	15		15	22, 23, 24		Set F, p. 243	Set F, p. 245	69	69	69

Grade 3 Chapter 8 Form for Individualizing

Student Name _____

Geometry and Measurement

See page 61 for scoring.

	Date	Score
Pretest		
Posttest		

Objectives	Text Pages	Review/Test in PE — Item Numbers	Forms A & B — Item Numbers	Item Numbers	Forms C & D	Alternative Assessment	Reteaching	More Practice	P	R	E
70 Identify cubes, spheres, rectangular prisms, and cylinders.	254–257	1	1	1, 2, 3					70	70	70
71 Identify circles, triangles, squares, rectangles, pentagons, hexagons, and octagons.	258–261	2	2	4, 5, 6			Set A, p. 288	Set A, p. 290	71	71	71
72 Identify angles including right angles.	262–263	3	3	7, 8, 9			Set B, p. 288	Set B, p. 290	72	72	72
73 Identify lines of symmetry and complete figures when given lines of symmetry.	264–265	4, 15	4	10, 11, 12			Set C, p. 288	Set C, p. 290	73	73	73
74 Identify congruent segments and figures.	266–267	5	5, 17	13, 14, 15			Set D, p. 288	Set D, p. 290	74	74	74
75 Solve problems using data from graphs.	270–271	14	16	16, 17, 18					75	75	75
76 Find volume by counting cubic units.	272–273	6	6	19, 20, 21					76	76	76
77 Choose an appropriate customary measure of capacity using cup, pint, quart, or gallon.	274–275	7	7	22, 23, 24			Set E, p. 289	Set E, p. 291	77	77	77
78 Choose an appropriate metric measure of capacity using milliliter or liter.	276–277	8	8, 9	25, 26, 27			Set F, p. 289	Set F, p. 291	78	78	78
79 Choose an appropriate customary measure of weight using ounce or pound.	278–279	9	11	28, 29, 30			Set G, p. 289	Set G, p. 291	79	79	79
80 Choose an appropriate metric measure of weight (mass) using gram or kilogram.	280–281	10, 11	10, 12	31, 32, 33			Set H, p. 289	Set H, p. 291	80	80	80
81 Solve problems using recipes, and identify problems with too little information.	282–283	13	15	34, 35, 36					81	81	81
82 Estimate weights and volumes for pictured situations.	284–285	12	13, 14	37, 38, 39					82	82	82

Column groupings: Test Records — Review/Test in PE, Forms A & B, Forms C & D, Alternative Assessment. Review Options — Independent Study (Reteaching, More Practice), Supplements (P, R, E).

Student Name _____

See page 61 for scoring.

	Date	Score
Pretest		
Posttest		

Division Concepts

Objectives	Text Pages	Test Records — Item Numbers	Review/Test in PE — Item Numbers	Forms A & B — Item Numbers	Forms C & D — Item Numbers	Alternative Assessment	Independent Study — Reteaching	Independent Study — More Practice	Supplements P	Supplements R	Supplements E
83 Understand the concept of division as sharing.	296–298	1, 2		1, 2	1, 2, 3		Set A, p. 322	Set A, p. 324	83	83	83
84 Understand the concept of division as grouping.	300–303	3, 4		3, 4	4, 5, 6		Set B, p. 322	Set B, p. 324	84	84	84
85 Complete division sentences.	304–305	5		5	7, 8, 9		Set C, p. 322	Set C, p. 324	85	85	85
86 Write quotients for division facts using 2 or 3 as the divisor.	306–307	6, 7, 10, 11		6, 7, 10, 11	10, 11, 12		Set D, p. 323	Set D, p. 325	86	86	86
87 Write quotients for division facts using 4 as the divisor.	308–309	8, 12		8, 12	13, 14, 15		Set E, p. 323	Set E, p. 325	87	87	87
88 Solve problems by using try and check.	312–313	18		18	16, 17, 18				88	88	88
89 Write quotients for division facts using 5 as the divisor.	314–315	9, 13		9, 13	19, 20, 21		Set F, p. 323	Set F, p. 325	89	89	89
90 Solve problems by writing number sentences.	316–317	19, 20		19, 20	22, 23, 24				90	90	90
91 Identify multiplication and division sentences that belong to a family of facts.	318–319	14, 15, 16, 17, 21		14, 15, 16, 17, 21	25, 26, 27		Set G, p. 323	Set G, p. 325	91	91	91

Grade 3 Chapter 10 Form for Individualizing

Student Name _____

See page 61 for scoring.

	Date	Score
Pretest		
Posttest		

Division Facts

#	Objectives	Text Pages	Item Numbers	Review/Test in PE — Item Numbers	Forms A & B — Item Numbers	Forms C & D	Alternative Assessment	Reteaching (Independent Study)	More Practice (Independent Study)	Supplements P	Supplements R	Supplements E
92	Write quotients for division facts using 6 as the divisor.	330–331	1, 7	1, 7	1, 2, 3			Set A, p. 352	Set A, p. 354	92	92	92
93	Write quotients for division facts using 7 as the divisor.	332–333	6, 8	6, 8	4, 5, 6			Set B, p. 352	Set B, p. 354	93	93	93
94	Write quotients for division facts using 8 as the divisor.	334–335	4, 9	4, 9	7, 8, 9			Set C, p. 352	Set C, p. 354	94	94	94
95	Write quotients for division facts using 9 as the divisor.	336–337	3, 10	3, 10	10, 11, 12			Set D, p. 353	Set D, p. 355	95	95	95
96	Identify multiplication and division sentences that belong to a family of facts.	338–339	11, 12, 23	11, 12, 23	13, 14, 15			Set E, p. 353	Set E, p. 355	96	96	96
97	Solve problems by choosing addition, subtraction, multiplication, or division.	342–343	17, 18, 19, 20	17, 18, 19, 20	16, 17, 18					97	97	97
98	Write quotients for division facts involving zero and 1.	344–345	2, 5	2, 5	19, 20, 21			Set F, p. 353	Set F, p. 355	98	98	98
99	Divide a two-digit number by a one-digit number to get a one-digit quotient with a remainder.	346–347	13, 14, 15, 16	13, 14, 15, 16	22, 23, 24			Set G, p. 353	Set G, p. 355	99	99	99
100	Solve problems by interpreting remainders.	348–349	21, 22	21, 22	25, 26, 27					100	100	100

Student Name _____

Fractions and Decimals

See page 61 for scoring.

	Date	Score
Pretest		
Posttest		

		Test Records				Review Options				
		Review/Test in PE	Forms A & B	Forms C & D		Independent Study		Supplements		
Objectives	Text Pages	Item Numbers	Item Numbers	Item Numbers	Alternative Assessment	Reteaching	More Practice	P	R	E
101 Write a fraction for part of a whole.	360–363	1	1, 2, 22	1, 2, 3		Set A, p. 396	Set A, p. 398	101	101	101
102 Write a fraction for part of a set.	364–365	2	3	4, 5, 6		Set B, p. 396	Set B, p. 398	102	102	102
103 Write equivalent fractions.	366–367	3	4, 5	7, 8, 9		Set C, p. 396	Set C, p. 398	103	103	103
104 Use division to find a fractional part of a set.	368–369	4	6, 7	10, 11, 12		Set D, p. 396	Set D, p. 399	104	104	104
105 Solve problems by using try and check.	370–371	17, 18	21	13, 14, 15				105	105	105
106 Compare two fractions.	372–373	7	8, 9	16, 17, 18				106	106	106
107 Order fractions from least to greatest.	374–376	8	10	19, 20, 21		Set E, p. 397	Set E, p. 399	107	107	107
108 Write decimals involving tenths.	380–381	9, 10	11, 12	22, 23, 24		Set F, p. 397	Set F, p. 399	108	108	108
109 Give the place value for numbers involving tens, ones, and tenths.	382–383	12, 13, 14	14, 15, 16	25, 26, 27				109	109	109
110 Write decimals involving hundredths.	384–387	11	13	28, 29, 30				110	110	110
111 Compare two decimals involving tenths or hundredths.	388–389	5, 6	17, 18	31, 32, 33		Set G, p. 397	Set G, p. 399	111	111	111
112 Solve problems by using more than one strategy.	390–391	16, 17, 18	20, 21	34, 35, 36				112	112	112
113 Use decimals to count, measure, and estimate.	392–393	15	19	37, 38, 39		Set H, p. 397	Set H, p. 399	113	113	113

Grade 3 Chapter 12 Form for Individualizing

Student Name _____

See page 61 for scoring.

	Date	Score
Pretest		
Posttest		

Time and Money

Objectives	Text Pages	Review/Test in PE — Item Numbers	Test Records — Forms A & B — Item Numbers	Test Records — Forms C & D — Item Numbers	Alternative Assessment	Review Options — Independent Study — Reteaching	Review Options — Independent Study — More Practice	Supplements — P	Supplements — R	Supplements — E
114 Tell time to the nearest minute using a standard clock.	408–411	1, 2	1, 2	1, 2, 3		Set A, p. 432	Set A, p. 434	114	114	114
115 Read and interpret a yearly calendar.	412–413	3, 4	3, 4	4, 5, 6		Set B, p. 432	Set B, p. 434	115	115	115
116 Solve multiple-step problems involving time.	414–415	15, 16	15, 16	7, 8, 9				116	116	116
117 Identify and write values for coins and bills through $10.00.	416–417	5, 6, 17	5, 6, 17	10, 11, 12		Set C, p. 432	Set C, p. 434	117	117	117
118 Use the dollar sign and decimal point to record amounts of money involving coins and bills through $10.00.	420–421	7, 8	7, 8	13, 14, 15		Set D, p. 433	Set D, p. 435	118	118	118
119 Add or subtract amounts of money.	422–423	9, 10	9, 10	16, 17, 18		Set E, p. 433	Set E, p. 435	119	119	119
120 Find amounts of change.	424–425	11, 12	11, 12	19, 20, 21		Set F, p. 433	Set F, p. 435	120	120	120
121 Solve problems by working backward.	426–427	14	14	22, 23, 24				121	121	121
122 Estimate amounts of money.	428–429	13	13	25, 26, 27		Set G, p. 433	Set G, p. 435	122	122	122

Grade 3 Chapter 13 Form for Individualizing

See page 61 for scoring.

	Date	Score
Pretest		
Posttest		

Student Name _____

Multiplication Computation

Objectives	Text Pages	Review/Test in PE — Item Numbers	Forms A & B — Item Numbers	Forms C & D — Item Numbers	Alternative Assessment	Independent Study — Reteaching	Independent Study — More Practice	Supplements P	Supplements R	Supplements E
123 Explore multiplying with multiples of 10 and 100.	440–441	1	1	1, 2, 3		Set A, p. 464	Set A, p. 466	123	123	123
124 Multiply a number by 10 and 100.	442–443	2, 3	2, 3	4, 5, 6		Set B, p. 464	Set B, p. 466	124	124	124
125 Estimate the product of two numbers by using rounded numbers.	444–445	4, 5, 21	4, 5, 21	7, 8, 9		Set C, p. 464	Set C, p. 466	125	125	25
126 Explore multiplying a two-digit number by a one-digit number with renaming from ones to tens.	446–449	6	6	10, 11, 12		Set D, p. 465	Set D, p. 467	126	126	126
127 Multiply a two-digit number by a one-digit number with renaming.	450–451	7, 8, 9	7, 8, 9	13, 14, 15		Set E, p. 465	Set E, p. 467	127	127	127
128 Solve problems with too much information.	454–455	17	17	16, 17, 18				128	128	128
129 Multiply a two-digit number by a one-digit number to get a three-digit product.	456–457	10, 11, 12	10, 11, 12	19, 20, 21		Set F, p. 465	Set F, p. 467	129	129	129
130 Solve problems by choosing addition, subtraction, multiplication, or division.	458–459	18, 19, 20	18, 19, 20	22, 23, 24				130	130	130
131 Multiply a three-digit number by a one-digit number with renaming.	460–461	13, 14, 15, 16	13, 14, 15, 16	25, 26, 27		Set G, p. 465	Set G, p. 467	131	131	131

Grade 3 Chapter 14 Form for Individualizing

Student Name _____

See page 61 for scoring.

	Date	Score
Pretest		
Posttest		

Statistics, Graphing, and Probability

Objectives	Test Records				Review Options				
	Text Pages	Review/Test in PE — Item Numbers	Forms A & B — Item Numbers	Forms C & D — Alternative Assessment	Independent Study — Reteaching	Independent Study — More Practice	Supplements P	Supplements R	Supplements E
132 Solve problems by collecting data.	472–473	1	1, 2, 3				132	132	132
133 Make and interpret tally charts.	474–475	9	4, 5, 6		Set A, p. 498	Set A, p. 500	133	133	133
134 Read and interpret pictographs.	476–479	2	7, 8, 9		Set B, p. 498	Set B, p. 500	134	134	134
135 Read and interpret bar charts.	480–482	3	10, 11, 12		Set C, p. 498	Set C, p. 500	135	135	135
136 Solve problems by making bar graphs or tables.	486–487	10	13, 14, 15				136	136	136
137 Locate points for number pairs, and write number pairs for points.	488–489	4, 5	16, 17, 18		Set D, p. 499	Set D, p. 501	137	137	137
138 Understand the concept of probability.	490–491	6	19, 20, 21		Set E, p. 499	Set E, p. 501	138	138	138
139 List possible outcomes of events.	492–493	7	22, 23, 24		Set F, p. 499	Set F, p. 501	139	139	139
140 Interpret and record data for probability experiments.	494–495	8	25, 26, 27		Set G, p. 499	Set G, p. 501	140	140	140

See page 61 for scoring.

Student Name _____

Division Computation

				Test Records						Review Options					
		Review/ Test in PE		Forms A & B		Forms C & D	Alternative Assessment		Independent Study		More Practice	Supplements			
Objectives	Text Pages	Item Numbers	Item Numbers		Item Numbers				Reteaching			P	R	E	
141 Understand the concept of division as sharing.	506–507	1, 2, 17	1, 2, 17		1, 2, 3				Set A, p. 526	Set A, p. 528		141	141	141	
142 Identify multiplication and division sentences that belong to a family of facts.	508–509	3, 4, 5	3, 4, 5		4, 5, 6				Set B, p. 526	Set B, p. 528		142	142	142	
143 Divide a two-digit number by a one-digit number to get a two-digit quotient with a remainder.	510–512	6, 7, 8	6, 7, 8		7, 8, 9				Set C, p. 527	Set C, p. 529		143	143	143	
144 Solve problems that involve interpreting remainders.	514–515	9	9		10, 11, 12							144	144	144	
145 Divide a two-digit number by a one-digit number to get a one- or two-digit quotient and a remainder.	518–521	10, 11, 12, 13, 14	10, 11, 12, 13, 14		13, 14, 15				Set D, p. 527	Set D, p. 529		145	145	145	
146 Solve problems by choosing addition, subtraction, multiplication, or division.	522–523	15, 16	15, 16		16, 17, 18							146	146	146	

	Date	Score
Pretest		
Posttest		

Grade 3 Cumulative Tests Form for Individualizing

Student Name _____

See page 61 for scoring.

Objectives	Text Pages	Item	Cum. Test Ch. 1–3	Item	Cum. Test Ch. 1–7	Item	Cum. Test Ch. 1–11	Item	Cum. Test Ch. 1–15	Reteaching	More Practice	P	R	E
1 Identify uses of numbers.	4–5	1								Set A, p. 28	Set A, p. 30	1	1	1
2 Use basic addition and subtraction facts to find sums and differences.	6–7	3, 4, 6		1						Set B, p. 28	Set B, p. 30	2	2	2
3 Find missing numbers and operation signs in addition and subtraction facts.	8–9	2								Set C, p. 28	Set C, p. 30	3	3	3
4 Solve problems by using a problem-solving guide.	10–11	7										4	4	4
5 Use families of facts to solve problems.	12–15	5, 8								Set D, p. 29	Set D, p. 31	5	5	5
6 Identify even and odd numbers.	18–19	9								Set E, p. 29	Set E, p. 31	6	6	6
7 Solve problems by using data from pictures.	20–21	11										7	7	7
9 Solve problems by finding patterns.	24–25	13							1			9	9	9
10 Use place-value materials to understand hundreds.	36–39	14								Set A, p. 66	Set A, p. 68	10	10	10
11 Write digits in the proper sequence for pictured hundreds, tens, and ones, and numbers through 999 in standard and expanded form.	40–41	15								Set B, p. 66	Set B, p. 68	11	11	11
12 Compare numbers less than 1,000 using < and >.	42–43	10, 16		2		1				Set C, p. 66	Set C, p. 68	12	12	12
13 Order three-digit numbers.	44–45	12, 17, 18							2	Set D, p. 66	Set D, p. 68	13	13	13
14 Find patterns in a number chart.	46–47	19								Set E, p. 67	Set E, p. 69	14	14	14
15 Round numbers to the nearest ten and nearest hundred.	48–49	20							3	Set F, p. 67	Set F, p. 69	15	15	15
16 Solve problems by using logical reasoning.	52–53	21										16	16	16
17 Write numbers through 9,999 in standard form.	54–57	22, 23								Set G, p. 67	Set G, p. 69	17	17	17

Test Records

Review Options — Independent Study — Supplements

Grade 3 Cumulative Tests Form for Individualizing (continued)

Student Name _____

Objectives	Text Pages	Item	Cum. Test Ch. 1-3	Item	Cum. Test Ch. 1-7	Item	Cum. Test Ch. 1-11	Item	Cum. Test Ch. 1-15	Reteaching	More Practice	P	R	E
18 Compare and order numbers less than 9,999.	58–59	24								Set H, p. 67	Set H, p. 69	18	18	18
19 Write numbers and give place value for numbers through 999,999.	60–61	25, 26		5						Set I, p. 67	Set I, p. 69	19	19	19
20 Solve problems by choosing sensible answers.	62–63	27										20	20	20
21 Solve problems by choosing addition or subtraction facts.	74–75	28, 35, 39										21	21	21
22 Rename numbers by changing ones to tens and tens to ones.	76–79	29								Set A, p. 98	Set A, p. 100	22	22	22
23 Add 2-digit numbers with and without renaming ones as tens.	80–81	30, 33		6, 7						Set B, p. 98	Set B, p. 100	23	23	23
24 Use mental math strategies to find the sum of two numbers.	82–83	34		4						Set C, p. 98	Set C, p. 100	24	24	24
25 Add three or four numbers of one and two digits whose sums do not exceed 99.	84–85	31								Set D, p. 98	Set D, p. 101	25	25	25
26 Subtract numbers with up to two digits, renaming tens as ones.	88–89	32		8						Set E, p. 99	Set E, p. 101	26	26	26
27 Use mental math strategies to find the difference between two numbers.	90–91	36		9						Set F, p. 99	Set F, p. 101	27	27	27
28 Estimate the sum or difference between two numbers.	92–93	37		3, 14						Set G, p. 99	Set G, p. 101	28	28	28
29 Solve addition problems by using estimation.	94–95	38		11								29	29	29
30 Use pennies, dimes, and dollars to rename.	110–113			12						Set A, p. 142	Set A, p. 144	30	30	30
32 Add three-digit numbers with one renaming.	118–119			10		2		4		Set C, p. 142	Set C, p. 144	32	32	32
33 Add three- and four-digit numbers with more than one renaming.	120–121			13						Set D, p. 142	Set D, p. 144	33	33	33
37 Subtract three-digit numbers with one renaming.	132–133			15, 16		3		5		Set G, p. 143	Set G, p. 145	37	37	37

Test Records — Review Options: Independent Study / Supplements

Grade 3 Cumulative Tests Form for Individualizing (continued)

See page 61 for scoring.

Student Name _____

Objectives	Text Pages	Item	Cum. Test Ch. 1–3	Item	Cum. Test Ch. 1–7	Item	Cum. Test Ch. 1–11	Item	Cum. Test Ch. 1–15	Reteaching	More Practice	P	R	E
38 Subtract three-digit numbers with up to two renamings involving zeros.	134–135			17						Set H, p. 143	Set H, p. 145	38	38	38
39 Subtract three- and four-digit numbers with three renamings involving zeros.	136–137			18						Set I, p. 143	Set I, p. 145	39	39	39
41 Tell time to the nearest minute using standard and digital clocks.	150–153			20		4		26		Set A, p. 178	Set A, p. 180	41	41	41
42 Read and interpret a calendar for three months.	154–155			21						Set B, p. 178	Set B, p. 180	42	42	42
43 Measure objects to the nearest inch and half inch.	156–157							10		Set C, p. 178	Set C, p. 180	43	43	43
44 Choose an appropriate customary unit of length using inch, foot, yard, or mile.	158–159			22						Set D, p. 178	Set D, p. 180	44	44	44
45 Measure objects to the nearest centimeter and decimeter.	160–161			23		5				Set E, p. 179	Set E, p. 181	45	45	45
47 Solve problems by making tables.	166–167			37		6						47	47	47
48 Find perimeters.	168–169			25						Set G, p. 179	Set G, p. 181	48	48	48
52 Join groups of equal size.	186–187			26						Set A, p. 212	Set A, p. 214	52	52	52
53 Write and solve addition and multiplication sentences.	188–191			19						Set B, p. 212	Set B, p. 214	53	53	53
54 Use arrays to find products.	192–193			24						Set C, p. 212	Set C, p. 214	54	54	54
55 Find products using 5 as a factor.	194–195			27		7		6, 7		Set D, p. 212	Set D, p. 215	55	55	55
59 Find products using 4 as a factor.	204–205			28		16				Set G, p. 213	Set G, p. 215	59	59	59

Column group headers: **Test Records** (Cum. Test Ch. 1–3, Cum. Test Ch. 1–7, Cum. Test Ch. 1–11, Cum. Test Ch. 1–15); **Review Options** — Independent Study (Reteaching, More Practice), Supplements (P, R, E).

Grade 3 Cumulative Tests Form for Individualizing (continued)

Student Name _____

See page 61 for scoring.

Objectives	Text Pages	Test Records: Item (Ch. 1–3)	Cum. Test Ch. 1–3	Item (Ch. 1–7)	Cum. Test Ch. 1–7	Item (Ch. 1–11)	Cum. Test Ch. 1–11	Item (Ch. 1–15)	Cum. Test Ch. 1–15	Review: Reteaching	More Practice	P	R	E
60 Solve problems with too much information.	206–207			38								60	60	60
61 Find products using zero or 1 as a factor.	208–209			29						Set H, p. 213	Set H, p. 215	61	61	61
62 Write products for multiplication facts using 6 through 9 as factors.	220–221			30, 31, 32		8, 9				Set A, p. 242	Set A, p. 244	62	62	62
64 Solve problems by choosing addition, subtraction, or multiplication.	224–225			34, 35, 39								64	64	64
65 Use patterns to multiply.	226–227			33						Set C, p. 242	Set C, p. 244	65	65	65
67 Find products with 6, 7, 8, or 9 as a factor.	232–235							9		Set E, p. 243	Set E, p. 245	67	67	67
68 Solve problems by finding patterns.	236–237					10						68	68	68
69 Find products of three factors using volume models.	238–239			36				8		Set F, p. 243	Set F, p. 245	69	69	69
72 Identify angles and right angles.	262–263					11		11		Set B, p. 288	Set B, p. 290	72	72	72
73 Identify lines of symmetry and complete figures when given lines of symmetry.	264–265							12		Set C, p. 288	Set C, p. 290	73	73	73
78 Choose an appropriate metric measure of capacity using milliliter or liter.	276–277					12				Set F, p. 289	Set F, p. 291	78	78	78
79 Choose an appropriate customary measure of weight using ounce or pound.	278–279							13		Set G, p. 289	Set G, p. 291	79	79	79
86 Write quotients for division facts using 2 or 3 as the divisor.	306–307					22				Set D, p. 323	Set D, p. 325	86	86	86
87 Write quotients for division facts using 4 as the divisor.	308–309					19				Set E, p. 323	Set E, p. 325	87	87	87
88 Solve problems by using try and check.	312–313					15						88	88	88
89 Write quotients for division facts using 5 as the divisor.	314–315					17		14		Set F, p. 323	Set F, p. 325	89	89	89

Grade 3 Cumulative Tests Form for Individualizing (continued)

See page 61 for scoring.

Student Name _____

Objectives	Text Pages	Cum. Test Ch. 1–3 Item	Item	Cum. Test Ch. 1–7 Item	Item	Cum. Test Ch. 1–11 Item	Item	Cum. Test Ch. 1–15 Item	Item	Reteaching	More Practice	P	R	E
91 Identify multiplication and division sentences that belong to a family of facts.	318–319						13, 14			Set G, p. 323	Set G, p. 325	91	91	91
92 Write quotients for division facts using 6 as the divisor.	330–331						18			Set A, p. 352	Set A, p. 354	92	92	92
93 Write quotients for division facts using 7 as the divisor.	332–333						20			Set B, p. 352	Set B, p. 354	93	93	93
94 Write quotients for division facts using 8 as the divisor.	334–335						21			Set C, p. 352	Set C, p. 354	94	94	94
95 Write quotients for division facts using 9 as the divisor.	336–337						23		15	Set D, p. 353	Set D, p. 355	95	95	95
96 Identify multiplication and division sentences that belong to a family of facts.	338–339						27			Set E, p. 353	Set E, p. 355	96	96	96
97 Solve problems by choosing addition, subtraction, multiplication, or division.	342–343						26, 28, 36					97	97	97
98 Write quotients for division facts involving zero and 1.	344–345						24		16	Set F, p. 353	Set F, p. 355	98	98	98
99 Divide a two-digit number by a one-digit number to get a one-digit quotient with a remainder.	346–347						25		17	Set G, p. 353	Set G, p. 355	99	99	99
100 Solve problems by interpreting remainders.	348–349						29		18			100	100	100
101 Write a fraction for part of a whole.	360–363						30			Set A, p. 396	Set A, p. 398	101	101	101
102 Write a fraction for part of a set.	364–365								20	Set B, p. 396	Set B, p. 398	102	102	102
103 Write equivalent fractions.	366–367						31			Set C, p. 396	Set C, p. 398	103	103	103
104 Use division to find a fractional part of a set.	368–369						32		19	Set D, p. 396	Set D, p. 399	104	104	104
106 Compare two fractions.	372–373								21			106	106	106
108 Write decimals involving tenths.	380–381								22			108	108	108

Grade 3 Cumulative Tests Form for Individualizing (continued)

Student Name _____

See page 61 for scoring.

Objectives	Text Pages	Item (Ch. 1–3)	Item (Ch. 1–7)	Item (Ch. 1–11)	Item (Ch. 1–15)	Reteaching	More Practice	P	R	E
110 Write decimals involving hundredths.	384–387		33		24			110	110	110
111 Compare two decimals involving tenths or hundredths.	388–389		35		23	Set G, p. 397	Set G, p. 399	111	111	111
112 Solve problems by using more than one strategy.	390–391		34					112	112	112
116 Solve multiple-step problems involving time.	414–415				25			116	116	116
118 Use the dollar sign and decimal point to record amounts of money involving coins and bills through $10.00.	420–421				27	Set D, p. 433	Set D, p. 435	118	118	118
119 Add or subtract amounts of money.	422–423				28	Set E, p. 433	Set E, p. 435	119	119	119
120 Find amounts of change.	424–425				29	Set F, p. 433	Set F, p. 435	120	120	120
125 Estimate the product of two numbers by using rounded numbers.	444–445				30	Set C, p. 464	Set C, p. 466	125	125	125
127 Multiply a two-digit number by a one-digit number with renaming.	450–451				31	Set E, p. 465	Set E, p. 467	127	127	127
131 Multiply a three-digit number by a one-digit number with renaming.	460–461				32	Set G, p. 465	Set G, p. 467	131	131	131
133 Make and interpret tally charts.	474–475				33	Set A, p. 498	Set A, p. 500	133	133	133
135 Read and interpret bar charts.	480–482				34	Set C, p. 498	Set C, p. 500	135	135	135
144 Solve problems that involve interpreting remainders.	514–515				35			144	144	144
146 Solve problems by choosing addition, subtraction, multiplication, or division.	522–523				36, 37			146	146	146

Test Records — Cum. Test Ch. 1–3, Cum. Test Ch. 1–7, Cum. Test Ch. 1–11, Cum. Test Ch. 1–15

Review Options — Independent Study (Reteaching, More Practice); Supplements (P, R, E)

334